EXERCISE

Benefits, limits and adaptations

EDITED BY

Donald Macleod, Ron Maughan
Myra Nimmo, Thomas Reilly
and
Clyde Williams

London
E. & F.N. SPON
New York

First published in 1987 by
E. & F.N. Spon Ltd
11 New Fetter Lane, London EC4P 4EE
Published in the USA by
E. & F.N. Spon
29 West 35th Street, New York 10001
© *1987 This collection: The Edinburgh Post-Graduate Board for Medicine*
Printed in Great Britain at the
University Press, Cambridge

ISBN 0 419 14220 7 (Hardback)
ISBN 0 419 14140 5 (Paperback)

British Library Cataloguing in Publication Data

Exercise: benefits, limits and adaptations.
  1. Exercise—Physiological aspects
  I. Macleod, Donald A.D.
  612' .044   QP301

  ISBN 0-419-14140-5

Library of Congress Cataloging-in-Publication Data

Exercise: benefits, limits, and adaptations.

  Edited by Donald A.D. Macleod and others.
  Includes bibliographies and index.
  1. Exercise—Physiological aspects—Congresses.
2. Adaptation (physiology)—Congresses. I. Macleod,
Donald A. D.   II Commonwealth and International
Conference on Sport, Physical Education, Dance,
Recreation, and Health (8th : 1986 : Glasgow,
Strathclyde) [DNLM: 1. Exertion—congresses.
  2. Fatigue——congresses.   3. Sports—congresses.
QT 260 E957 1896]
QP301.E94 1986   613.7'1   86-19762
ISBN 0-419-14220-7
ISBN 0-419-14140-5 (pbk.)

Contents

The Edinburgh Post-Graduate Board of Medicine

Organised post-graduate medical education in Edinburgh began in 1905 with the formation of a Post-Graduate Executive Committee and this tradition has continued to the present day through the work of the Edinburgh Post-Graduate Board for Medicine. The Board, whose governing body consists of an equal representation from the University of Edinburgh, the Royal College of Surgeons of Edinburgh and the Royal College of Physicians of Edinburgh has, as its remit, the organisation and review of formal post-graduate teaching both for doctors in Edinburgh and the surrounding region and for the large number of post-graduate students and specialists who come to Edinburgh from other parts of the United Kingdom and the rest of the world. It is appropriate therefore that the Post-Graduate Board is sited, in part, within the buildings that once accommodated the Edinburgh Colleges' School of Medicine in Surgeon's Hall, which itself was one of the earliest medical schools in the country. It is also appropriate that the Board has taken as its own motto that of the old School of Medicine 'EN ΤΩ ΔΕΣΜΩ Η ΙΣΧΥΣ' which, when translated, reads 'In the Bond the Strength' since it signifies a close relationship between the University and Colleges in furthering medical education and at the same time the strong associations that exist between the Board and its students, which tend to continue for many years after their departure.

Although the principle activity of the Board has been the organisation of courses in the Basic Sciences, in Surgery and in Medicine and have been directed towards the needs of surgeons and physicians in training, it has, at the same time constantly reviewed the latest developments in the specialties of Medicine and in the related Sciences. By means of a series of specialist courses and regular scientific symposia held in the Board's Pfizer Foundation it has offered both education and training to doctors and scientists of all grades who are actively involved in these specialties.

Foremost among these special interests has been the recent developments in Sports Medicine and the Sports Sciences which, for the past eight years, have been a regular feature on the Board's educational programme.

JOHN A. STRONG
Emeritus Professor,
Chairman, Edinburgh Post-Graduate Board for Medicine

Organising Committee

Chairman

Mr Donald A.D. Macleod
M.B.Ch.B., F.R.C.S.Ed.

Consultant Surgeon; Assistant Director of Studies (Surgery), Edinburgh Post-Graduate Board of Medicine.

Session Conveners

Dr Ron Maughan
B.Sc.(Hons), Ph.D.

Research Lecturer, Department of Environmental and Occupational Medicine, University of Aberdeen.

Dr Myra Nimmo
B.Sc.(Hons), Ph.D.

Senior Lecturer (Research), Department of Physiotherapy, The Queen's College, Glasgow.

Dr Thomas Reilly
B.A., D.P.E., M.Sc., Ph.D., M.I.Biol., F.Erg.S.

Reader in Sports Science, Department of Sports and Recreation Studies, Liverpool Polytechnic.

Professor Clyde Williams
B.Sc., M.Sc., Ph.D.

Professor of Sports Science, University of Technology, Loughborough.

Members

Sir James Fraser Bt
B.A., Ch.M., F.R.C.S., F.R.C.P.

Post-Graduate Dean, Edinburgh Post-Graduate Board for Medicine.

Mr Peter Edmond
C.B.E., M.B.Ch.B., F.R.C.S.Ed.

Chairman, Medical Services Committee, XIIIth Commonwealth Games, Scotland.

Dr Elizabeth McSwan
M.B.Ch.B.

Medical Officer, Dunfermline College of Physical Education, Edinburgh.

Contributors

Professor P.O. Åstrand   Department of Physiology III, Karolinska Institute, Lidingovagen I, S-114 33 Stockholm, Sweden.

Mr L.H. Boobis   Senior Surgical Registrar, Department of Surgery, Clinical Sciences Building, Leicester Royal Infirmary, Leicester, LE2 7LX, UK.

Professor G.A. Brooks   Director, Exercise Physiology Laboratory, University of California, Berkeley, California, 94720, USA.

Mr M.G. Everitt   Senior Lecturer in Computer Science, Department of Systems and Computer Studies, N.E. London Polytechnic, Longbridge Road, Dagenham, Essex RM8 2AS, UK.

Dr W.I. Faser   Consultant Psychiatrist, Gogarburn Hospital, Corstorphine Road, Edinburgh, UK.

Dr E.C. Frederick   Nike Research, RFD 1, Haigh Road, Exeter, New Hampshire, 03833, USA.

Dr J.A. Muir Gray   Community Physician, Radcliffe Infirmary, Woodstock Road, Oxford, UK.

Dr M.H. Harrison   RAF Institute of Aviation Medicine, Farnborough, Hants, GU14 6SZ, UK.

K. Hede — Department of Clinical Physiology, Rehabilitation Institute, University Hospital, Tagensvej 22, DK-2200, Copenhagen, Denmark.

Professor E. Hultman — Department of Clinical Chemistry II, Huddinge University Hospital, S-141 86 Huddinge, Sweden.

B. Kiens — August Krogh Institute, University of Copenhagen, 13 Universitetsparken, DK-2100, Copenhagen, Denmark.

Dr I. Jacobs — Defence and Civil Institute of Environmental Medicine, P.O. Box 2000, Downsview, Ontario, Canada, M3M 3B9, UK.

Dr A.B. Loucks — Assistant Research Reproductive Endocrinologist, Department of Reproductive Medicine, T-002, University of California, San Diego, La Jolla, California, 92093, USA.

Professor J.N. Morris — London School of Hygiene and Tropical Medicine, University of London, Keppel Street, London, WC1E 7HT, UK.

Mr D.S. Muckle — Consultant Orthopaedic Surgeon, Middlesbrough General Hospital, Middlesbrough, Cleveland, TS5 5AZ, UK.

Dr N. Mutrie — Assistant Director, Department of Physical Education and Recreation, Glasgow University, Stevenson Building, Glasgow, G12 8LT, UK.

Dr E.A. Newsholme — Department of Biochemistry, University of Oxford, South Parks Road, Oxford, OX1 3QU, UK.

Professor E. Nygaard   Department of Clinical Physiology, Rehabilitation Institute, University Hospital, Tagensvej 22, DK-2200 Copenhagen, Denmark.

Dr J.C. Prior   Assistant Professor, Department of Medicine, Division of Endocrinology and Metabolism, University of British Columbia, Suite 3318, 910 West 10th Avenue, Vancouver, British Columbia, Canada, V5Z 1M9.

Professor P.B. Raven   Associate Professor, Department of Physiology, Texas College of Osteopathic Medicine, Camp Bowie at Montgomery, Fort Worth, Texas, 76107, USA.

Dr T. Reilly   Reader in Sports Science, Department of Sport and Recreation Studies, Liverpool Polytechnic, Byrom Street, Liverpool, L3 3AF, UK.

Professor B. Saltin   August Krogh Institute, University of Copenhagen, 13 Universitetsparken, DK-2100 Copenhagen, Denmark.

G. Savard   August Krogh Institute, University of Copenhagen, 13 Universitetsparken, DK-2100 Copenhagen, Denmark.

Dr A.M. Semmence   Chief Medical Adviser, Civil Service Medical Advisory Service, Tilbury House, Petty France, London SW1H 9EU, UK.

K. Söderlund   Department of Clinical Chemistry II, Huddinge Hospital, Stockholm 14186, Sweden.

Dr L.L. Spriet   School of Human Biology, University of Guelph, Guelph, Ontario, Canada N1G 2W1.

Dr J.R. Sutton

Ambrose Cardio-Respiratory Unit, Department of Medicine, McMaster University, 1200 Main Street West, Hamilton, Ontario, Canada, L8N 3Z5.

Dr A. Young

Consultant Physician in Geriatric Medicine, The Royal Free Hospital, New End Hospital, New End, Hampstead NW3 1JB, UK.

Dr G.A. Zitnay

Director of Mental Retardation Programs, The Joseph P. Kennedy, Junior Foundation, 1350 New York Avenue, NW, Suite 500, Washington DC, 20005-4709, USA.

Mr A. Stuart

The Scottish Sports Council, 1 St. Combe Street, Edinburgh EH3 6AA, UK.

Participants

Dr D. Ballantyne Consultant Physician and Cardiologist, The Victoria Infirmary, Glasgow, G42 9TY, UK.

Mr S. Brooks Department of Physical Education and Sports Science, University of Technology, Ashby Road, Loughborough, Leicestershire, LE11 3TU, UK.

Miss M. Cheetham Department of Physical Education and Sports Science, University of Technology, Ashby Road, Loughborough, Leicestershire, LE11 3TU, UK.

Dr M. Farrally Department of Physical Education, University of St. Andrews, St. Andrews, Fife, UK.

Dr M. Gleeson Department of Environmental and Occupational Medicine, University of Aberdeen, Foresterhill, Aberdeen, AB9 2ZD, UK.

Mr P.L. Greenhaff Department of Environmental and Occupational Medicine, Aberdeen University, UK.

Dr A. Hardman Department of Physical Education and Sports Science, University of Technology, Ashby Road, Loughborough, Leicestershire LE11 3TU, UK.

Dr R.C. Harris Exercise Physiology Unit, The Animal Health Trust, Balaton Lodge, Snailwell Road, Newmarket, Suffolk, CB8 7DW, UK.

Dr S. Hillis Consultant Cardiologist, Stobhill Hospital, Glasgow, UK.

Dr P. Jakeman Division of Sport and Science, Crewe and Alsager College, Alsager, Stoke-on-Trent, ST7 2HL, UK.

Dr E. Jansson Department of Clinical Physiology, Karolinska Hospital, 10401 Stockholm, Sweden.

Dr R.P. Knill-Jones Department of Community Medicine, University of Glasgow, UK.

Dr J.M. Kowalchuk Department of Biochemistry, University of Oxford, South Parks Road, Oxford, OX1 3QU, UK.

Dr S.J. Legg Army Personnel Research Establishment, Farnborough, Hants, UK.

Dr E. Lloyd Consultant Anaesthetist, Royal Infirmary, Edinburgh, UK.

Mr D. MacLaren Department of Sport and Recreation Studies, Liverpool Polytechnic, Byrom Street, Liverpool L3 3AF, UK.

Mr G.R. McLatchie Consultant Surgeon, The General Hospital, Hartlepool, Cleveland, UK.

Mr D. McLean Department of Physiotherapy, The Queen's College, 1 Park Drive, Glasgow, UK.

Professor H.J. Montoye Professor and Director, Biodynamics Laboratory, 2000 Observatory Drive, Madison, WI 53706, USA.

Mr R.H. Mukherjee   Consultant Orthopaedic Surgeon, Victoria Hospital, Kirkcaldy, UK.

Dr F.J. Nagle   Biodynamics Laboratory, 2000 Observatory Drive, University of Wisconsin, Madison, Wi 53706, USA.

Professor J.R. Poortmans   Chimie Physiologique, Institut Superieur d'Ed Physique, Universite Libre de Bruxelles, 28 Av. P. Heger, Brussels B1050, Belgium.

Dr P. Radford   Head of Department, Department of Physical Education and Recreation, Glasgow University, Stevenson Building, Glasgow, G12 8LT, UK.

Dr H. Simpson   Pathology Department, Royal Infirmary, Glasgow, G4 0SF, UK.

Dr N.C. Spurway   Department of Physiology, University of Glasgow, Glasgow, G12 8QQ, UK.

Professor R.A. Stockwell   Department of Anatomy, University Medical School, Teviot Place, Edinburgh, UK.

Mr D.M. Tumilty   Australian Institute of Sport, P.O. Box 176, Belconnen A.C.T., Australia 2616.

Dr S.A. Wootton   Nutrition Department, Southampton University, Bassett Crescent East, Southampton, SO9 3TU, UK.

E R R A T A

p. v: line 4 up to read
L.H. Boobis, C. Williams, M.E. Cheetham and S.A. Wooton

line 3 up to read
Lactate production during exercise: oxidizable substrate

p. xi: line 9 up to read
Dr W.I. Fraser   Consultant Psychiatrist, Gogarburn

p. xiv: line 3 up to read
Mr R.A. Stuart   The Scottish Sports Council, 1 St.

p. 85: title to read
Muscle pH, glycolytic ATP turnover and the onset of fatigue

p. 116: authorship to read
L.H Boobis, C. Williams, M.E. Cheetham and S.A. Wooton

p. 159: line 14 up to read
Changes in $\dot{V}O_2$ peak and peripheral factors were evident only in the trained

p. 193: line 5 up
'capacity' to read 'output'
line 3 up
'capacity' to read 'power'

p. 217: line 6
to have a full stop after 'possibility'

P. 366: line 8 up
'alleviate' to read 'accentuate'

EXERCISE: *Benefits, limits and adaptations.*
Edited by Donald Macleod, Ron Maughan, Myra Nimmo, Thomas Reilly and Clyde Williams. ISBN 0 419 14140 5

PART I   EXERCISE AND MEDICINE

'Exercise and Temperance can preserve something
of our early strength even in old age'.
Cicero (106-43 BC)

In pre-Christian Rome Cicero recognised that regular exercise and
temperance would ensure a 'positive' lifestyle, which would be an
advantage to the citizens of Rome. Cicero's message has been lost
to much of our technological world where societies have adopted a
'negative' lifestyle, which has, in turn, led to the modern
epidemic - 'The Western way of dying' - through cardiovascular
disease and malignancy.

Over the last 30 to 40 years, with increasing momentum in the
last decade, exercise has been recommended in health conscious
societies as an essential element in a normal lifestyle, both to
maintain good health and to ameliorate disease, disability and
depression. The opening session of the Symposium was therefore
planned to emphasise the benefits of exercise to the old and middle-
aged as well as to the young; to those with medical ailments; and
to people with mental and physical illness or handicap.

One of the founding figures of this movement, recognising that
regular vigorous exercise and aerobic work protects the exerciser,
was Professor J.N. Morris, and his experience with the employees of
London Transport and British Government civil servants has received
world wide recognition. The Academic Committee planning the
Symposium were delighted when Professor Morris agreed to open the
Meeting with a review of his work coupled with his thoughts as to
where future epidemiological and physiological research would lead.

Professor Morris gave an outstanding opening address which set a
high standard and acted as a stimulating challenge to all
subsequent speakers.

Dr Samuel Johnson (1709-1784 AD) visited Scotland on his
Highland Journey in 1773. Following this epic journey he announced
'The noblest prospect that a Scotchman ever sees is the high road
that leads to London' and J.M. Barrie (1860-1937 AD), the author of
Peter Pan, noted that 'there are few more impressive sights in the
world than a Scotsman on the make'.

The next two speakers in the opening session of the Symposium were Scotsmen who have taken the high road to London and made outstanding contributions to the care and health of the community, with particular reference to the elderly.

Dr A. Young, who works in a London Teaching Hospital as a Senior Lecturer and Consultant Physician in Geriatric Medicine, contributed the section on sports medicine in 'The Oxford Textbook of Medicine' published by the Oxford University Press. Dr Young's remit for the Symposium was to review the value of exercise in chronic disease and he met this responsibility with flair, presenting a succinct and lucid wide-ranging review of the many chronic ailments that can be ameloriated by exercise. Dr Young stressed that, if exercise is to become an accepted prescription for patients, there is an urgent need to stress its importance in the teaching of medical undergraduates as well as postgraduates.

Dr J.A.M. Gray is employed in Oxford as a Consultant Physician specialising in Community Medicine with responsibility for the Geriatric Services. He is the author of many books and papers on sport and community health, including 'Rugby Injuries' published by Offox Press and 'Man Against Disease' published by the Oxford University Press. Dr Gray was invited to address the problem of Exercise and Ageing. In his paper, which gave an excellent review of this complex subject, he confirmed that the elderly can benefit greatly from training programmes enabling them to maintain an independent and active lifestyle and he emphasised the need to change the philosophy behind the management of the elderly in society from one of 'caring' to 'stimulating and supporting'.

The closing paper in this session of the Symposium was entitled Exercise and Sport for the Mentally Handicapped. This paper was due to be presented by Dr G.A. Zitnay, Director of Mental Retardation Programs at the Joseph P. Kennedy Jnr Foundation in Washington. Unfortunately Dr Zitnay could not be present because of ill health and his paper was read by the Post-Graduate Dean, Sir James Fraser. The paper published in this volume has been prepared by Dr W.I. Fraser, Consultant Psychiatrist at Gogarburn Hospital for the Mentally Handicapped, Edinburgh, and Mr R.A. Stuart who is a member of the staff of the Scottish Sports Council with responsibility for developing sporting facilities for mentally handicapped people. Dr Fraser is editor of The Journal of Mental Deficiency Research and Mr Stuart was a member of the Disabled Lung working party which published 'Give us a Chance'. This report was subsequently made into a highly acclaimed film.

Dr Fraser and Mr Stuart have expanded the material presented at the Symposium and have demonstrated the great value of exercise to the mentally handicapped, irrespective of their degree of disability. The individual's self-esteem is raised, as well as the esteem of handicapped people in the community. They have also given an excellent review of the problem of atlanto-axial instability in patients with Down's Syndrome.

I would like to aknowledge the gratitude felt by the Organising Committee of the Symposium and the Edinburgh Post-Graduate Board for Medicine to Dr Fraser and Mr Stuart for the major contribution they have made to this publication.

The range of papers presented at the opening session of the Symposium have confirmed that 'Exercise for All' should be an everyday and continuing part of our lifestyle. The medical profession must be encouraged to accept that exercise is a suitable prescription for treatment of illness as well as valuable in the prevention of disease. For a doctor to undertake this responsibility competently, it is essential that the teaching of exercise physiology is improved and that the medical profession is aware of work that is being undertaken in the sports sciences and by epidemiologists. This Symposium is an attempt to bridge the gap between these various professional groups, confirming that the medical profession increasingly accepts the relevance of a joint approach to the benefit of the community and patients. The development of increasing co- operation between interested professionals will follow the precepts set by the Edinburgh Post-Graduate Board for Medicine in its motto - 'In the Bond, the Strength'.

Mr Donald A.D. Macleod

Exercise and coronary heart disease

J.N. MORRIS, M.G. EVERITT

and A.M. SEMMENCE

The hypothesis drawn from the original occupational studies, that
high levels of physical activity are associated with a lower
incidence of coronary heart disease, has not been confirmed in
prospective studies of exercise taken in leisure activities by
sedentary British office workers. These studies only show
substantial and consistent reduction of coronary heart disease in
association with vigorous aerobic activities. Men taking such
levels of exercise are manifestly self-selected, but this does not
affect the main observation: as in the earlier investigations men
reporting adequate levels of exercise experienced less coronary
heart disease, irrespective of their predispositions to avoid or
experience this condition.

Possible mechanisms of the exercise - coronary heart disease
association are considered and the author expresses scepticism
about the relevance of the high density lipoprotein hypothesis for
these men, though regrettably, direct observations remain to be
undertaken. The author speculates about endurance fitness as a
possible protective factor.

1. Physical activity of occupation

Initial prospective studies at the close of the 1940s and extending
through the 1950s found that men in physically active jobs, e.g.
the conductors of London's double-decker buses and postmen, had a
lower incidence of coronary heart disease - fewer first clinical
episodes - than comparable men in sedentary jobs, e.g. bus drivers,
or office clerks in postal or other government service (Morris et
al., 1953). Different men select, and are selected for, different
jobs. The underlying problem in this type of research was
immediately apparent. What proportion of the risk of developing
the disease is due to these selective factors, and what proportion
to the subsequent experience of the men - for example, their
different levels of physical activity over ten, twenty or thirty
years? One very obvious feature was that bus conductors were more
lightly built than bus drivers and we were able to confirm that
this difference was present from the time of taking up employment
with London Transport. The answer to the main question became
clear as the incidence of 'first coronaries' accumulated: bus
conductors suffered fewer such episodes than drivers, irrespective
of their physique, slim or portly, tall or short. Table 1 relates

the trouser waist band measurement to the most serious form of coronary heart disease, namely its first clinical appearance as 'sudden death'. Both the hypothetical 'predisposition' and the behavioural 'cause' seem to be contributing to the benefit of the conductors.

Table 1. Occupation, physique, and the incidence of 'sudden death' as first clinical manifestation of coronary heart disease in London busmen.

Uniform trouser-waist (inches)	Rates per 1000 p.a.	
	Bus conductors	Drivers
<32	0.5	1.1
34-37	0.5	0.8
38&+	0.7	2.0
All men	0.5	1.2

Men aged 35-64. Age-standardised. 1949-52-58, (Heady et al., 1961).

This result is typical of numerous studies undertaken since the 1950s which have attempted to explain and observe the association between physical activity and the incidence of coronary heart disease. Moreover, San Francisco dock workers allowed no personal selection of jobs, showed similar gradients of coronary heart disease with the level of physical activity associated with their occupation (Paffenbarger and Hale, 1975).

2. Exercise during leisure hours

By the 1960s it was evident that if physical activity was to contribute to the prevention of the 'modern epidemic' of coronary heart disease it would be through the medium of exercise taken in leisure time. People were becoming increasingly sedentary as physical effort, in particular anything strenuous, was progressively eliminated from work. In the 1960s this trend was already evident with mechanisation and automation; the development of robots and computers in conjunction with the growth of 'human service industry', etc., has further eliminated effort from work.

Table 2. Physical activity and the incidence of coronary heart disease in male executive grade civil servants.

	214 first clinical episodes	428 matched controls
(A) Total physical activity 'scores'*		
Fatal first attacks	628	653
Non-fatal	633	639
(B) 'Actual activity' scores**		
Rapidly fatal first attacks	231	256
Non-fatal myocardial infarction	220	230
Angina. etc	261	236

	Coronary Rates per cent
(C) Moderate activity*** Fatal first attacks, 1968/70-77	
Low third of men (0)	2.8
Mid third (4-80)	2.8
High third (81-880)	2.7
(D) Total activity, and vigorous exercise*** Fatal first attacks, 1968/70-77	
Low third of men (523)	2.7
Mid third (608)	3.1
High third (731)	2.2
Men reporting VE	0.9

Men aged 40-64 at entry to survey in 1968/70.

*Sum of points given for all physical activity in the two sample days, ranging from 1 point for 5 minutes sitting or lying awake to 7 points for 5 minutes of vigorous sports. No points given for sleeping. Working time was regarded as sitting and so rated. Periods of less than 5 minutes were disregarded (Yasin et al., 1967). Incidence of CHD, 1968/70-72.

**Scores for sitting time, and for very light standing activities off the job that were given 2 points per 5 minutes, were deducted from the totals of *. Incidence 1968/70-2.
***E.g., painting and decorating; lawn mowing; golf, table-tennis. 4 points per 5 minutes. Means of all the moderate activity that was reported in brackets. Rates are age-standardised.
****Men reporting 'vigorous exercise' (see text) were identified and analysed separately from the remainder. Means of total activity point scores in brackets.

A prospective study was undertaken of a large group of desk-bound office workers. The sample consisted of men in the executive grade of the British civil service, a narrow, homogeneous, educational, occupational and economic band of the middle class. At entry to the survey the men were given points for each five minutes' activity in an unannounced, two-day sample log that they completed for us (Morris et al., 1973). This assessment of physical activity was shown to give an acceptably valid account of habitual behaviour. We found little or no association between the incidence of coronary heart disease and the estimates of their total activity levels, Table 2 (A) and (B), so contradicting the hypothesis we had drawn from the earlier occupational studies. In Table 2 (C) the figures are particularly revealing as two thirds of the men engaged in such 'Do-it-Yourself' activity or recreation; again there was no correlation between the amount of moderate activity and the incidence of coronary heart disease. Deducting actual activity scores (B) from total physical activity scores (A) gives an estimate of inactivity, and this again showed no material difference between subjects developing coronary heart disease and their closely matched controls.

The figures for total activity and vigorous exercise, Table 2 (D), provided a possible explanation. Scrutiny of the records shows substantially more vigorous exercise among the controls and this was confirmed in systematic analysis of the total 'population': in men who reported vigorous exercise the rate of coronary heart disease was significantly lower. The category 'Vigorous Exercise' represents the most strenuous activities recorded, and these activities were further assessed by a threshold - as liable, on average, to entail peaks of energy expenditure of 7.5 kcal per minute, a standard definition of heavy industrial work. Typical examples are swimming, badminton, hill-walking, stair climbing, and 'vigorous getting about' such as walking at over four mph (6.4 kmph). We classify these activities as 'VE sports'. Other common forms of vigorous exercise undertaken during leisure time by these men such as digging, concreting and the heaviest jobs on the car, were classified as 'VE heavy work'. Such vigorous exercise was above the customary level of activity of these average middle-aged men and sufficient, we postulated, to produce 'overload' rather than mere energy output.

Sports will involve free, rhythmic, movement of large muscle masses, i.e. largely 'dynamic' activity. These activities are often sustained over considerable periods and can therefore be expected to entail some training or conditioning effect. These are commonly called 'aerobic', though the exercise and activity in general of such men is, of course, predominantly 'aerobic'. The Heavy Work is more heterogeneous. It is liable to be intermittent, involving more limited movement, often of smaller muscles, and with considerable pushing, pulling, lifting or carrying of heavy objects. This type of activity produces more static, isometric and 'anaerobic' effort. Associations of Heavy Work with the incidence of coronary heart disease were weaker and less consistent than for the vigorous Sports (Aerobic activity) which are now the main focus of enquiry.

Table 3 illustrates that though men involved in vigorous Sports smoked a little less than their colleagues not participating in vigorous exercise, but the different smoking rates in no way accounted for their lower incidence of coronary heart disease. The advantage bestowed by vigorous exercise in each category of smoker/non-smoker applied to other factors considered; similar beneficial results were found for vigorous exercise among the range of physiques in the study groups, on the analysis of parental mortality, with sundry medical conditions including hypertension, and with cholesterol levels (Morris, 1975; Epstein et al., 1976).

Table 3. Vigorous aerobic exercise (VE Sports), smoking, and the incidence of coronary heart disease in male executive civil servants.

Smoking*	1968/70-1978 Vigorous Sports*		No vigorous exercise	
	No. of men	CHD rate%	CHD rate %	No. of men
Never smoked	475	1.5	3.8	2465
Ex-smokers	635	2.1	5.1	3850
Pipe/cigar only	320	3.1	6.2	1930
All these	1430	2.1**	**5.0	8245
Cigarette Smokers:				
1-10 p.d.	270	5.3	8.3	1610
11+ p.d.	510	4.6	10.1	4225
All these	780	4.9**	**9.7	5835

* At entry, 1968/70.
**$p < 0.001$.

Age-standardised rates, men aged 40-64 at entry. 1136 first clinical episoders CHD in 17,944 men. Morris et al., 1980.

3. A new hypothesis

We now had a quite different hypothesis on the relationship
between physical activity and the incidence of coronary heart
disease. High total levels of physical activity were no longer
considered to be the crucial factor, the emphasis having turned to
the thresholds achieved in episodes of vigorous aerobic exercise.
Plainly in the present 'exercise revolution', and the general
encouragement of exercise for health promotion, it is necessary to
be clear about the type of exercise to be recommended for reducing
the incidence of coronary heart disease. This is a limited view
point, as exercise has also been shown to confer many other
physiological benefits; as well as the stamina that vigorous
aerobic exercise will induce - exercise can be considered as one of
the body's defences, important for weight regulation, and in
muscular strength and joint flexibility, etc.). Moreover, American
studies while confirming that vigorous sports were the most
beneficial, also found that there was a lower rate of coronary
heart disease in individuals achieving lower levels of aerobic
sportsplay (Paffenbarger et al., 1978).
    We therefore decided to mount a further prospective survey to
test this new hypothesis directly. A more direct method for
assessing habitual exercise was identified, seeking more
information about the exercise actually taken and exploring also
the characteristics of those who do and don't take various forms of
exercise to try and further clarify the abiding underlying problem
of self-selection bias.

4. Further survey: dose response

The method chosen for testing this new hypothesis was a four week
recall, a system developed over many years by the National Office
of Population Censuses and Surveys (GHS, 1973, 1978, 1982). Table 4
gives some preliminary results. The gradation of coronary heart
disease rates percent with frequency of vigorous exercise is
reassuring, though the advantage with occasional Sports (1-3 times
in the previous four weeks, i.e. less than once a week) raises
questions which are currently being addressed. Another aspect of
dose response, to the intensity of the exercise, is being studied
by way of assessing symptoms such as sweating and getting out of
breath. These symptoms it may be postulated, will indicate that
the vigorous exercise is utilising more than 60% of the maximum
oxygen intake, on average, of such middle-aged men, more than, say,
25 ml/kg/min. Preliminary analysis suggests that the rate of
coronary heart disease, when vigorous Sports produce these
symptoms, will be significantly lower than when they do not,
3.1% compared with 4.7%.

Table 4. Frequency of vigorous sports, and the incidence of coronary heart disease in male executive grade civil servants.

| | 1976-1985 CHD rates per cent | | | |
| | Vigorous sports in past 4 weeks* | | | |
	None	1-3 times	4-7	8&+
Fatal first clinical episodes	2.6	1.4	1.0	0.7
Non-fatal	3.7	3.7	2.5	1.3
Total	6.3	5.1	3.6	2.0

* Reported at entry, 1976.

Age-Standardised rates, men aged 45-59 at entry. 485 first clinical episodes CHD in 7820 men.
Overall rate with VE sports = 4.0%.
Preliminary result: Leisure - Activity Study, work in progress.

5. Exercise and exercisers

The possibility of selection-bias in this study is being approached by trying to identify which individuals choose to undertake differing forms of vigorous exercise.

Table 5 records the incidence of coronary heart disease in the study group in conjunction with a history of athleticism when younger. The middle-aged civil servants who were athletic when young (defined as engaging in the most vigorous exercise such as rugby and track and field sports) may be presumed to have been selectively fit at that stage of their lives, which may be related to upbringing and/or genetically dictated. Those who then gave up exercise derived no advantage in incidence of coronary heart disease in later life unless they were currently also engaged in vigorous Sport. And civil servants who were undertaking vigorous Sport in later life had a lower incidence of coronary heart disease irrespective of their history of athleticism as young men.
It is interesting to compare the results of the study on British civil servants with the study undertaken by Paffenbarger on Harvard Alumni which quite independently gave the same answer (Paffenbarger, Wing and Hyde, 1978).

Table 5. Athleticism when young, current vigorous sports, and the incidence of coronary heart disease in male executive grade civil servants.

	Athletic history %
Men reporting current VE sports*	9.5
Not reporting current VE sports*	6.1

	CHD incidence rate %**
Athletic history present	5.6
Athletic history absent	5.1
Athletic history present	
Current regular VE sports***	2.9
No VE sports	5.9
Athletic history absent	
Current regular VE sports	2.3
No VE sports	5.3

Men aged 45-59 at entry in 1976. Athletic history when young as
  given at entry.
  *In past 4 weeks, at entry.
 **incidence, first clinical episodes 1976-1984.
***4 or more times in past 4 weeks.
  Preliminary result.

    Another aspect of the present study is to consider the men's attitudes to health and preventive medicine to identify relevant differences between people. Table 6 records attitudes to the possibilities of control of health and current vigorous exercise levels. Over-all the group with a positive attitude to health enjoyed a somewhat lower incidence of coronary heart disease. However, the table illustrates a falling incidence of coronary heart disease in association with increasing levels of vigorous exercise in both groups, irrespective of a positive or other attitude to health. So it is again irrelevant to the main hypothesis that, as expected, there were somewhat more 'definites' among the VE sportsmen (74% compared with 58%).

Table 6. Attitudes to health and prevention, current vigorous sports, and the incidence of coronary heart disease in male executive grade civil servants.

| | 1976-1985 CHD rates per cent | | |
| | Vigorous sports in past 4 weeks | | |
	None	Occasional	Regular
'Definitely can do something to prevent ill-health in future'	6.1	4.5	2.8
Other men	6.6	5.7	3.2

Age-standardised rates, men aged 45-59 at entry.
Preliminary result.

6. Other exercise

Analysis is under way of the many other forms of physical activity undertaken by the men in the second survey. The preliminary results are disappointing and there is little of interest. Table 7 illustrates that the incidence of coronary heart disease is not significantly affected by the number of hours spent dancing or undertaking 'heavy work' as defined during the four week base line study period.

Table 7. Other physical activity and the incidence of coronary heart disease in male executive grade civil servants.

| | 1976-1985 CHD rates per cent Hours in past four weeks | | | | |
	0	1-3	4-7	8-11	12&+
Dancing	6.2	5.8	8.2	11.11	3.1
Heavy work	6.2	5.9	6.1	5.6	4.1

Age standardised rates, men aged 45-59 at entry
Preliminary result.

7. Specificity of effect?

The evidence suggests that adequate vigorous exercise is a defence against myocardial ischaemia and its consequences. It remains an open question whether the 'protective factor' of vigorous exercise is limited to this. The recent important paper by Paffenbarger and his colleagues (1984) is summarised in Table 8. Exercise in leisure-time (Sportsplay) was associated with lower rates of all cardiovascular deaths, including coronary heart disease and stroke, as well as deaths due to respiratory disease. There was no influence on deaths from cancer. Our own unpublished data agrees.

Table 8. Physical activity/exercise in leisure-time, and death rates in Harvard alumni.

1962-1978

Rates per 10,000 man-years of observation

Cause of death	Physical activity index, kcal/week		
	<500	500-1999	2000&+
All causes (n=1,413)	84.8	66.0	52.1
Total cardiovascular disease (n=640)	39.5	30.8	21.4
Coronary heart disease (n=441) (1/3 all deaths)	25.7	21.2	16.4
Stroke (n=103)	6.5	5.2	2.4
Total respiratory diseases (n=60)	6.0	3.2	1.5

16936 men aged 55-74 at entry. Rates are standardised for age, cigarette smoking and history of hypertension. Paffenbarger et al., 1984.

8. Possible mechanisms

Self-selection must give rise to bias: there is no doubt that those participating in vigorous aerobic exercise on a regular basis are a self-selected group of men. Equally, there is no evidence that such favourable predispositions account for the protection against coronary heart disease, as is highlighted in Table 3. 21.5% of men participating in vigorous exercise had never smoked compared with 17.5% of the less active. This is a significant and by no means negligible difference. However the men who were moderate or heavy smokers also showed an undoubted beneficial effect from participating in vigorous exercise. Similarly, (see Table 5) more of the men engaging in vigorous sports had been athletic when young (9.5% compared with 6.1%), but it was only vigorous exercise in middle-age that gave any protection against coronary heart disease.

Despite a vast effort there is no clear understanding of the mechanisms whereby exercise lowers the incidence of coronary heart disease, atherosclerosis and/or myocardial ischaemia. To date, two main lines of work have yielded no convincing explanation.

First it is suggested that adequate exercise moderates the standard risk factors of coronary heart disease, for example, smoking and blood lipid patterns. In general this is so, though there are exceptions, and, as a result, an overall lowering of coronary risk factor are to be expected with adequate exercise. However, there is no indication that such associations wholly or largely account for the substantial variation of coronary rates with exercise that are increasingly being reported (Morris, 1975; Epstein et al., 1976; Brand et al, 1979; Morris, 1983), as Table 3 of the present paper again exemplifies; and there are corresponding data on weight, blood pressure and cholesterol. However welcome these benefits, the main question remains open.

I have always been sceptical about the high density lipoprotein hypothesis. Jogging eight miles (13 km) a week, which is the threshold for raising high density lipoprotein levels (Wood et al., 1983; Haskell, 1984), seems to me to be more exercise - more intense and longer - than can be postulated to underlie the beneficial experience of our civil servants. We now need studies of apoproteins, lipoprotein lipase, etc. Lipid patterns among the London Transport staff, see Table 9, are relevant: the alpha correspond to high density lipoproteins. On the other hand, triglycerides carried in the Sf fractions 20-400 are expectedly low. (Unfortunately we were unable to study these men in the fasting state, examining them as assorted pairs as they came off work, at variable times in relationship to their last meal). Findings at 40-49 and 60-64 were similar.

Table 9. Lipid patterns in London Busmen mg/100ml.

	Conductors (n=100)	Drivers (n=165)
Total plasma cholesterol	235	251
∝lipoprotein	45	49
β lipoprotein	190	201
Sf20-400	101	156

Sample of working men, aged 50-59, with no clinical or ECG evidence of coronary heart disease. Kagan, 1960; Morris et al., 1966. G.L. Mills, Courtauld Institute.

An earlier clue to possible mechanisms is illustrated in Table 10. In this study, individuals dying from non-vascular disorders were shown to have a lower prevalence of thrombotic/occlusive coronary artery disease if their occupation involved heavy work

(Morris, 1975). Today, we require population studies of factor 7, fibrinolytic activity, etc., in relationship to physical activity patterns. Data on exercise and stress, in relation to coronary heart disease, is quite deficient.

Table 10. Physical activity of occupation, and the prevalence of coronary atherosclerosis and ischaemic heart disease at necropsy in deaths from other than vascular disease.

| | Rates, per cent | | |
| | | Occupation | |
	Heavy	Active	Light
Coronary atherosclerosis			
Mural disease			
Present	82%	82%	89%
Severe	15	15	16
Calcified	18	18	19
Occlusion*	2.5	3.0	3.7
Ischaemic heart disease			
Small myocardial scars	4.2	4.7	6.6
Large fibrous patch	0.6	1.6	2.6

*Complete, or near-complete, occlusion of main coronary artery.
2,700 necropsies. National Necropsy Study (Morris, 1975).
Men aged 45-70. Age standardised rates.

The main finding in the present studies is that habitual vigorous aerobic exercise for sustained periods, involving the movement of large muscle masses, is the only exercise factor which is consistently and substantially associated with a lower incidence of coronary heart disease. This type of exercise improves 'physical fitness' and its principal components, <u>aerobic power</u> or VO_2 max; and even more, <u>aerobic capacity</u>, stamina, and endurance fitness, which means the capacity to function for prolonged periods at a high proportion of VO_2 max whatever the level of that may be. Reduction in the endurance fitness of the population, because of its strong dependence on such habitual vigorous exercise may well be one of the main physiological consequences of the progressive elimination of vigorous activity in work and the rest of daily life in advanced industrial and urbanised society. It is this type of society which is experiencing the modern epidemic of heart attacks. The VO_2 max itself is likely to have been less affected because it is so strongly genetically determined and it is therefore less likely to be less relevant to this predominantly behavioural/environmental disease. Aerobic capacity, on the other hand, is highly susceptible to improvement by vigorous aerobic exercise.
Is it possible that improved physical fitness, improved cardiovascular function is in itself an important mechanism whereby appropriate exercise protects against coronary heart disease? Putting it at its most simple the hypothesis would be that physical

fitness is a defence against coronary heart disease. The central
and peripheral processes that might be involved need to be considered
in the slowing and sparing of the heart, increased myocardial
power, moderation of blood pressure rises, changes in muscle, etc.
The difficulty in testing this hypothesis is that there is no
satisfactory method presently available for measuring endurance
fitness in a population. Identifying such a method is now the main
concern, and the main obstacle to progress, of the British National
Fitness survey, inspired by the Canadian studies. When this
particular problem is solved, and after 2 1/2 years study this now
looks more hopeful, we should be able to launch large scale
prospective studies of exercise patterns, fitness levels and the
incidence of coronary heart disease in free living populations.

I would like to comment on health education. The many studies
referred to above have indicated the type of exercise that may be
beneficial. The question arises, however, of the quantity of
exercise that maybe beneficial. Conventional wisdom, derived mainly
from laboratory training experiments monitoring $\dot{V}O_2$ max suggest
that 20-30 minutes of sub-maximal aerobic work a week is necessary.
Again we need a lot more information on diverse populations, with
diverse end points: a job once more for epidemiologists and
physiologists, hopefully working together.

Acknowledgements

The authors are deeply grateful to the collaborators in these
studies: to the late Dr S.P.W. Chave; Dr E.H. Burgess, Medical
Adviser, the Inland Revenue; and the many thousands of men who have
participated in these studies over the years. Mrs D. Cook is
responsible for the documentation, Miss K. Gulliford for the
clerical work, and both for the coding. The research is funded by
MRC Special Project Grant 7504263.

References

Brand, R.J., Paffenbarger R.S., Sholtz, R.I., Kampert, J.B. (1979).
    Work activity and fatal heart attacks studied by multiple
    logistic analysis. Am. J. Epidemiol. 110:52-62.
Epstein, L., Miller, G.J., Stitt, F.W., Morris, J.N. (1976).
    Vigorous exercise in leisure-time, coronary risk factors, and
    resting electrocardiogram in middle-aged male civil servants.
    Br. HtJ. 38:403-409.
General Household Survey, Report. 1973, 1977, 1982. London:
    H.M.S.O.
Haskell, W.L. (1984). Exercise-induced changes in plasma lipids and
    lipoproteins. Prev. Med. 13:23-36.
Heady, J.A. Morris, J.N., Kagan, A., Raffle, P.A.B. (1961).
    Coronary heart disease in London busmen: a progress report with
    particular reference to physique. Br. J. Prev. & Soc. Med.
    15:143-153.
Kagan, A. (1960). Atherosclerosis of the cornary arteries -
    epidemiological considerations. Proc. R. Soc. Med. 53:18-22.

Morris, J.N. (1951). Recent history of coronary disease. Lancet.
    i,1-7, 69-73.
Morris, J.N. (1975). Uses of Epidemiology. London & New York:
    Churchill-Livingston. Reprinted 1983.
Morris, J.N. (1983). Exercise, health and medicine. Br. Med. J.
    287:357-358.
Morris, J.N., Heady, J.A., Raffle, P.A.B., Roberts, C.G., Parks,
    J.W. (1953). Coronary heart disease and physical activity of
    work. Lancet. ii, 1053-1057, 1111-1120.
Morris, J.N., Kagan, A., Pattison, D.C., Gardner, M.J., Raffle,
    P.A.B. (1966). Incidence and prediction of ischaemic heart
    disease in London busmen. Lancet. ii,553-559.
Morris, J.N., Chave, S.P.W., Adam, C., Sirey, C., Epstein, L.,
    Sheehan, D.J. (1973). Vigorous exercise in leisure-time and the
    incidence of coronary heart disease. Lancet. i,333-339.
Morris, J.N., Everitt, M.G., Pollard, R., Chave, S.P.W.,
    Semmence, A.M. (1980). Lancet. ii,1207-1210.
Paffenbarger, R.S. and Hale, W. (1975). Work activity and coronary
    heart mortality. N. Engl. J. Med. 292:545-550.
Paffenbarger, R.S., Wing, A.L., Hyde, R.T. (1978). Physical
    activity as an index of heart attack risk in college alumni.
    Am. J. Epidemiol. 108:161-175.
Paffenbarger, R.S., Hyde, R.T., Wing, A.L., Steinmetz, C.H. (1984).
    A natural history of athleticism and cardiovascular health.
    JAMA. 252:491-495.
Wood, P.D., Haskell, W.L., Blair, S.N., Williams, P.T., Krauss,
    R.M. Lindgren, F.T., Albers, J.J., Ho, P.H., Farquhar, J.W.
    (1983). Increased exercise level and plasma lipoprotein
    concentrations; a one-year randomised, controlled study in
    sedentry middle-aged men. Metabolism. 32:31-39.

Discussion

Professor Åstrand, Stockholm, Sweden
Could you comment on Professor Paffenbarger's studies of Harvard
Alumni, where he is more concerned about the total extra energy
output achieving 2000 kilo-calories per week and he places less
emphasis on how vigorous the exercise is.

Professor Morris, London, England
The exercise that Paffenbarger reports is mainly aerobic, of
course, and he gets more positive effects in men who undertake what
we call 'vigorous exercise'. However he also reports positive
findings with ordinary walking which we did not find, and we have
spent a lot of time trying to sort out this difference. So far we
have been unable to resolve the difference but I have a hunch that
his men are, in general, much less active than our men.

Dr J.R.Sutton, Ontario, Canada

When you looked at the incidence of coronary heart disease relating
to activity, did the people with the highest activity levels have a
chronic history of activity as well as vigorous activity within the
last four weeks? The reason I ask is because of concern that a
middle aged person who suddenly adopts vigorous activity patterns
may well be at a slightly higher risk of developing a coronary
incident. Were you able to look at that aspect?

Professor Morris, London, England

Very little. Our first study of exercise in leisure-time was done
in 1968-70 and the second in 1976. What we can say is that men
undertaking vigorous exercise in 1976 were much more likely to have
done so also in 1968-70. Equally, we now have a third survey from
1982-84 and we can say from this study that unless you are doing
vigorous exercise by middle age it is very unlikely that you will
adopt it in later life; but we haven't a direct answer to the
question.

Professor Montoye, Wisconsin, USA

Thank you, Professor Morris for a very nice review of your work.
I would like to ask you about mechanisms and invite you to hazard
a guess as to what are the effects of exercise in terms of whether
it affects the atherosclerotic process or is the process related
to diet? Does exercise somehow affect the heart in such a way that
it enables people to live longer with atherosclerosis?

Professor Morris

To what extent does exercise affect atherosclerosis? I wish to be
cautious in my comments about this because of the work that is
being presented by Kramsch and colleagues who are studying
primates. They have shown dramatic beneficial effects of exercise
on the presence of atherosclerotic lesions in the coronary arteries
disease among primates. These observations are more positive than
anyone has shown before. Until we have absorbed these studies we
must be cautious in their interpretation, but they are showing
substantially less coronary atherosclerosis, including occlusive
lesions, in those monkeys undertaking vigorous aerobic exercise.

Our previous work suggested that exercise is related only to the
frequency of occlusive lesions. There was no difference in the
amount of coronary mural disease in different occupations; but we
found a real difference in the number of occlusive lesions, i.e.
major obstruction of major coronary arteries and this is the
interesting hypothesis: this is what appears to have increased in
the 20th century giving rise to the modern epidemic.

In more general terms of mechanism, the main work done on this
area focuses on the possibility that exercise moderates standard
risk factors. Exercise does affect the standard risk factors to
some extent in many but not all studies, but this is often to quite
a small degree in biological terms though statistically it can be
very significant. There is lowering of cholesterol levels and men
undertaking heavy activity have lower blood pressures but these
advantages do not add up to an explanation. Then the high density
lipoproteins story came along and we thought here was a chance of
salvation. I have always been suspicious, you might say prejudiced

against the lipoprotein story, for two reasons. First the Stanford studies have shown that you have to jog for more than eight miles a week to produce a real rise in high density lipoprotein levels. We, and others, are showing benefits in terms of coronary heart disease at lower exercise levels than that. The second reason I am sceptical about the high density lipoproteins story is because of the observations on lipoproteins we made a long time ago in our original studies of busmen (Table 8). There is no difference in alpha levels.

I think we now have to look seriously at cardiovascular fitness itself as a possible protective factor against coronary heart disease. The studies we are thinking of now, following advice from members of this audience, including Professor Clyde Williams, indicate the importance of differentiating between aerobic power, which is under genetic control and can only be modified to a minor extent by exercise, and endurance fitness which is very heavily influenced by exercise. The kind of exercise my people are doing which is giving them some sort of protection against coronary heart disease is the kind of exercise which produces endurance fitness. The big physiological change in modern times, we can speculate, has been the reduction of endurance fitness-activities in daily life. The hypothesis we need to test is that endurance fitness is a protective factor against coronary heart disease and here there are difficulties in identifying a method of study in the population.

If a valid technique for measuring endurance fitness is identified we should be able to raise all sorts of questions on the function of the heart and muscles and hopefully add to the many small bits of explanation available at present with regard to the benefits of exercise.

Exercise and chronic disease

A. YOUNG

Regular physical activity and participation in sport can increase
endurance, strength, joint mobility, co-ordination, confidence, and
self-esteem. An understanding of the underlying physiology is
essential for the optimal management of any patient whose
functional abilities are limited.

This is especially true in old age. Advancing age brings an
increasing prevalence of chronic disease and an apparently
obligatory loss of muscle mass and physical performance, placing
many elderly people perilously close to 'thresholds' for
functionally important activities. Any further loss, no matter how
slight, has a major impact on the quality of life.

Nevertheless, the intrinsic strength and the aerobic metabolism
of muscle seem to be just as trainable in old age as in youth.
Moreover, the improvements most relevant to everyday life may be
many times greater than the changes in maximal performance.

There are important applications of physical training in the
prevention, treatment and/or amelioration of many diseases,
including ischaemic heart disease, airflow obstruction, peripheral
arterial disease, osteoporosis, obesity, diabetes mellitus, and
hypertension. This is still not reflected in conventional medical
teaching.

1. Introduction

'The restoration of patients to their fullest physical, mental and
social capability'. (Mair, 1972)

Mair's definition of rehabilitation is an excellent statement of
the clinician's aim for any patient with chronic disease.
Sometimes, that aim may be achieved by treating the underlying
disease. More often, measures are also required to reduce the
impact on the individual patient of the disease itself and of the
residual, irreversible impairment which remains after specific
treatment of the disease. Regular physical activity and
participation in sport can increase endurance, strength, joint
mobility, co-ordination, confidence, and self-esteem. It is not
surprising, therefore, that there are many situations where
exercise and sport may be important for the patient with chronic
disease.

Two recent symposia have attempted to bring current exercise
physiology to the attention of practising doctors: one in the
United Kingdom (sponsored by the Medical Research Society, the
Sports Council, and the Health Education Council) and the other in
Sweden (an Acta Medica Scandinavica Symposium). The proceedings of
both have been published (Smith et al., 1984; Åstrand and Grimby,
1986) and are recommended. This short review attempts to highlight
some aspects of the role of exercise in relation to chronic disease
and disability.

2. Physical ability in old age

Chronic diseases are commonest in elderly people. Moreover, even
healthy elderly people suffer from a general loss of physical
ability. If this could be prevented or minimised, it would improve
the quality of life for a large number of people and reduce the
social and economic cost of supporting an infirm aged population.

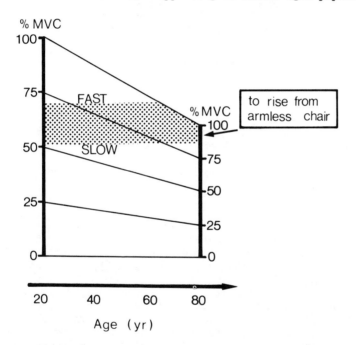

Figure 1. Effect of age on the estimated percentage of a maximal
voluntary contraction (%MVC) of the quadriceps muscles required
to raise a healthy woman from a low, armless, chair (Young, 1986).
(By permission of the Editor, Acta Medica Scandinavica).
(c.f. figure devised by Saltin (1980) for the effect of age on
aerobic power and the oxygen costs of everyday activities).

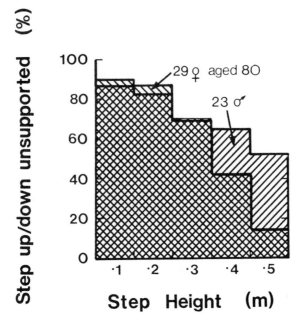

Figure 2. Ability of healthy elderly people to step unsupported
up and down different heights of step (Danneskiold-Samsøe et al.,
1984).
(Reproduced from Young (1986) by permission of the Editor,
Acta Medica Scandinavica).

2.1 'Thresholds'
Muscle mass and strength (for references see Young et al., 1984,
1985) and aerobic power (for references see Shephard, 1978) decline
at about 1% per annum. This probably places many elderly people
perilously close to 'thresholds' for functionally important
activities (Saltin, 1980; Young, 1986).

Any further loss of strength, no matter how slight, may well
have a major impact on the quality of life. It seems likely that
the healthy 80-year-old woman is at, or very near to, the threshold
value of quadriceps strength for rising from a low, armless chair
(or from the lavatory) (Fig. 1). In a Danish study (Danneskiold-
Samsøe et al., 1984), nearly 40% of healthy 80-year-old women were
unable to step up on to, and down from, a 40cm step without
support. Most were unable to manage a 50cm step without support
(Fig. 2).

Similarly, the loss of aerobic functional reserve means that
even a small further decline in aerobic power may render some
everyday activities impossible to sustain, or so dependent on
anaerobic metabolism as to be unpleasant. For example, for the
average 70 to 75-year-old woman, just walking at 5km/hr (3.1mph) is
already maximal aerobic exercise (Saltin, 1980).

There have been remarkably few studies of functional ability in old age which have attempted to examine its relationship with accurate measurements of muscular strength and aerobic power. It would be valuable if a hierarchy of strength-related thresholds could be defined, along with their relationship to laboratory measurements of strength. An equivalent hierarchy of thresholds for the ability to perform aerobic exercise would also be valuable. It would then be possible to identify those people closest to important thresholds and intervene before they cross them.

2.2 The effect of training

It seems clear that advancing age brings an obligatory loss of physical performance. Nevertheless, it also seems clear that most of the training effects of regular exercise are much the same, in relative terms, in old age as in youth.

2.2.1 Strength training

The strength of elderly muscles can be increased by physical training. A 10 to 20% improvement in the isometric and isokinetic strength of the quadriceps muscles of 70-year-old men can be produced fairly readily (Aniansson and Gustafsson, 1981), effectively postponing strength-related thresholds for at least another 10 to 20 years.

Training studies with younger subjects suggest that some of the potential benefits may be even greater than this. Strength-training produces an improvement in weight-lifting ability which is greater than the improvement in the strength of the muscle concerned (Rutherford and Jones, 1986). After several weeks of weight-training, which will produce some 15% increase in the isometric strength of the quadriceps, there may be a 200% increase in the maximum weight which can be lifted by knee extension. Although simple compared to many daily activities, weight-training movements are more complex than measurements of isometric, or isokinetic, strength. They require the co-ordinated activation of other muscles, to stabilise the body. If an elderly person's functional deficit is due, in part, to a loss of skill and co-ordination, it may be possible to produce improvements in functional ability which are much greater than the improvements in the strength of individual muscles. The choice of rehabilitation activity will be important; 'practice' may be at least as important as 'training'.

2.2.2 Endurance training

At least up to age 70, there appears to be no unusual difficulty in producing a 10 to 25% improvement training (for review see Sidney, 1981). In even older subjects, there is a suggestion that maximal oxygen uptake may not be increased quite as readily, although the heart rate response to submaximal exercise is still reduced (Benestad, 1965).

In younger subjects, the ability to sustain exercise at a fixed proportion of the maximal oxygen uptake is much more sensitive to training than is the maximal oxygen uptake itself. The time for which exercise can be sustained at 75% of the maximal oxygen uptake may increase by 200 to 500% when the maximal uptake itself has increased by only 5 to 20%. It seems likely that this is equally true for elderly people. Just as with strength, the improvements most relevant to everyday life may be many times greater than the changes in maximal performance.

3. Exercise to reverse the effects of disuse

Even healthy volunteers put into bed for two or three weeks suffer a dramatic loss of fitness. In one famous study (Saltin et al., 1968) five students were put to bed for three weeks. Before the bed rest, their average heart rate while exercising at an oxygen consumption approximately equivalent to walking on the level at four and a half miles per hour was 129 beats per minute. This rose to 154 beats per minute following the period of bed rest. This change was associated with a 25 to 30% drop in their maximum aerobic power.

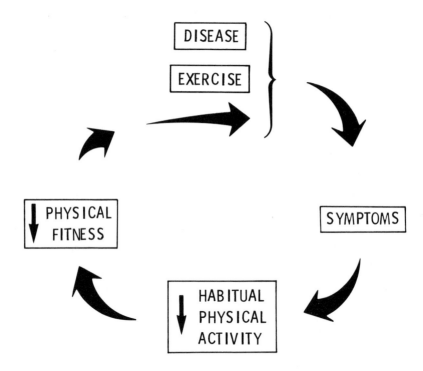

Figure 3. The 'disuse ↔ disability' spiral (Young, 1981). (By permission of the publisher).

There is a vicious circle that may ensnare patients with exercise-related symptoms, with the result that they become less active, less fit, and have their symptoms provoked by progressively lower levels of exercise (Fig. 3). The descending spiral of disuse and disability may turn through so many revolutions that a patient with only moderate disease becomes severely disabled by their low exercise tolerance.

For example, a patient with angina may be advised to avoid symptoms by 'taking it easy'. This, however, will cause him to lose fitness and his heart rate response to a given submaximal level of exercise will rise. The result will be that the intensity of exercise required to push his myocardial work-rate past his angina threshold will become progressively lower. This vicious circle may also operate in other conditions, such as chronic bronchitis or intermittent claudication.

Elderly people are probably even more likely to fall into this trap. At 85, two weeks in bed may mean that just dressing and undressing provoke a maximal heart-rate response, the production of lactate, and a corresponding sense of effort and dyspnoea.

4. Exercise to compensate for residual impairment

In addition to reversing the effects of disuse, the body's adaptations to an increase in habitual physical ability may help patients compensate for the impairment which still remains after optimal concentional treatment of their disease. The wheelchair athlete's greater than normal arm strength goes some way towards compensating for the loss of lower-limb function.

4.1 Intermittent claudication

Intermittent claudication provides another, less obvious, example of enhanced fitness compensating for residual physical impairment. Walking training greatly increases the distance that can be walked before the onset of claudication pain. There is little or no improvement in the maximal blood flow to the affected calf muscles but the trained muscles' greater content of oxidative enzymes and greater capillarity makes them better able to extract oxygen from the small amount of blood which reaches them. A doubling of the walking tolerance can be expected after three to four months of training (Dahllöf et al., 1983). It has been suggested that all patients with uncomplicated intermittent claudication should be treated by physical training before surgery is considered, that more is likely to be achieved than by surgery, that training has fewer complications than surgery, and that it may even give better long-term results (Scherstén, 1984).

4.2 Angina

Angina occurs when myocardial oxygen demand is greater than the delivery of oxygen to the myocardium. The heart rate is one of the most important factors determining the oxygen requirement of the myocardium. Aerobic training reduces the heart rate response to a constant sub-maximal level of exercise. It therefore reduces the myocardial oxygen requirement for that level of physical activity. Thus, a level of exercise which would have produced angina at a heart rate of, say, 140 beats per minute, will be performed after training with a heart rate of perhaps 130 beats per minute. This will be below that patient's angina threshold and he will be able to exercise at that intensity for longer and without symptoms. Despite the fact that the severity of his ischaemic heart disease will almost certainly be unchanged, it will be less disabling.

4.3 Chronic airflow obstruction

Before the exercise tolerance of a patient with chronic airflow
obstruction can be increased, it is necessary to understand the
nature of the factor limiting performance. The approach to that
particular patient's rehabilitation will vary depending on whether
the limiting factor is the airflow obstruction itself,
deconditioning, respiratory muscle fatigue, anxiety, or respiratory
discomfort (Young, 1983). A recent editorial gives a succinct
review of the place of arm muscle training, leg muscle training and
respiratory muscle training in different categories of patients
with respiratory impairment (Casaburi and Wasserman, 1986).
Despite the undoubted benefit that many patients derive from
exercise training, in virtually none does the residual airflow
obstruction itself become less severe.

5. Exercise to counter the psychological effects
   of physical disease and disability

Depression and anxiety often follow a myocardial infarction and can
be relieved by physical training. The ability to perform physical
exercise can improve a patient's self-image and renews 'feelings of
control over (the) body, promotes self-esteem, and helps dissipate
tension and anger' (Cohn, 1982).

Children with diabetes, asthma or epilepsy benefit from the
opportunity to participate in sport or, better still, the
opportunity to excel in sport. Children stop seeing themselves as
invalids; they are just as good as their friends. This, however,
requires that doctors should be able to prescribe each child's
drugs in a regime appropriate to the chosen pattern and intensity
of exercise. They should also be able to guide the choice of
sport.

For very elderly people, there may also be other potential
benefits. The performance of floor exercises may help assuage the
disabling dread of being unable to rise from a fall, as well as
contributing to the retention of this crucial skill. I am also
impressed by anecdotal accounts of the emotional benefit derived
from socially acceptable, but non-clinical, touching, when
exercising in pairs.

6. Exercise to treat the underlying disease

6.1 Diabetes Mellitus

Physical training may improve the control of maturity-onset diabetes
by partially restoring peripheral insulin sensitivity. It also
reduces the insulin requirements of the insulin-dependent patient
whose diabetes is well-controlled, but this is of limited practical
value in management. These topics are discussed in greater detail
elsewhere (e.g. Berger et al., 1982; Kemmer and Berger, 1983;
Berger, 1984; Macleod and Sönksen, 1985).

Holloszy (1986) suggested to the Acta Medica Scandinavica
symposium that, if the exercise is vigorous enough, the age-related
decline in the glucose tolerance of normal subjects, and the

increase in insulin resistance, may even be completely abolished
by physical training.

It is still far from clear to what extent these phenomena are
the result of the acute effects of each bout of exercise or of a
cumulative, 'training' effect, Holloszy asked whether the effect of
training is merely that it enables the subject to exercise hard
enough to produce the insulin-like acute effects of vigorous
exercise.

6.2 Hypertension

It is also possible that mild or moderate hypertension may be
reduced by physical training. Unfortunately, many of the studies
in this area have been methodologically inadequate. Nevertheless,
there does seem to be an important effect (Tipton, 1984; Hagberg,
1986) but it is again far from clear whether this is a true
training effect or whether it is an acute effect of exercise,
persisting from one training bout to the next. An important
clinical point is that it is still not known whether the sequelae
of hypertension are more effectively avoided when pressure is
reduced by exercise than by drugs.

7. Exercise to prevent disease

7.1 Ischaemic heart disease

The apparently considerable protective effect of regular, vigorous
exercise is discussed elsewhere in these proceedings by Professor
J.N. Morris.

7.2 Obesity

The contribution of regular exercise to the prevention of obesity
has probably been underestimated in the past, but is now more
widely recognised (Royal College of Physicians of London, 1983).
It has been proposed that an important mechanism may be a slight
elevation of metabolic rate persisting for many hours after
vigorous exercise has ceased (Newsholme, 1984).

A potential pitfall for the clinician is that findings with
normal subjects cannot be assumed to apply to grossly obese
patients; the levels of exercise involved may be quite unrealistic.
Weight control always depends on keeping a balance between energy
intake and expenditure. Garrow (1986) has suggested that exercise
may be more important for those with a Quetlet index less than
$30kg/m^2$. The challenge now is to determine the relative
importance of exercise and diet between 30 and $40kg/m^2$, that is
for the majority of patients with clinically important obesity.

7.3 Osteoporosis

Physical exercise is one of the most important factors in achieving
peak bone mass and in maintaining it thereafter. It seems that the
loss of skeletal calcium following the menopause can be slowed by a
programme of regular physical activity (e.g. Smith et al., 1981).

The preservation of bone mineral is a highly specific response
to exercise, localised to the bone(s) being subjected to mechanical
stress (Smith, 1986). Bone strength is also improved by
remodelling, in response to the applied stresses (Lanyon and Rubin,

1983; Smith, 1986). Future work must concentrate on the practical implications of these new examples of the specificity of training.

8. Recommendations

It is important for all doctors to know more about when and why to promote or prescribe exercise, and to know how to ensure that all may exercise safely and enjoyably. A sound understanding of the physiology of muscular exercise and of the associated homoeostatic mechanisms should be the starting point for much of clinical practice but these matters receive scant attention in conventional medical teaching. The usual 'static' concept of the patient even means that physical examination too rarely includes an analysis of the patient's ability to walk, run, lift, carry, climb stairs, bend down, stand up, dress and undress.

A recent survey of final-year medical students throughout the United Kingdom (Young et al., 1983) indicated that the students recognised the need for more teaching on medical aspects of exercise. It seems that even fundamental exercise physiology is not successfully taught; 57% of the students did not know that physical training reduces the heart rate response of elderly subjects to submaximal exercise and 19% did not even know that this was true for young adults. Clearly, there is a major medical education task ahead of us. This is discussed by Dr M. Gray (this volume), along with steps to change public attitudes to exercise participation by elderly people and by people with chronic disease, the importance of sports participation if regular exercise is to be continued, the training of lay people to lead exercise groups, and the architectural and other changes which will have to take place if if everyone who would benefit from exercise is to obtain access to appropriate facilities.

References

Aniansson, A. and Gustafsson, E. (1981). Physical training in
    elderly men with special reference to quadriceps strength and
    morphology. Clin. Physiol. 1:87-98.
Åstrand, P.-O. and Grimby, G. (editors) (1986). Physical activity
    in health and disease. Acta. med. scand. Suppl. (in press).
Benestad, A.M. (1965). Trainability of old men. Acta Med.
    Scand. 178:321-327.
Berger, M. (1984). Exercise in the prevention and management of
    diabetes mellitus. In Exercise, Health and Medicine;
    Proceedings (edited by A. Smith et al.,) pp. 37-38.
    London: Sports Council.
Berger, M., Christacopoulos, P. and Wahren, J. (1982). Diabetes
    and Exercise. Bern: Hans Huber.
Casaburi, R. and Wasserman, K. (1986). Exercise training in
    pulmonary rehabilitation. New Engl. J. Med. 314:1509-1511
Cohn, A.H. (1982). Chemotherapy from an insider's perspective.
    Lancet i:1006-1009.

Dahllöf, A,.-G., Holm, J. and Schersten, T. (1983). Exercise
   training of patients with intermittent claudication.
   Scand. J. Rehab. Med. Suppl. 9:20-26.
Danneskiold-Samsøe, B., Kofod, V., Munter, J., Grimby, G., Schnohr,
   P. and Jensen, G. (1984). Muscle strength and functional
   capacity in 78-81 year old men and women. Eur. J. Appl.
   Physiol. 52:310-314.
Garrow, J. (1986). Effects of exercise on obesity. In Physical
   Activity in Health and Disease (edited by P.-O. Astrand and G.
   Grimby), Acta med. scand. Suppl. (in press).
Hagberg, J. (1986). The effects of exercise on hypertension.
   In Physical Activity in Health and Disease (edited by P.-O.
   Astrand and G. Grimby), Acta med. scand. Suppl. (in press).
Holloszy, J. (1986). Effect of exercise on glucose tolerance and
   insulin resistance. In Physical Activity in Health and Disease
   (edited by P.-O. Astrand and G. Grimby), Acta med. scand.
   Suppl. (in press).
Kemmer, F.W. and Berger, M. (1983). Exercise and diabetes
   mellitus: physical activity as a part of daily life and its role
   in the treatment of diabetic patients. Int. J. Sports Med.
   4(2):77-88.
Lanyon, L. and Rubin, C.T. (1983). Regulation of bone mass in
   response to physical activity. In Osteoporsis, a
   Multidisciplinary Problem (edited by A. St. J. Dixon, R.G.G.
   Russell and T.C.B. Stamp), pp.51-61. Royal Society of Medicine
   International Congress and Symposium Series No.55,
   London: Academic Press.
Macleod, A. and Sönksen, P. (1985). Exercise for diabetics.
   Update. 30:468-474.
Mair, A. (chairman) (1972) Medical rehabilitation: the pattern
   for the future. Report of a sub-committee for the Standing
   Medical Advisory Committee, Scottish Home and Health Department
   and Scottish Health Services Council. London: Her Majesty's
   Stationery Office.
Newsholme, E.A. (1984). Exercise and obesity. In Exercise Health
   and Medicine; Proceedings (edited by A. Smith et al.,) pp.
   41-42. London: Sports Council.
Royal College of Physicians of London (1983). Obesity; a report.
   J. Roy. Coll. Phys. Lond. 17:5-65.
Rutherford, O. and Jones, D.A. (1986). The role of learning and co-
   ordination in strength training. Eur. J. Appl. Physiol.
   (in press).
Saltin, B. (1980). Fysisk praestationsevne. Aerob Kapacitet.
   Manedsskrift for praktisk laegegerning. 58:193-216.
Saltin, B., Blomqvist, G., Mitchell, J.H., Johnson, R.L.,
   Wildenthal, K. and Chapman, C.B. (1968). Response to exercise
   after bedrest and training. Circulation 38: Suppl.7.
Scherstén, T. (1984). Exercise and physical training in the
   management of peripheral arterial insufficiency. In Exercise,
   Health and Medicine: Proceedings (edited by A. Smith et al.,)
   pp.33-34. London: Sports Council.
Shephard, R.J. (1978). Physical Activity and Aging. London: Croom
   Helm.

Sidney, K.H. (1981). Cardiovascular benefits of physical activity
    in the exercising aged. In Exercise and Aging; the Scientific
    Basis. (edited by E.L. Smith and R.C. Serfass), pp131-147.
    Hillside, New Jersey: Enslow Publishers.
Smith, A. et al. (editors) (1984). Exercise, Health and Medicine:
    Proceedings. London: Sports Council.
Smith, E.L. (1986). Osteoporosis and physical activity. In
    Physical Activity in Health and Disease (edited by
    P.-O. Astrand and G. Grimby), Acta. med. scand. Suppl.
    (in press).
Smith, E.L., Reddan, W. and Smith, P.E. (1981). Physical activity
    and calcium modalities for bone mineral increase in aged woman.
    Med. Sci. Sports Ex. 13:60-64.
Tipton, C.M. (1984). Exercise, training, and hypertension.
    Ex. Sports Sci. Rev. 12:245-306.
Young, A. (1981). But of course, exercise wouldn't help me! -
    physical conditioning for patients and normal subjects. In Good
    Health - Is There a Choice? (edited by P.H. Fentem), pp.37-50.
    London: Macmillan.
Young, A. (1983). Rehabilitation of patients with pulmonary
    disease. Ann. Acad. Med. Sing. 12:410-416.
Young, A. (1986). Exercise physiology in geriatric practice. In
    Physical Activity in Health and Disease. (edited by P.-O
    Astrand and G. Grimby), Acta med. scand. Suppl. (in press).
Young, A., Gray, J.A.M. and Ennis, J.R. (1983). 'Exercise
    medicine': the knowledge and beliefs of final-year medical
    students in the United Kingdom. Medical Education 17:369-373.
Young, A., Stokes, M. and Crowe, M. (1984). Size and strength of
    the quadriceps muscles of old and young women. Eur. J. clin.
    Invest. 14:282-287.
Young, A., Stokes, M. and Crowe, M. (1985). The size and strength
    of the quadriceps muscles of old and young men. Clin. Physiol.
    5:145-154.

Discussion

Professor Raven, Texas, USA
One of the things you were showing today was the drop in both
isometric and isokinetic strength with ageing. You will be aware
of the Valsalva maneuvre when people go to the toilet and sudden
death that occurs. Equally this can follow the isometric challenge
of undoing a stuck jar. These are things that I think the exercise
movement in the United States is ignoring i.e. the afterload
stresses that are put on by these maneouvres. Have you any
comments on the incidence of sudden death in relation to this type
of exercise.

Dr Young, Hampstead, England
Specifically in the elderly - no: I think everyday tasks like
opening jars etc. do not show up greatly in the literature whereas
events like pushing cars and shovelling snow are much better
reported. If we turn away from death and think more of
rehabilitation, we do neglect the many isometric activities in
everyday life. I think this has occurred because people have been

so cautious to ensure that they co not provoke the type of events
that you have been talkinig about and have therefore left isometric
activities out of their therapeutic exercise programmes.
Paradoxically these are the very activities that should be included
because they occur in everyday life. I believe there is a lot of
scope for trying to see the effects of including isometric work in
rehabilitation programmes.

Professor Morris, London, England
Can I make a point with regard to the whole question of sudden
death and it is that we don't know the blood pressure raising
potential of normal everyday activities. Digging, for instance is
classified simply as aerobic activity but this is a very different
type of aerobic activity compared with swimming or jogging and
I would suggest that digging involves quite a bit of isometric
work. This seems to be a real gap in the physiological literature.

Dr Young
The ambulatory monitoring people haven't really got into that area
at all as far as I can see.

Dr Sutton, Ontario
With reference to the last comments there are quite profound blood
pressure changes during strenuous exercise; the more strenuous the
acitivity the greater the rise. In one study by my own group,
using indwelling arterial lines on subjects doing very vigorous
activity such as double leg contractions, you could raise the main
blood pressure to something like 350mm of mercury and in one
weight lifter the systolic blood pressure rose to 480mm of
mercury. We were surprised, looking at these pressure levels, that
people undertaking these activities did not blow cerebral vessels
and inevitably the following week one of our neurologists reported
seeing such a patient who did develop a cerebral haemorrhage.
    The question I have to ask you, Dr Young, with regard to your
presentation relates more the the perceptual aspects of your
studies. You hinted when you showed the one asthmatic you had
trained that the patient's perception of his ability to exercise
had increased as well as having achieved objective heart rate and
ventilatory changes. I wonder whether you felt that this is an
area that requires more emphasis in that the perception of a
persons disability, particularly with reference to the elderly, is
more important than its physiological benefits.

Dr Young
Yes, I am sure that is correct.

Dr Sutton
I presume the linkage between these two parameters is fatigue.

Dr A. Young, Hampstead
Yes.

Dr Ballantyne, Glasgow, Scotland
I am interested in heart disease and the effects of training on

people with heart disease and I am still, after having read the literature and doing work in this field, unsure if the effects I am producing which are beneficial in terms of psychological well-being and improved exercise tolerance are related to peripheral muscle or cardiac muscle effects. Do you think that the increase in exercise tolerance in patients with angina for example is related to peripheral muscle or is it some change in the heart?

Dr Young
Professor B. Saltin will comment on this question in his paper. My prejudice is that the vast majority of these beneficial effects are peripheral.

Exercise and ageing

J.A. MUIR GRAY

There is increasing evidence about the benefits of exercise in old age. Physical activity cannot only prevent many of the problems that have hitherto been assumed to be the normal concomitance of ageing but can also improve fitness and thus lead to an improvement in performance levels.

The evidence of surveys is that elderly people are, by and large, convinced of the benefits of exercises and want guidance on the most appropriate type of exercise to take, but do not receive helpful advice from the professionals they meet.

1. Introduction

Physical activity is usually associated with youth, both in developed and developing countries, but there is increasing evidence that exercise is of even greater importance to older people than to young people.

It is important to emphasise at the outset that there is no sharp threshold at which 'old age' starts and that the physical conditions of people in their 60s and 70s is in part a function of their whole life's experience, physical, social and psychological, and it is also important to emphasise that generalisations about 'old people' have to be made, and read, with great caution, for older people differ from one another in many more ways than they are similar to one another and cohorts of people of the same age show increasing diversity the older they become; a population of people aged 70 can range from Prime Ministers to people suffering from severe intellectual deterioration, whereas a population of people aged 20 is usually compressed within a narrower range of ability. In spite of these difficulties this chapter will focus on the benefits of exercise as a means of reducing disability and dependency in old age.

2. The ageing process

Ageing is a normal biological process. Certain cell lines age and die at an early age, for example the cell lines in the thymus, but in general ageing as a process starts after the phase of growth and development is over. There appears to be no stable biological phase between growth and development and between the phase of ageing, analogous to the relatively stable social stage of adult life between childhood and retirement. The phase of growth and the phase of ageing merge into one another.

Although a loss of capacity and ability is often regarded as a hallmark of ageing, there is a more important effect of ageing and that is the loss of reserve, namely the loss of the body's ability to respond to challenge. The young person who develops pneumonia becomes dehydrated and acidotic but when the bacteria are killed with antibiotics the homeostatic mechanisms òf the body correct the dehydration and the acidosis; when pneumonia develops at an advanced age, however, the homeostatic mechanisms do not show the same ability to correct deviations from the normal range, and although it is possible to kill bacteria in old people it is the loss of reserve, the inability to respond to the challenge of dehydration and acidosis, that has fatal results. Similarly, the older a person is, the less able they are to respond to changes such as a change in environmental temperature, or to respond to the challenge of inactivity.

2.1 Disability and inactivity

For some people inactivity is caused by physically disabling disease and five of the eight types of disability in the World Health Organisation's 'International Classification of Impairments, Disabilities and Handicaps' are disabilities which reduce the activity levels of the individual suffering from a particular type of impairment. These disabilities cause a wide range of handicap, for example problems with physical independence, mobility, occupation, and social integration, but in all these types of disabilities the vicious cycle of disability develops with, eventually, a proportion of the individual's disability being the result not of the disease that caused the basic impairment but of the inactivity caused by the disability itself.

This occurs particularly when other individuals take over the tasks formerly performed by the person with the disability. The problems faced by people with disabilities are complicated by the unhelpful social attitudes that they encounter.

In many societies the 'cripple' has traditionally been pale, thin and weak and his or her altered social status has depended in part on this type of image as well as on the loss of mobility that has caused the individual to be dependent on others.

In recent years there has been a notable change in attitude resulting not from educational programmes to make able-bodied people pay more respect to people with disabilities but from the activities of disabled people themselves. It has been the participation of people with disabilities in sporting events, particularly those confined to wheelchairs, which has caught the public attention and the person who is disabled who also looks fit and strong is no longer an exception or a cause for comment. Furthermore, the justifiably angry demands of people with disabilities for the opportunity to work and earn precludes the possibility that they will be accused of malingering, for while the sick person in many societies has been excused from the normal social obligation to work or to seek work they have also been expected to act like a sick person and to look unwell and unfit.

The majority of people with disabilities have vigourously rejected the identification of disability with illness in the last decade and have carved out a new social position of being healthy and disabled, and sport and physical training has played a part in changing the self image of people with disabilities and the attitudes of other people towards them.

Considerable though the advances have been, much remains to be done and people with disabilities need more information about exercise than they receive from health professionals at present; easier access to sporting facilities, both in reaching those facilities and in actually using the facilities when they reach them; and perhaps most important of all, the opportunity to participate in sports with people without major disabilities as well as having the opportunity to participate with other people with similar disabilities.

3. The challenge of inactivity

Inactivity is a biological challenge. However, inactivity is a challenge which presents not only as a result of severe illness and injuries; decreasing levels of activity are also a feature of life in industrialised countries, particularly for men.

It is a paradox that those least in need of exercise take most. Children in the school playground are active and lively whenever they have the opportunity but as we grow older interests, opportunities and attitudes change and people adapt a decreasing level of exercise the older they become. The more senior people get in an organisation the less likely they are offered the opportunity for exercise - consider the way in which the oldest and most senior members of an organisation usually have a car parking space nearest the door - and attitudes change, for, with certain notable exceptions, most senior people regard physical activity during the working day as behaviour which would be an affront to their dignity and status.

4. Cumulative effects of inactivity

When capacity is plotted against age the pattern that is depicted in Fig.1 is observed. Some people have a flat turning point maintaining a higher level of capacity in their 20s by dint of commitment to training programmes, but with some people the turning point is sharp and results from the sudden cessation of physical activity on leaving school or college. As can be seen a gap widens between the best possible level of performance and the actual level of performance. In youth this gap is relatively unimportant, except for those who wish to participate in sport, but in old age the gap can be of great significance. Let us imagine that point A on the vertical axis represents the capacity required to climb two flights of stairs. From the graph it can be seen that a person's capacity to do this task, which is absolutely essential for those who live in second floor flats, can drop below this level at a certain age due to the combined effects of ageing and loss of fitness, and that an improvement in the level of fitness will allow the person to be able to continue climbing the steps to their apartment for an additional number of years.

Thus, loss of fitness can have a major impact on the ability of older people to look after themselves and enjoy life.

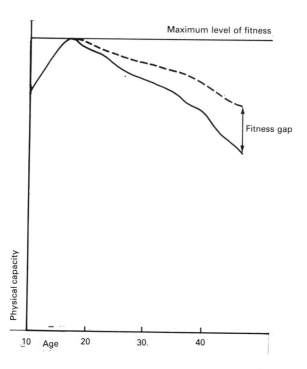

Figure 1. Rate of change of physical capacity with age. Broken line is the rate of decline due to ageing alone if fitness is not lost. Continuous line is the actual rate of decline.

5. Ageing, unfitness and disease

The relationship between inactivity and chronic disease is described elsewhere in these proceedings by Dr A. Young, but it is worth emphasising the interactive relationship between loss of fitness, disease, and ageing, for the older people are when they contract chronic disease, the less their physiological reserves and the greater the impact of inactivity and immobility.

The older an individual is, the more likely is he to develop the adverse effects previously described by Dr Young, in part because he, like the person of any age, may suffer from a disease which makes activity and physical exercise more difficult, but older people face an additional problem, namely the attitudes of other people. The general attitude of society towards old people may be summed up in the word 'care', which of course means many things ranging from intensive care with a high level of intervention and strenuous efforts to modify pathological processes, to a very

passive style of care which is found in the worst types of
residential institution. In general younger people have low
expectations of older people and when they see older people
disabled by disease they are moved to try to do thing for them,
rather than helping them regain the ability to do things for
themselves. This attitude stems in part from the mistaken belief
that all the problems of older people are caused by the biological
and immutable, process of ageing, but in many instances it stems
from guilt. Society is aware of the fact that elderly people are not
well treated, in the broadest sense of the word, as exemplified by
the relationship between the average income of an older person and
the average income of a person who is working and because society
feels guilty it wishes to relieve the feelings of guilt by doing
things for older people. The general image of older people that
is portrayed is of a passive dependent and disabled group whereas
people with these characteristics are only a minority of older
people who are, as a whole, a group that is active, independent
and able. Old people who struggle to do things or who are at risk
cause anxiety to their family, neighbours and friends, and the
response to this anxiety is too often a request to professionals to
remove the old person or to modify the environment in such a way
as to reduce the degree to which the old person has to struggle
and to reduce the degree of risk. In some cases, particularly
where the old person is incompetent because of Alzheimer's
disease, this type of approach is appropriate, but it is
frequently advocated by friends, neighbours and family when the
old person is competent and wishes to retain their independence,
even though they have to struggle and are at increased risk
because they are doing things for themselves.

6. The scope for health promotion

The factors described in the previous sections outline the reasons
why exercise and the promotion of exercise is important in old age;
exercise is important because it can prevent a number of problems
that are regarded as the consequences of ageing and the promotion
of exercise is important because of the attitudes which prevail.
    The case for exercise and exercise promotion is strengthened
each year by the publication of research which demonstrates the
benefits of exercise in old age and there is now evidence that
older people who increase their levels of activity can regain
stamina, strength, suppleness and skill, and that they, like other
groups with disabilities, gain considerable psychological benefits
from exercise.

6.1 Regaining strength
In Goteborg, where the most important and comprehensive
longitudinal studies of normal ageing are being conducted, research
workers have examined the effects of physical training on muscle
strength (Aniansson et al., 1980; Aniansson and Gustafsson, 1981).
Significant increases in both static and muscular strength were
demonstrated following a 12 week training programme. Futhermore,
muscle biopsies were taken and although the number of subjects,

nine, was small there was an increase noted in the elative area of
type 2 fibres (Fig.2).

There is therefore clear evidence that strength can be not only
maintained but improved in old age.

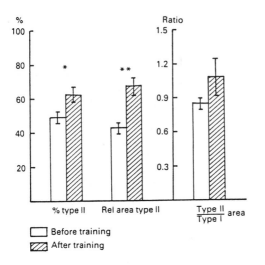

Figure 2. Relative number and relative area of Type II fibres and
ratio between the mean fibre area of Type II and Type I fibres in
the right vastus lateralis before and after training in 69-74 year
old men (n=9). Mean and SE are given, * and ** denote P<0.05 and
P<0.01 respectively (Aniansson and Gustafsson, 1981).

6.2 Regaining stamina
There have been numerous studies of the effect of training on
aerobic aspects of fitness (Bassey, 1978). One of the most
important conclusions was drawn by Sidney and his colleagues
(Sidney et al., 1977) for the authors concluded not only that
aerobic power could be increased by training but that 'maximum
oxygen intake returned quite quickly to the level anticipated in a
sedentary person 10 to 20 years younger than the test subject'.
This improvement in aerobic capacity is, as in younger ages, due to
a combination of improvement in the cardiovascular and respiratory
systems which transport oxygen round the body and to an improvement
in the muscular enzymes which extract and use the oxygen brought to
the cells (de Vries, 1970).

6.3 Regaining suppleness
Less research has been done on suppleness because stiffness and
suppleness are much more difficult to measure than muscular
strength or aerobic power. This is unfortunate because loss of
suppleness presents major problems for older people and research
which studies the effects of training on suppleness should be a
high priority for work in this area. One encouraging study

(Chapman et al., 1972) demonstrated that a training programme could decrease the torque necessary to move a joint passively and another study (Munns, 1981) demonstrated that a thrice weekly exercise and dance programme, of 12 weeks duration, produced an increase in movement in neck, wrist, shoulder, knee, ankle and in the hip and back.

Chapman's study was particularly encouraging because he concluded that there was no difference between the response of young subjects and old subjects to the training programme (Table 1).

There is therefore sufficient evidence to advocate those types of exercise which promote suppleness, for example music and movement and swimming but, as indicated above, more research in this area is needed.

Table 1. Effect of training on torque necessary to move index finger passively about metacarpophalangeal joint (Chapman et al., 1972).

	Pre-training		Post-training	
	Mean	SE	Mean	SE
Young				
Experimental	1.458	0.104	1.148	0.097*
Control	1.291	0.087	1.183	0.076
Old				
Experimental	2.166	0.235	1.709	0.123*
Control	2.144	0.168	1.931	0.145

*Significance of pre-post difference, $p < 0.05$ Torque is measured in Kg-Cm.

6.4 Regaining skill

This is another aspect of fitness in which there has been relatively little research carried out but the research that has been done has demonstrated that people who remain active do not experience so great an increase in reaction times as those who become inactive as they age (Sherwood and Selder, 1979), but most of the interesting results are not available in English as many of the studies have been conducted in the Soviet Union and published in Russian. However, an interesting review of the Russian literature (Gore, 1972) provides encouraging information about the benefits of training.

This is also a topic which requires further research particularly in view of the results of Sherwood and Selder's study (Fig. 3) for they demonstrated that training is of relatively greater benefit in old age.

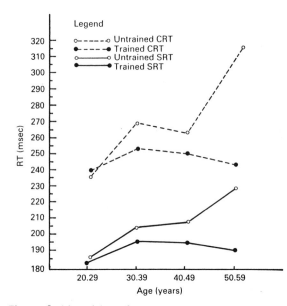

Figure 3. The relationship of reaction time, age and fitness level. (SRT=simple reaction time; CRT=choice reaction time) (Sherwood and Selder, 1979).

6.5 Psychological benefits of exercise

As in younger age groups, it has been demonstrated that participation in an exercise programme can have psychological as well as physical benefits and the study by Blumenthal and Williams showed that there was an improvement in anxiety levels following a ten week exercise programme (Fig.4).

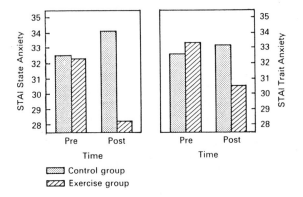

Figure 4. Comparison of exercise and control group scores on state (left) and trait (right) anxiety before and after the ten-week exercise programme (Blumenthal and Williams, 1982).

7. The risk of exercise

The promotion of exercise entails some risk but provided people are advised to build up exercise levels slowly the principal adverse effect is an increased risk of soft tissue injury, and there is no evidence to suggest that exercise promotion will harm more people than it benefits. Neither is there evidence to suggest that older people need a medical examination before increasing their exercise levels, although those who suffer from chronic disabling disease are well advised to discuss with their medical adviser the most appropriate type of exercise for their particular condition. This assumes, of course, that their professional advisers are able to advise them on exercise which is, unfortunately, an unwarranted assumption at present.

8. Implications for sport and recreation managers

The implications of the evidence cited are wide ranging for managers of sport and recreation centres and for the providers of education, for there are benefits from psychological and physical stimulation in old age. All public services must recognise the demographic changes that are taking place and must consider the contribution that they can make to health promotion in old age, a point emphasised by the World Health Organisation in its recent report on health promotion in old age (WHO, 1986). Services which have currently been orientated towards youth, for example sport, recreation and education services, must face up to the changes that are occurring in society and to the changing nature of older people. Older people today are better educated and more assertive than older people were in the past and this trend will continue as the cohorts recruited to old age are increasingly well educated and organised.

Managers of sports facilities should review the use of their facilities, comparing the use with the population figures for the catchment area they serve, and if there is evidence of under-representation of older people they should identify the reasons and try to increase participation. Some centres will need access improved, either by adapting the structure of the building or by improving transport to the centre. In other cases the timing of exercise programmes for older people may have to be adjusted in recognition of the fact that the low level of car ownership and in some cities, a fear of going out in the dark. Finally, recreation managers should link with education department staff to promote exercise in old age, making use of established groups and networks such as old people's clubs or retirement fellowships.

9. Implications for public education

Surveys of older people demonstrate their optimism and their positive attitude to life and they also demonstrate that many older people already believe in the benefits of exercise. There are a few people, however, who believe that all their problems are due to ageing and that nothing can be done to slow down or reverse the decline in ability and capacity. In addition there is evidence that older people wish more information about exercise and about the steps they can take to improve their own health. Much attention has been given to the need for better education of older people and although this is true it is important to bear in mind the fact that it is the professionals who are probably in greater need of education than older people.

The over protective attitudes of the public towards elderly people, arising as they do not only from ignorance or mistaken beliefs but from feelings of guilt and paternalism, are difficult to change. Simply providing information about the benefits of exercise in old age will not change the behaviour of those people who are very concerned about older people and who demonstrate their concern by trying to do things for older people, thus forcing them into a passive dependent lifestyle.

The most important step is to help older people become more self confident and assertive and this is, of course, taking place as the cohorts of people becoming old have a different social, educational and political experience from those who are very elderly today.

10. Implications for professional education

Professional education, by and large, provides very little teaching about exercise and this is in part due to the fact that exercise lies within the province of a number of different disciplines. Teaching about old age is also poorly organised in a number of professional training courses, again in part, because it is a topic which stands within so many disciplines that it requires an integrated approach to teaching which few institutions appear to be able to manage. Thus both exercise and ageing are poorly taught in many professional training programmes, so that it is scarcely surprising that the benefits of exercise in old age have been poorly taught.

Professional training should help the trainee acquire two types of skill. The first type of skill is an education skill for there is evidence that older people wish for more information about exercise than they are offered by their professional helpers (McHeath, 1984). However, the second type of skill which they require is a rehabilitative skill.

Too often the professional response to the development of a problem in old age is a prosthetic response, the supply of a prosthesis, using the term 'prosthesis' to include not only wheelchairs and appliances but any intervention which carries out tasks for an older person, for example the provision of meals on wheels or the provision of home help. Meals on wheels and home help are extremely important elements in the support of elderly people in their own homes but only if they are provided for the older person when it is clear that the old person cannot be helped to regain the skills which will allow him to perform these tasks for himself.

An idealised approach to functional problems in old age is set out in the handicap algorithm.

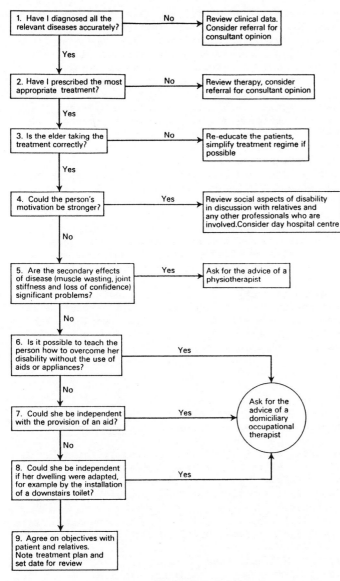

1. Have I diagnosed all the relevant diseases accurately? — No → Review clinical data. Consider referral for consultant opinion

Yes ↓

2. Have I prescribed the most appropriate treatment? — No → Review therapy, consider referral for consultant opinion

Yes ↓

3. Is the elder taking the treatment correctly? — No → Re-educate the patients, simplify treatment regime if possible

Yes ↓

4. Could the person's motivation be stronger? — Yes → Review social aspects of disability in discussion with relatives and any other professionals who are involved. Consider day hospital centre

No ↓

5. Are the secondary effects of disease (muscle wasting, joint stiffness and loss of confidence) significant problems? — Yes → Ask for the advice of a physiotherapist

No ↓

6. Is it possible to teach the person how to overcome her disability without the use of aids or appliances? — Yes →

No ↓

7. Could she be independent with the provision of an aid? — Yes → Ask for the advice of a domiciliary occupational therapist

No ↓

8. Could she be independent if her dwelling were adapted, for example by the installation of a downstairs toilet? — Yes →

↓

9. Agree on objectives with patient and relatives. Note treatment plan and set date for review

The handicap algorithm.

This algorithm is, as has been stated, an ideal approach, for few health services have the resources to take this approach for all the practical problems that occur in old age. Nevertheless, it is important that the sharp split between health services and social services which exists in most countries as the social work profession has become an independent profession, separate from the health profession, results in old people presenting with problems that are classified as social problems, for example difficulty in coping with housework, meeting a social response, a prosthetic response, when their problem is in fact a symptom of an underlying and correctable physical problem, either disease or loss of fitness or, most commonly, a combination of both.

There are obvious ethical problems inherent in this approach and advocating a system in which elderly people will be bullied and harassed to become more active and to do things for themselves. Nevertheless, it is my opinion that it is important to state the case for exercise, and the promotion of exercise, clearly, unequivocally, and emphatically, becuase of the general tendency to underestimate the abilities of older people and deny them the right to be active, even if that means that they have to struggle and be at risk.

The major problem is to change professional behaviour and thus minimise functional decline in the elderly. I would argue for the promotion of exercise as this will help keep older people in their own homes, if that is what they want, and improve the quality of life for residents in institutional care.

References

Aniansson, A., Grimby, G., Rundgren, A., Svanborg, A. and Orlander, J. (1980). Physical training in old men. Age and Ageing 9:186-187.

Aniansson, A. and Gustafsson, E. (1981). Physical training in elderly men with special reference to quadriceps muscle strength and morphology. Clinical Physiology 1:87-98.

Bassey, E.J. (1978). Age, inactivity and some physiological responses to exercise. Gerontology, 24:66-77.

Blumenthal, J.A. and Williams, R.S. (1982). Duke University Centre for the Study of Aging and Human Development. Advances in research 6:3.

Chapman, E.A., deVries, H.A. and Swezcy, R. (1972). Joint stiffness: effects of exercise on young and old men. Journal of Gerontology 27:218-221.

deVries, H.A. (1970). Physiological effects of an exercise training regime upon men aged 52 to 88. Journal of Gerontology 25:325-336.

Gore, I.Y. (1972). Physical activity and ageing - a survey of the Russian literature. Gerontologia Clinica 14:65-85.

MacHealth, J.A. (1984). Activity, health and fitness in old age. Croom Helm, London.

Munns, K. (1981). Effects of exercise on the range of joint motion in elderly patients. In: Smith, B.L., and Serfass, R.C. (eds). Exercise and Aging. (Enslow, p.167-178).

Sherwood, D.E. and Selder, D.S. (1979). Cardiorespiratory health, reaction time and aging. Medicine and Science in Sports 11:168-169.

Sidney, K.H., Shephard, R.J. and Harrison, J.E. (1977). Endurance training and body composition of the elderly. American Journal of Nutrition 30:326-333.

World Health Organisation (1986). The International Classification of Impairments, Disabilities and Handicaps. W.H.O. Geneva.

Discussion

Professor Raven, Texas, USA

I have a comment. What happens in America is that people are penalised when they get old because at the age of 65 there is mandatory retirement and society tells these people that they are useless. In fact many people can work in to old age and we have just lost V.B. Dell at the age of 95 and he was still walking in the desert at the age of 90 with his meals and continuing to work. J.C. Penny was working in his office at 88 when he died. I consider the problem is that we tell people at 65 that they are not capable of work and this policy of mandatory retirement is creating a psychosocial problem.

Dr Gray, Oxford, England

My own view is that mandatory retirement is a major psychological issue. The experience has been that most people will retire before mandatory retirement if pension arrangements are suitable and if you remove mandatory retirement it has an negligible impact on the labour market because most people will get fed up with the job they are doing and want to retire. You don't have major problems with people holding up promotion. It might be different in the National Health Service where at the moment we have certain problems in our medical structure pyramid. I believe that mandatory retirement is something we should challenge and we are going to bring it up locally.

Dr Legg, Farnborough, England

Do you think there are any lessons we might learn from considering the social attitudes that the Chinese or the African nations have towards the aged. They tend to revere the aged and listen to them much more carefully than we would tend to. Have you considered this?

Dr Gray

The Western world believes that it is facing a challenge with regard to this ageing population but this challenge is nothing compared to the problems facing the third world. In Brazil, for example, the number of people over 70 will double in the next 20 years in addition to all other problems that country faces. The first thing to take into account is the impact of urbanisation. Many of the idyllic views of the third world countries are views of a country before urbanisation, inflation and unemployment and what we are seeing is the break up of the extended family in many of these countries. This occurs because some members of the family move to the city, send money back home, but then there is inflation, and unemployment and the money can't go back home. As a result you get destitute old people living back in rural areas and this is something which third world countries are having to come face to face with. In the Far Eastern cultures it does seem that the role of the extended family is incalcated into society and it is accepted by both sides. We enjoyed an interesting contribution from Thailand at a recent World Health Organisation Conference reviewing this aspect of Far Eastern culture but one has to be very careful about shifting examples from culture to culture.

If you want to look back to the good old days where the old man kept control until he was finally pushed out I would suggest you read King Lear again. That is a classic example which you can still see in some farming communities of the old man keeping control for far too long and this nice intergenerational relationship deteriorates into very severe tension. So I believe that with European and North American cultures, generational independence is what people want rather than being dependent one upon the other. So there are two points: first you have to look at the third world countries after urbanisation and second the third world countries in the Far East have got some very attractive models but I believe they are difficult to translate to Western society because old people in our society would rather be independent of their children than dependent upon them.

Dr Mutrie, Glasgow, Scotland
I was very interested in what you said about the education of general practitioners regarding exercise programmes. I wonder if it is really possible for general practitioners to do this type of work given their very pressed time-tables.

Dr Gray
You sound very like a GP speaking.

Dr Mutrie
I was wondering what you thought of employing physical exercise specialists to work within general practices, equivalent to a dietician, to assist the general practitioner in this type of work.

Dr Gray
Looking ahead at public funding, even with a change of government, I make all my assumptions on zero or very little more than zero growth. I certainly would like to have physical education experts more involved in Health Service development but, in more practical terms, what we have to try to do is change the nature of consultations. I think Professor Morris gave an appropriate epidemiological approach in that if we could change the content of 75% of consultations by 5% we would have a much greater impact on the publics health than by changing the content of 5% of consultations by 75%. What we really have to do is change the whole style of professional work, change the nurses attitudes to

what they see as nursing, change the physiotherapists attitudes to
what they see as physiotherapy. All professionals must learn to
work with the assumption that self care is the most important form
of care and professionals should see their job as helping
individuals look after themselves which may require a prescription
or an operation or some other service but professionals must stop
looking at the patient as a dependent person who is receiving some
professional gift. I would like to see more involvement of people
with the right physical education background in general practice
particularly as the new people coming through physical education
courses are well prepared biologically and psychologically in terms
of their education but we really have to look at the size of the
problem and identify a practical solution. There are a million
consultations in general practice each day in the United Kingdom
and we have to identify a technique which will influence the
majority of these consultations. I believe the present pattern of
service will carry on and accordingly we have to try and influence
professional behaviour. There may be a place for specialist
services but I think that the scale of the challenge is so big we
will achieve quicker results if we change the way the professionals
in the Health Service work.

Dr Wootton, Southampton, England
Nutritionists are increasingly concerned with the risk of
hyponutrition in the elderly, with decreasing appetite and the
associated anorexia that develops with ageing. Do you know of any
work that has been done on the role of physical activity in
offsetting this anorexia?

Dr Gray
I don't know of any work directly that has been done on appetite
and exercise but I am very concerned about one aspect of this area
namely meals on wheels. There has been a very welcome move to
"lunch clubs" in the last few years but again these have been
groups where old people have been brought together, sat down at
tables and brought food. In one old peoples' home I went to they
even buttered the bread and stirred the tea of elderly people who
could easily have managed themselves. I think we should be
developing exercise and cooking clubs because I believe the major
problem with regard to loss of appetite is poor motivation as
opposed to inability to buy and prepare food.

Dr Lloyd, Edinburgh, Scotland
Some old people seem to expect that when they have reached a
certain age they are entitled to assistance from the family and
society. This is an educational problem and we must teach both
families and the social services to encourage mobility and
independence in the old. The old must be given the ambition of
keeping physically and intellectually active.

Dr Gray
The home help services have to be very careful because the eyes of
society are on them. I have seen this in old peoples' homes that I
have worked with and heard statements like 'Why don't we have a
jumble sale to buy wheel chairs so none of the old people need to

walk'. There is a marked cultural difference between being employed to provide care and being employed to provide treatment and rehabilitation for old people. The pressure on the caring services is that they should do things for old people and protect them from risk.

It is very fashionable in British society to look for cases of abuse of the elderly by families in the home or staff in institutions caring for the elderly. I think old people usually abuse and exploit their families and the carers more than they are abused by them.

Exercise and sport for mentally handicapped people

W.I. FRASER and R.A. STUART

Sporting opportunities, such as the Special Olympics, create an environment in which mentally handicapped people can benefit from participating in challenging activities. Limitations to activities are few, but individuals with Down's Syndrome require careful assessment to identify the possible presence of Atlanto-Axial instability and appropriate activities must be selected for this group of athletes.

1. Introduction

In 1968, Mrs Eunice Kennedy Shriver, sister of the late President John F. Kennedy, began a summer programme of swimming and exercise for mentally handicapped people. The purpose was to demonstrate that the mentally handicapped could participate in sports events like other athletes. From that early (backyard) programme utilising volunteer high school students as coaches, has grown the Special Olympics. Today, over one million athletes participate in Special Olympics in the United States and over 50 nations have Special Olympics programmes for mentally handicapped individuals, and this year the Peoples Republic of China joined the Special Olympics movement.

Special Olympics is an international movement which believes that people with mental retardation benefit physically, mentally, socially and spiritually by training and competing in sport. Families are strengthened and the community at large, through participation and observation, is united with mentally handicapped people in an environment of equality, respect and acceptance (Cipriano, 1980).

While Special Olympics quickly flourished in the United States, the picture in the U.K. was somewhat confused, there being little or no information about the extent and range of activities that were being undertaken by mentally handicapped people.

It was at this juncture that the Disabled Living Foundation, a private trust concerned about the daily living of disabled and handicapped people, determined to find out what mentally handicapped people could, should and were doing in the field of sport, physical recreation and leisure.

The results of their study, a book called 'Give Us The Chance' (Latto, 1981) and a film of the same name, clearly show that for the majority of mentally handicapped people participation in sport is beneficial.

2. Benefits

Participation in exercise and sports programmes by mentally handicapped individuals has undoubtedly improved physical wellbeing in the individual (Hayden, 1974; Rarick, 1978). Involvement, especially in motor activity, is of great importance because it is the principle means through which individuals interact with their environment and by so doing the mentally handicapped individual has a better image of self and, at the same time is more acceptable in the eyes of his or her peers (Connolly, 1984).

Tilley (1986), conducted a study in British Columbia on Special Olympics athletes in which he demonstrated that these athletes showed a marked improvement with regard to physical fitness when compared to mentally handicapped people who had not benefitted from a training programme or participated in the Special Olympics Programme. Other studies have indicated that physical exercise programmes have reduced considerably absenteeism in sheltered workshops. Krebs (1986) reporting on studies in mentally handicapped children showed that simple reaction time and choice reaction time can be improved if they are provided with physical exercise training and training in simple sports activities that require choice. Finally, Guttman (1973) commented that leisure time and recreational opportunity for mentally handicapped people are greatly enhanced if they are provided with an opportunity to take part in sports programmes. All of these studies have indicated that sport contributes to the physical health of mentally handicapped people (Sherrell, 1982) and to an improvement in motor performance (Rarick, 1976).

Vermeer (1985) in utilising Wolfenberger's definition (1983) of normalisation; that is 'the creation, support and defence of valued social roles for people who are at risk of social devaluation' examined the stigma reductions and change of attitude in society by studying a group of Dutch mentally handicaped athletes who took part in the 1983 International Summer Special Olympics. His study evaluated the enhancement of the mentally handicapped social image, or of the perceived values in the eyes of others and the enhancement of their competencies as a result of their participation in the games. His study confirmed the impression that sport has a positive effect on bodily competencies and equally on emotional, mental and social competencies. He also verified the enhancement of this social image on the individual athlete, the athlete's parents and those working with the athlete. There was an improved positive opinion of self, and improved self-esteem. There was also an improved positive attitude about mentally handicapped persons in communities with appropriate sports programmes.

The greatest benefits of sports to mentally handicapped people are said to be emotional rather than physical but sweeping generalisations about 'emotional adjustment' are inappropriate since the range of disability, motivation and intellect varies widely.

Beneficial games for the profoundly handicapped include simply learning to 'take turns'and Movement Therapists and Psychologists at Edinburgh University are developing these games techniques to study the origins of communication with profoundly handicapped adults.

Institutions have, over the past 100 years, provided gymnastics for the severely mentally handicapped with the object of 'burning up' the surplus energy of overactivity. This was not however the main way that they were calmed, rather it helped the severely retarded people by assisting them to behave better, by giving them skills and ensuring that they received precious, scarce attention.

Sport is just as vital to the much larger number of moderately retarded people who live outside hospital. To a flabby, gawky Down's anomaly living with elderly parents; over-protected, timid and never having succeeded in anything; sport does indeed bring liberation. It brings a sense of belonging, of adventure, and excitement which parents might be reluctant to permit; and the unambiguous adult role; no longer a half-child but an adult, intent on mastery. Sport brings a topic of conversation; it improves communication for the handicapped, brings personal success and confidence. In many countries such as Scotland when athletic events are promoted for the mentally handicapped every athlete is provided with a momento of participation and to witness how mentally handicapped persons cherish these medals or ribbons is vindication enough. At the same time, those who win, display their tokens of victory for weeks or months after the event and are never slow to tell of their achievements. Sport also makes it plain to the handicapped persons that there is a need for stamina quite apart from the need for clean socks and vest!

However the most testing time for such a person lies ahead when the parents become infirm and he or she must leave the shelter of the home. Exercise in these circumstances can be an antidote to realistic anxiety and reactive depression (Van Andel and Austin 1984) and anxiety and depression are the most common nervous problems for the mentally retarded. In the same way, with the great social pressure from the new philosophy of normalisation which is to discharge retarded people and to close hospitals, it is vital that we do not consign them to boredom and isolation. It is essential they have proper sport and leisure counselling before these great changes and relocations occur, in order that they can, through sport, face a simulated stress, learn courage and can draw on their sport as a solace in times of real crisis.

Well meaning community care is at present failing to meet the recreational needs of borderline handicapped people who now live outside hospital and still frequently visit their former hospitals which come to be perceived as their alma mater. Directionless, they exist in dismal surroundings. These backward 'dropouts' (Spencer, 1982) talk wistfully of the days of soccer matches and competitions in the vanishing institutions.

3. Barriers and limitations

There are undoubted barriers both perceived and real, to the participation of mentally handicapped people in a full range of sport. The perceived barriers include parents' interventions and the handicapped person's lack of an initial motivation - very similar to the situation in school athletics. Availability and access to facilities can also present major barriers. The use of

sports halls and swimming pools restricted to unsocial hours; an
inflexible approach to supervision, to overtime, to insurance
together with veiled fears of infection and sometimes even
undisguised prejudice. There may be a lack of staff;
unsympathetic attitudes in newly appointed and often inexperienced
bureaucrats in the sport institution or in the nursing hierarchy
and finally flagging staff enthusiasm. Most mentally handicapped
people will talk nostalgically about sports schemes they loved,
but which for some reason have abruptly stopped!

Real medical barriers to participation are few. It is only a
matter of transforming the sport to the individual's handicaps.
There are many sports such as the marathon and mountain races - one
of our patients was 11th in the race up Ben Nevis the highest
mountain in the United Kingdom - netball and dinghy sailing where
handicapped people can reach normal competitive standards.
Excellence is rare because of training problems, but over-training
is also uncommon because all training is coach-orientated and
regulated. Many mentally handicapped people are prescribed
medication the purpose of which is to help them lead a full life
and which shouldn't deter them from taking part in sport. Epilepsy
affects one in four and provided that the staff are aware of the
situation, there is little reason to eliminate epileptics from a
full programme of sport.

One problem of current widespread concern, however, is Atlanto-
Axial Subluxation in Down's Syndrome because it illustrates the
dilemma of taking risks with mentally handicapped people. Since
1965 we have been aware that people with Down's Syndrome (which is
the commonest mental handicapping condition) are particularly prone
to Atlanto-Axial Subluxation (Tishler and Martell, 1965). It can
cause deterioration in walking and bladder control, neck pain,
limitation, neurological signs, hypertonicity, hyper-reflexia,
clonus, and in vigorous exercise where there is hyper-extension or
severe flexion, sudden death. To draw attention to these risks the
Kennedy Foundation has published articles in the newsletter of the
American Academy of Family Physicians and the American Association
for Retarded Citizens, advising that Special Olympic Athletes with
Down's Syndrome be restricted from participating in gymnastics,
diving, butterfly stroke when swimming, high jump, pentathlon and
warm-up exercises placing pressure on the head and neck muscles
until they have been physically examined and until X- rays have
excluded this condition. Last year a wave of over- reaction swept
the United Kingdom when some education authorities stopped all
forms of athletics for the mentally handicapped. Although the Royal
Society for Mentally Handicapped Adults and Children (MENCAP)
issued a press statement to clarify the risks, this did nothing to
allay the fears and it was left to the Chief Medical Officer of the
DHSS to issue the following statement in May 1986. 'Perhaps 2 or
3% of the people with Down's Syndrome will have instability between
the atlas and the axis bones at the top of the neck, which can lead
to pressure on the spinal cord and in exceptional circumstances to
death. In some of these individuals, spinal cord compression
develops slowly over a number of years, while in others, accident
or injury produces immediate damage. The question arose therefore,
whether, given this knowledge, the lives of people with Down's
Syndrome were being put at unreasonable risk, and in what way the

risk should be limited. The Standing Medical Advisory Committee
were asked to advise the Secretary of State on this matter, and I
am writing now to let you know their views. The first thing to say
is that at present only one case of injury to the neck and
spinal cord during sporting activity has been reported in the
world literature and that occurred during unsupervised
trampolining to a girl already known to have nerve damage.
Deaths have occurred, however, in a variety of other circumstances
including car accidents involving whiplash injury, to which these
individuals are more vulnerable. It is possible to identify the
instability by x-ray from the age of 6 onwards and one response
has been to suggest radiological investigation for all people with
Down's Syndrome. Although this might be appropriate if there was
an effective treatment available, current advice is that this is
not so, and that it is not possible to stabilise the bones
satisfactorily by surgery. The Standing Medical Advisory
Committee therefore recommend the following compromise:

(1) That people with Down's Syndrome should continue to
participate in a full range of daily activities including running,
jumping and horse riding.
(2) Where more vigorous sporting activity such as diving or
trampolining, which involve acute flexion of the neck, or violent
contact sports, such as karate, are envisaged, the individual
should first be x-rayed.
(3) Where an instability is demonstrated, the individual should
be medically examined. In the event that compression of the
nervous system is demonstrated, consultant advice should be sought
without delay. Where there is no evidence of compression,
individuals should be encouraged to continue previous activities
but be dissuaded from more vigorous activities such as diving or
trampolining.
(4) Care should be taken to support the body and head of a
person with Down's Syndrome when travelling by use of seat belts
and head rests.
(5) Because pressure on the spinal cord occasionally develops
without any accident or injury, examination of the central nervous
system should form an integral part of the medical examination of
all people with Down's Syndrome. On finding exaggerated knee jerks
the doctor should arrange radiological investigation to exclude
Atlanto-Axial instability.
(6) At the time of a general anaesthetic or following a road
traffic accident, particular attention should be paid to people
with Down's Syndrome because of the possibility of instability and
its attendant complications.'

In spite of the above statement from the Chief Medical Officer
it should be noted that Burke and colleagues (1985) pointed out in
the American Journal of Bone Surgery that Atlanto-Axial
subluxation can develop in adolescence with progressive
instability and neurological deficits. Thus, negative findings at
age 10 could give a false sense of security and negative signs at
any age is not a guarantee against subsequent instability from
cumulative minor trauma. The medical literature also report a
wide variation in the incidence of Atlanto-Axial Subluxation or

instability, much greater than 3%. Cooke (1984) reported 10 to 17% and in Manchester 37% of Down's have been found to have radiological instability. The operation of Atlanto-Axial fusion is established as effective, and should be considered in healthy patients with instability whose activity cannot be restricted. The DHSS Advisory Committee Statement that a full range of daily activity is permissible could include somersaulting but the only suspected Atlanto-Axial death in Scotland occurred in a soft play area. Death, in any case, would not necessarily be reported in the scientific literature. Thus, neither extreme alarm nor total reassurance is justified, but surely this does not mean radically curtailing the physical education curriculum, until more clinical, as opposed to radiological, evidence is available.

While Atlanto-Axial Subluxation is a problem area among some mentally handicapped athletes perhaps there are greater concerns. Stuart (1983) has questioned whether in fact mentally handicapped athletes should participate in competitive sport at all, given its almost total emphasis on 'winning at all costs'. While he argues that competition in sport can be beneficial and rewarding to mentally handicapped athletes he is emphatic that such competition must be undertaken in the clear understanding that it is the participation that is important, not the winning and certainly not the losing. As he states 'for too long mentally handicapped people have been viewed as a group unable to achieve, unable to acquire knowledge and unable to function in society at large. It is time therefore to alter this by focusing, not on what the individual cannot do, but on what he or she can do. Perhaps we should begin with the humane spirit of looking at the person first and the game situation second and instead of trying to eliminate competitive activities we must examine the real source of negativism associated with competition. Competition is a way of life and is here to stay. Let us not deny mentally handicapped people the opportunity to compete in sports events simply because of our misuse of competition'.

Acknowledgements

The author would like to acknowledge the major contribution made by Dr G.L. Zitnay of the Joseph P. Kennedy Jnr. Foundation, Washington DC, USA in the preparation of this paper.

References

Burke, S., Graeme French, H., Roberts, J., Johnstone, C., Whitecloud, T. and Edmund J. (1985). Chronic Atlanto-Axial Instability in Down Syndrome. Journal of Bone & Joint Surgery 6:1356-1360.
Cipriano, R.E. (1980). Reading in Special Olympics. Special Learning Corporation, Connecticut.
Connolly, K.J. (1984). The assessment of motor performance in children. In Biozek, J., Schurch, B. (Eds). Malnutrition and Behaviour : critical assessment of key issues. Ed. Jesef Biozek and Beat Schurch, Lausanne, Switzerland. Nestle Foundation.

Cooke, R. (1984). Atlanto-Axial Instability in People with Down Syndrome. Adapted Physical Activity Quarterly. 1:194-196.

DHSS Atlanto-Axial Instability in peiple with Down Syndrome C.M.O. (86) 9.

Guttmann C. (1973). Sport and recreation for the mentally and physically handicapped. Royal Society of Health Journal 93: pp 208-212.

Hayden, F.J. (1974). Physical education and sport. In Wortis J. (ed). Mental Retardation and Developmental Disabilities, 1974. Brunner, Mazel, New York.

Krebs, P. (1986). A comparison of simple and choice reaction time of developmentally disabled children to chronological age normal peers and mental age normal peers, unpublished study. Adelphi University, New York. Cited by Zitnay, G. Kennedy Institute, Washington.

Latto, K. (1981). Give us the chance, Disabled Living Foundation, London.

Rarick, G.L. (1976). The motor domain and its correlates in educationally handicapped children by Lawrence, S., Rarick, D., Dobbins, A. and Geoffrey, D. Broadhead, Englewood, Cliff, Prentice-Hall.

Rarick, G.L. (1978). Adult reactions to the Special Olympics. In Small, F. and Smith, R. (eds). Psychological perspectives in youth sports. New York, Helmstead Press.

Sherrill, C. (1982). Adapted physical education and recreation. William, C. Brown Co. New York.

Spencer, D. (1982). The mentally handicapped 'dropout'. Mental Handicap, 10:113-114.

Stuart, R.A. (1983). Should Mentally Handicapped Persons Participate in Competitive Sport - SSAD Edinburgh.

Tilley, A. et al. (1986). Physical fitness assessment of British Columbia Special Olympics athletes. University of British Columbia. Cited by Zitnay, G., Kenedy Institute, Washington.

Tishler, J. and Martel, W. (1985). Dislocation of the atlas in mongolism : preliminary report. Radiology. 84:904-906.

Van Andel, G. and Austin, D. (1984). Physical fitness and mental health : a review of the literature. Adapted Physical Activity Quarterly, i,207-220.

Vermeer, A. (1985). Sport for the mentally handicapped and Wolfensberger's concept of social role valorisation. Paper presented at the International Association for the Scientific Study of Mental Deficiency, New Delhi.

Wolfensberger, W. (1983). Social role valorisation : a proposed new term for the principle of normalisation. Mental Retardation, 21:234-239.

General Discussions

Dr Prior, Vancouver, Canada
I would like to recommend that stair climbing is a readily
available exercise which is part of normal daily life. We should
encourage this type of exercise in that you don't require extra
equipment and it provides aerobic work and improves quadriceps
strength. This simple activity would help prevent coronary heart
disease and promote rehabilitation in the elderly.

Dr Young, Hampstead, England
I must confess that my personal bias is that I will always take a
lift to go up six flights of stairs, if one is available, and I
cannot believe people will readily be educated to use stairs just
because it is good exercise. I believe we have to concentrate on
encouraging people to participate in recreational exercise. I
think people respond best to the motivation of enjoying themselves
rather than being told what is good for them.

Professor Morris, London, England
I would like to comment on the design of buildings. Modern
architects seem to make lifts the main feature of a building.
Delegating stairs to dark corners and designing them in such a way
that they are unattractive or even hazardous.

Professor Raven, Texas, USA
Would Professor Morris talk to the point which Paul Thompson raises
in the New England Journal of Medicine in 1982, namely that people
who are more active have a seven times greater chance of sudden
cardiac death if they have equal risk factors for cardiac disease.
This would imply that we have to be very careful that we are not
increasing the risk of sudden cardiac death in people with latent
cardiac disease.

Professor Morris
Yes: there is only one adequate study of this and that is Siscovitck's
study in the New England Journal of Medicine published in 1984. It
is exceptionally difficult to undertake studies of this type because
of the enormous numbers required to achieve significant statistical
evidence. The point is that there is an increased risk of cardiac
catastrophe during vigorous exercise. This is particularly so among
those who only occasionally participate in vigorous exercise. In
those who take habitual vigorous exercise the additional risk of
sudden cardiac death during that exercise is far outweighed by the
overall benefits and reduction in cardiac death.

Dr Young, Hampstead, England
Thomson's study made the point that the risk of sudden cardiac
death during vigorous exercise was seven times greater for his
whole group but if you took the people who had no premortem
evidence of coronary heart disease it came down to 3 1/2 times
increase of sudden cardiac death during exercise. Siscovitck's
study puts this in context, coming up with remarkably similar
figures for the increased risk of sudden cardiac death in people who
are habitually active. But he also pointed out that if you take

the whole 24 hour spread the risk of death in those who are
inactive was so much greater over the whole 24 hours compared
to those who are commonly active that the small increase during
activity gets lost in the whole 24 hour period. In other words you
gain more than you lose.

The other point, which is rather weak statistically because the
numbers in this group were not all that large, is that the risk to
an individual of sudden cardiac death during VE is greater if he is
habitually inactive. But, by definition, these people rarely take
VE. Therefore, SCD during VE may happen more often amongst those
who are habitually active, despite their lower individual risk.

Dr Ballantyne, Glasgow, Scotland

I agree entirely that the benefits of reducing overall risk of
regular vigorous exercise are quite clear and that sudden cardiac
death occurs in people who do take regular vigorous exercise. In
our study of sudden death on squash courts many of the players who
died suddenly were habitually taking vigorous exercise up to three
times a week and even then they died on the squash court. I think
there are some people who develop coronary artery disease in spite
of taking regular vigorous exercise.

Mr Macleod, Edinburgh, Scotland

Can you identify these individuals?

Dr Ballantyne

We looked at the standard risk factors of cardiac disease in these
people. There were more commonly smokers than average in the
population as a whole. They had risk factors like hypertension
and some of them were in fact known to have angina and two had had
previous myocardial infarctions. At post mortem, looking at those
who had detailed examinations of their hearts 2/3 of them had
severe coronary artery disease and that was despite taking regular
exercise. So we have not solved the problem yet.

Dr Newsholme, Oxford, England

I wonder if it is possible to distinguish, as we appear to be doing
so easily, between vigorous exercise which is assumed to be
aerobic and types of vigorous exercise which have a major anaerobic
component. Mechanistically you can argue that the anaerobic
component of vigorous exercise can be enormously dangerous from the
point of view of sudden death and coronary heart disease.
Therefore I wonder just how easily we can separate these activities
into aerobic and anaerobic exercise and assume that we are only
talking about aerobic exercise.

Professor G.A. Brooks, California, USA

We have been speaking about older people of whom more than 1/2 are
women. However most of the studies that have been carried out on
the elderly have been on men. I wonder if it is a local assumption
that the same parameters apply to women. We know that women
require specialised consideration. In the management of older
people what are the special considerations that should be given to
women particularly when thinking about conditions such as
osteoporosis.

Dr Gray, Oxford, England

My own view is that the link between osteoporosis and inactivity is strong and we should be promoting exercise among the elderly. There are obviously other factors involved and I think calcium deficiency is important. If you look at the problems of old age the high prevalence and severity of fractured neck of femur makes it one of the top two or three problems in society, so I think the prevention of osteoporosis should have the highest priority, by improving calcium intake in the diet and promoting exercise. I think we have to go right back to consider why girls give up exercise at school much earlier than boys and do not pursue exercise throughout adult life before we are going to be able to promote exercise as a significant technique in prevention of osteoporosis in elderly women.

Professor Brooks

Would you vary your exercise programme for older women?

Dr Gray

Not really: this is a cultural matter. Men by large do gardening more often than women. I think we have to suit the activity that women take part in in their 50s and 60s to suit the cultural environment in which they live. Unfortunately I don't think housework gives you suppleness or improves your bone strength sufficiently to protect against osteoporosis.

Professor Astrand, Stockholm, Sweden

Dr Barbara Drinkwater in the United States, reported that a women dies in the United States as a result of complications of fractured neck of femur. I think there is good evidence that the activity we should recommend to older women should be weight bearing so swimming for example is not that beneficial. I believe we should strongly promote prevention of osteoporosis by activity rather than attempting to treat it when it has developed.

PART II SHORT TERM ACTIVITY

The focus of attention of this section, entitled Short Term
Activity, is a consideration of the metabolic factors which are
associated with the onset of fatigue during short term, rather than
during prolonged, activity. Indeed it is appropriate that an
International Symposium organised for the purpose of providing a
forum in which to explore some of current questions about the
'Benefits, Limits and Adaptations to Exercise' should include a
section devoted to a consideration of the physiology and
biochemistry of short term activity. Its place in the programme
can be justified on the grounds that participation in recreational
activities provide most individuals with the opportunity for
regular exercise and, certainly for the younger members of the
community, the most popular recreational activities are those
involving brief periods of high intensity exercise accompanied by
intervals of rest or low intensity exercise. This type of short
term activity is common in what might be termed the 'multiple
sprint sports' such as football, hockey, rugby and squash to quote
only a few of the most popular participation sports. Even during
the daily round of what may appear, to the casual observer, to be
a totally sedentary life style it is not uncommon to witness brief
periods of high intensity exercise such as a dash for a bus or the
well timed sprint across a busy road. Physiologically we are
equipped for such brief bursts of high intensity exercise but it is
only during the preparation for and the participation in the
multiple sprint sports that we really explore our capacity for
such demanding activities.
  While recognising that brief periods of high intensity exercise
are part of the common experience irrespective of the arena in
which they are performed, this aspect of human performance has not
received as much attention as has, for example, prolonged low
intensity exercise. There has, however, been some confusion of
terms which may have given rise to the impression that this is a
well researched topic. The term maximum exercise has been
traditionally given, by exercise physiologists, to the exercise
intensity at which maximum oxygen uptake is achieved, however during
short term activity much higher exercise intensities can be
tolerated. For example during exercise of 5 or 6 seconds duration,
the period of maximum continuous activity observed in multiple-
sprint sports, the power outputs achieved are two to three times

higher than those recorded as 'maximum' during a test to establish an individual's maximum oxygen uptake. Therefore in previously reported studies which have declared that 'maximum' exercise can be tolerated repeatedly for 10 to 15 seconds without fatigue or a significant increase in the concentration of lactic acid, and as such have been commonly called 'alactic', it is important to recognise that in these studies 'maximum' refers only to the exercise intensity corresponding to the power outputs achieved during a maximum oxygen uptake test. Failure to appreciate this difference in terms leads not only to an over estimate of the amount of research information available on this particular topic but more importantly it leads to an over estimation of the tolerable amount of exercise an individual can perform repeatedly because 'maximum activity' in the practical context is interpreted as an all out effort for a short period of time. Recognising the short time-course over which maximum activity usually occurs, recent studies on human power output during exercise requiring a maximum effort have used instrumented cycle ergometers to follow the changes in power output during the development of fatigue. In addition the use of the needle biopsy procedure in conjunction with the techniques for following the development of fatigue have allowed repeated samples of working muscle to be obtained to provide a clearer description of the biochemical events associated with, and possibly responsible for, the phenomenon of fatigue.

Fatigue during high intensity exercise may be viewed as the result of a simple mismatching between the rate at which ATP is utilised and the rate at which ATP is produced in working muscles. The attention given, over the last two decades, to the study of the limitations to ATP production implies that the cause of fatigue may be the inability of the metabolic machinery to provide ATP fast enough for the energy needs of the working muscles to sustain force production. Lactic acid or more correctly the hydrogen ions formed during the rapid production of ATP by the degradation of muscle glycogen have been regarded as acting mainly as metabolic inhibitors of ATP production. There has, however, been more recent attention given to the inhibitory influence of hydrogen ions on the contractile activity of working muscles.

Set against this particular background, it is appropriate that the first paper in this section should be presented by Professor Eric Hultman who has made so many significant contributions to our present knowledge of human muscle metabolism. In his paper Professor Hultman presents an overview and a clear analysis of the available evidence on the metabolic events occurring in working muscles during the development of fatigue. He provides a well argued case for the cause of fatigue to be associated not with the rate of production of ATP but rather with the inhibitory influence of hydrogen ions and inorganic phosphate on cross-bridge cycling and on the further hydrolysis of ATP.

In the second paper Dr Lawrence Spriet presents the results of a series of experiments, performed in collaboration with Professor Hultman, in which intermittent electrical stimulation of the quadriceps muscles were used to examine the relationship between the changes in force production and ATP production in the presence

of increasing intramuscular acidosis. Using this particular
approach to the question of the mechanism underlying the onset of
fatigue, Dr Spriet provides substantial evidence in support of the
idea that inhibition of ATP provision is not the limiting factor to
the maintenance of force production even in the acidotic muscle.

In contrast to the examination of the performance of human muscle
during electrical stimulation, and as such involuntary contractile
activity, the third paper, by Dr Leslie Boobis, is a presentation
of the results of a series of studies in which the subjects
performed brief maximum dynamic cycling and running exercise. The
metabolic changes, for example the decrease in ATP resynthesis from
phosphocreatine and glycolysis as well as the decrease in ATP
concentration and the calculated intramuscular pH values following
a brief period of maximum exercise are of a similar order of
magnitude to those reported by Dr Spriet. This detailed metabolic
audit, presented by Mr Boobis, provides invaluable information
about the relationship between the changes in human power output
and the relative contributions to ATP resynthesis from
phosphocreatine and glycolysis during, what is effectively, freely
performed exercise. It therefore extends and confirms the results
reported by Dr Spriet and in so doing it also helps add a more
realistic perspective to the existing studies on the metabolic
aspects of fatigue during maximum exercise.

While muscle glycogen depletion during prolonged submaximal
exercise is generally accepted as playing a major role in the
development of fatigue, relatively little attention has been paid
to the affects of low muscle glycogen concentrations on the ability
to perform brief high intensity exercise. The fourth paper in this
section is presented by Dr Ira Jacobs and reports a series of
experiments which were designed to examine the influence of low
concentrations of muscle glycogen on leg strength and power output
in human subjects. Dr Jacobs presents information which shows the
detrimental influence of low glycogen concentrations on dynamic
strength and also a differential affect of reduced glycogen
concentrations on the fast twitch and slow twitch muscle fibres.
Thus this presentation by Dr Jacobs reminds us of the importance of
adequate substrate availability even for exercise of relatively
short duration and also that individual differences in the
proportion of fast and slow twitch fibres in muscle may play a part
in the rate of onset of fatigue.

It is entirely appropriate that the last paper in this section,
which has endorsed the central role of lactate formation as a major
contributor to the development of fatigue, should be addressed to
the question of the metabolic fate of lactate. Professor George
Brooks presents the results of a series of detailed experiments
which show the importance of lactate not as a metabolic end product
but as an oxidisable substrate capable of making a significant
contribution to energy metabolism during exercise of submaximal
intensity. Thus it appears from Professor Brooks' studies that
lactate produced in fast twitch muscle fibres may provide a useable
substrate for neighbouring slow twitch oxidative fibres during the
recovery periods which separate the brief periods of high intensity
exercise. In this way it exerts a glycogen sparing influence and
so it is an economic use of a limited substrate.

Thus collectively the papers presented in this section of the Symposium provide very real stepping stones towards greater understanding of the mechanisms underlying the development of fatigue during short term activity of maximum intensity.

Professor Clyde Williams

Energy metabolism and fatigue in working muscle

E. HULTMAN, L.L. SPRIET

and K. SÖDELUND

During short lasting maximum contractions the ATP turnover rate in the human quadriceps femoris muscle is of the order of 8-12mmol.kg^{-1}dm.s^{-1}. Initially [ATP] is unchanged due to resynthesis by the creatine kinase reaction and from glycolysis. During the first few seconds of contraction glycolysis accounts for approximately half of the ATP used. Continued contraction may result in the total depletion of the PCr store and this coincides with a loss in the subject's ability to sustain a voluntary isometric contraction at near maximum force (I.E. fatigue). Electrical stimulation can drive muscle contraction still further with decrease in [ATP] and continued glycolysis as sole providers of energy. Eventually the force may decrease to 20% or less of the initial value without signs of rigor. About 50% of the ATP is transformed to IMP and the pH decreases to 6.4. The ATP hydrolysis rate decreases during the same contraction period by 70-80%. It is suggested that the reason for the decrease in force and ATP hydrolysis is an inhibition of cross-bridge cycling primarily by increases in [Pi] and [H$^+$], produced by PCr-ATP splitting and glycolysis. During the last part of the contraction increase of free [Mg^{2+}] may also add to the inhibiting effect. Decreased repolarisation of sarcolemma and T-tubular membranes via product inhibition of the Na$^+$-K$^+$ ATPase could additionally decrease activation of the contractile system.

1. Introduction

1.1 Energy metabolism and fatigue in working muscles

A series of recent studies of energy metabolism utilising the needle biopsy technique in man has been focused on short term maximum exercise (Bergström et al., 1971; Boobis et al., 1983; Cheetham et al., 1985; Hultman and Sjöholm, 1983a; Jones et al., 1985). Under such conditions the ATP turnover rate is 500-600 times that at rest. Still there was no immediate decrease in the ATP store as rephosphorylation of ADP accelerated to the same rate as the ATP utilisation by anaerobic glycolysis and degradation of phosphocreatine (PCr). This, however, resulted in decreased PCr content and accumulation of lactate. If the exercise was prolonged to 30 seconds or more a decrease of the ATP content was also observed. The maximum or near maximum force could however be generated only during 5-20 seconds, thereafter the force decreased and the subjects experienced fatigue. This decrease in force generation is observed irrespective of the mode of muscle stimulation - i.e. volitionally via the central nervous system (Boobis et al., 1983; Cheetham et al., 1985; Jones et al., 1985) by electrical stimulation of a peripheral nerve (Edwards et al., 1977) or percutaneously via nerve-endings in the muscle (Hultman and Sjöholm, 1983) or by direct electrical stimulation of the muscle membranes (Lannergren and Westerblad, 1986). The fatigue mechanism thus seems to be localised to the contracting muscle and dependent on the metabolic environment of the muscle. In this paper some studies of anaerobic metabolism and relations between metabolism and force production will be discussed.

1.2 Processes involved in ATP turnover during contraction
1.2.1 Adenosine triphosphatases
ATP is hydrolysed during muscle contraction according to the formula

$$ATP + H_2O \longrightarrow ADP + P_i + H^+$$

Three different ATP splitting reactions are coupled to the contraction-relaxation cycle via 3 ATPases: actomyosin ATPase for formation and breaking of cross-bridges, Ca^{2+} transport ATPase for Ca^{2+} transport across the membrane of the sarcoplasmic reticulum and Na^+-, K^+ ATPase for electrolyte transport in the sarcolemma and the T-tubule system membranes. Of these ATPases the actomyosin ATPase has the highest activity. The maximum rate of ATP splitting in human muscle has been estimated during different types of activities. Margaria et al. (1964) estimated that the turnover rate during 3 seconds of stair climbing at top speed was 7 mmol $ATP.kg^{-1}$ dry muscle $(dm).s^{-1}$. Higher values, 25-30 $mmol.kg^{-1} dm.s^{-1}$ were estimated during 0.2 seconds of standing high jump (Davies, 1971; Di Prampero and Mogoni, 1981). In our studies with electrical stimulation of the quadriceps femoris muscle of man the ATP turnover rate varies with the stimulation frequency. With 20 Hz stimulation the ATP turnover rate at the start of stimulation is about 6.5 $mmol.kg^{-1} dm.s^{-1}$ and at 50 Hz about 10 $mmol.kg^{-1} dm.s^{-1}$ (Hultman and Sjöholm, 1983b).
The Ca^{2+}-transporting ATPase responsible for the transport of Ca^{2+} from the cytoplasm of the myofibrils to the sarcoplasmic reticulum has been calculated to utilise one ATP for two Ca^{2+} transported. During intermittent contraction the cytoplasmic Ca^{2+} content is $10^{-5} mol.l^{-1}$ during contraction and decreases to 10^{-7} during rest. During continuous tetanic stimulation there is probably a continuous cycling of CA^{2+} such that the free $[Ca^{2+}]$ remains at an elevated level of $10^{-5} mol.l^{-1}$. The ATP turnover rate due to Ca^{2+} cycling during exercise has not been determined but a reasonable estimate is 0.4 - 0.8 mmol $ATP.kg^{-1} dm.s^{-1}$ (Kushmerick, 1983).
The Na^+-K^+ pump restores the membrane potential after each action potential. The energetic cost to restore the initial conditions during recovery is about 10 μmol of energy-rich phosphate per kg dm for each depolarisation. The estimated energy cost for sodium transport during tetanic stimulation is in the order of 0.2-0.6 $mmol.kg^{-1} dm.s^{-1}$ (Kushmerick, 1983).
The remaining ATP turnover rate at start of contraction utilised

specifically in the actomyosin ATPase reaction would correspond to
5.9 mmol.kg^{-1}dm.s^{-1} at 20 Hz and 8.6 mmol at 50 Hz, The K$_m$
for ATP for the actomyosin ATPase is 0.78 mmol.kg^{-1}dm.

1.2.2 The creatine phosphokinase reaction
Phosphocreatine (PCr) is in near equilibrium with ATP via the
creatine phosphokinase (CPK) reaction

$$PCr + ADP + H^+ \rightleftharpoons ATP + Cr$$

The enzyme and reactants in the muscle cell are in close
contact with actomyosin ATPase reactants in the cytoplasm but
also in the myofibrils as a component of the M-band and in the
outer membrane of the mitochondria. The activity of CPK is higher
than ATPase activity which means that significant decreases in
[ATP]s are seen only when PCr is broken down to 60% of the value
in resting muscle or more (Hultman et al., 1967). Cr can only be
rephosphorylated by ATP. The creatine kinase reaction functions
to buffer ATP to ADP ratio in muscle and is thus active as a
stabiliser of intracellular adenylate gradients. The release of
phosphate (P$_i$) by PCr degradation is important in the regulation
of glycogenolysis and glycolysis during contraction (Chasiotis, 1983).
The initial rate of ATP production from PCr in human quadriceps
femoris muscle during maximum voluntary isometric contraction or
during electrical stimulation is about 8-9 mmol ATP.kg^{-1} dm.s^{-1}
calculated over the first 3-4 seconds (Bergström et al., 1971; Hultman
and Sjöholm, 1983b). The K$_m$ for PCr for the creatine phosphofructokinase is 5 mmol.kg^{-1}dm.

1.2.3 Adenylate kinase
ADP formed during ATP hydrolysis can also be catalysed by adenylate
kinase according to the reaction

$$2 \; ADP \longrightarrow AMP + ATP$$

The enzyme has a lower activity than CPK and the reaction is
assumed to be in equilibrium in the muscle cell. The free ADP in
resting cell is low but increases during contraction providing
substrate for formation of ATP and AMP. The effect of this is to
keep the ATP to ADP ratio high. The ratio is a determinant of the
free energy release by the ATPase reactions and thus also for the
question of force.

1.2.4 AMP Deaminase

$$AMP + H_2O + H^+ \quad \longrightarrow \quad IMP + NH_4^+$$

This enzyme AMP deaminase has a high activity especially in fast-twitch muscles fibres. The pH optimum for the enzyme is 6.5 (Setlow and Lowenstein, 1967) but it is active also at normal cell pH (Dudley and Terjung, 1985). The function of the enzyme during anaerobic exercise is to adjust the adenylate kinase equilibrium and thus to promote continued formation of ATP from ADP. During anaerobic exercise there is no resynthesis of AMP and IMP is accumulated together with NH_4^+. Both these metabolites have a stimulating effect on glycogen utilisation since IMP is shown to activate phosphorylase b (Aragon et al., 1980) and NH_4^+ formation stimulates phosphofructokinase (PFK) activity (Dobson et al., 1986).

1.2.5 Glycogen Phosphorylase

The enzyme glycogen phosphorylates glycogen producing glucose-1-phosphate (G-1-P).

The phosphorylase enzymes are in close contact with the glycogen molecule as a glycogen-protein complex in the cell. The enzyme exists in two forms, a, phosphorylated and b, non-phosphorylated. The transformations are mediated via phosphorylase kinase and a phosphatase respectively. The b form is probably inactive in the cell at normal levels of adenine nucleotides. It is inhibited by ATP and glucose 6-P and activated by AMP and IMP (Danforth, 1965; Aragon et al., 1980).

The a form which is low in the resting cell increases when phosphorylase kinase is activated. The activation is mediated via an increase in cytoplasmic $[Ca^{2+}]$ which also initiates muscle contraction. The activity of the enzyme is however also dependent on the availability of P_i as substrate for glycogen phosphorylation. The K_m of phosphorylase a for P_i is 27 mmol.l^{-1} in the absence of AMP but decreases to 6.8 when $[AMP]$ increases. The $[AMP]$ early in maximum contraction is probably sufficient to decrease the K_m for P_i but not to activate the b form of the enzyme (Chasiotis et al., 1982). The (P_i) in resting cell is difficult to determine chemically but by recent phosphorus nuclear magnetic resonance (N.M.R.) studies a concentration of 2-3 mmol.l^{-1} intracellular water was shown (Ackerman et al., 1980; Meyer et al., 1985). A significant increase of $[P_i]$ via degradation of PCr is thus necessary to activate glycogenolysis initially in contraction. The glycogenolytic rate observed during intense contraction is close to the $\dot{V}_{max}$ of the enzyme, estimated to 2.4 mmol glucosyl units.$kg^{-1}dm.s^{-1}$ with a range of 1.5-4.0 in the quadriceps femoris muscle (Chasiotis, 1983). The phosphorylase activity is dependent on the relative amounts of fast and slow-twitch fibres in the muscle: being 2-3 times higher in fast-twitch than in slow-twitch fibres in the quadriceps femoris muscle of man (Harris et al., 1976).

During continued stimulation a retransformation of the enzyme from a to b is observed in rat muscle (Conlee et al., 1979) and also in human muscle during isometric contraction or dynamic exercise (Chasiotis et al., 1982). The retransformation usually parallels a decrease in contraction force and could thus be explained as an effect of decreased Ca^{2+} release from the sarcoplasmic reticulum at least during intermittent isometric contraction and during dynamic work. However, in soleus muscle of rat a retransformation was observed without a decrease in force (Conlee et al., 1979). The mechanism for this retransformation is not known. Also the near $\dot{V}_{max}$ activity of the enzyme during the first 5 seconds of isometric contraction is difficult to explain as an effect of transformation and P_i increase.

1.2.6 Glycolysis - phosphofructokinase
The hexosephosphates produced in glycolysis are further metabolised by the phosphofructokinase (PFK) reaction. The enzyme activity is low in resting muscle and is inhibited by ATP, PCr, Mg^{2+}, H^+, citrate and some of the glycolytic three carbon intermediates but activated or de-inhibited by AMP, ADP, P_i, cyclic AMP, NH_4^+, K^+, fructose-6-phosphate (F-6-P) and fructose-1,6-diphosphate (F-1,6-DP) (for reviews see Bloxham and Lardy, 1956; Hoffman, 1976; Mansour, 1972; Uyeda, 1979; Uyeda et al., 1981). This means that PFK activity will increase as a result of ATP and PCr utilisation with formation of ADP AMP and P_i during the contraction. At start of exercise F-6-P produced by Ca^{2+} activated glycogenolysis will act both as substrate and activator.

The maximum rate of glycolysis during exercise is in the order of 1.5-2.2 mmol glucose.kg^{-1} $dm.s^{-1}$ in the quadriceps femoris muscle of man, corresponding to a rate of ATP formation from ADP of 4.5-6.6 mmol.kg^{-1} $dm.s^{-1}$. The maximum rate of glycolysis is not obtained at start of exercise, but increases during the initial part of the contraction. At maximum force the delay before glycolysis is fully activated is 4-5 seconds (Bergström et al., 1971) but at 70% of maximum force the time delay is about 20 seconds (Hultman and Sjöholm, 1983b). This can be explained as regulation of PFK activity by the concentrations of F-6-P, PCr, P_i and the adeninenucleotides which all will vary with the force generated and with the contraction time.

2 Energy metabolism during short term contraction

Energy metabolism and the development of fatigue were studied during short term exercise in three types of experiments.

(1) Voluntary isometric contractions of the knee extensors with different forces continued as long as the predetermined force could be sustained.
(2) Continuous electrical stimulation of the quadriceps femoris muscle during 50 seconds.
(3) Intermittent electrical stimulation of the quadriceps muscle prolonged until the force generation was close to zero in areobic muscle.

2.1 Isometric contraction sustained to fatigue

Fatigue is defined as the inability to sustain a predetermined force. The studies consisted of a series of isometric contractions by the quadriceps femoris muscle of man. The contractions were performed with different forces, given as a percentage (%) of the maximum voluntary contraction force (MVC). Each contraction was held as long as the predetermined % of MVC could be sustained. Muscle biopsy samples were obtained before the contraction, at different times during the contraction and at the end - i.e. the point of fatigue.

Biochemical analyses of the muscle tissue were done after freeze-drying and the muscle constituents were expressed per kg dry muscle.

The data presented here are taken from a series of studies in our laboratory (Bergström et al., 1971; Ahlborg et al., 1972; Harris et al., 1976; Harris et al., 1977; Sahlin et al., 1975) which were assembled by Roger Harris in his thesis (1981). Fig. 1 shows the ATP turnover rate, total ATP turnover, the rate of ATP formation by glycolysis and the holding time during the isometric contractions. The holding time follows a curvilinear function in relation to force (Rohmert, 1960) with a variation in time from 5 seconds at 100% MVC to 100 seconds at 40%. The ATP turnover rate was linearly related to force with a maximum rate of 9.5 mmol $ATP.kg^{-1} \cdot s^{-1}$, and the lowest rate about 2 mmol when the force corresponded to 40% MVC. ATP derived from glycolysis was also directly related to the force generated with a variation of 1-5 mmol $ATP.kg^{-1} \cdot s^{-1}$. At the highest contraction forces equal amounts of ATP are resynthesised via PCr degradation and glycolysis. At lower contraction forces glycolysis provides a larger fraction of the ATP turnover. In this graph only the anaerobic ATP turnover is included. Theoretically some ATP could additionally be derived from oxygen stored in the muscle before contraction. The available oxygen corresponds to 12 mmol $ATP.kg^{-1}$ (Harris et al., 1975). The total amount of ATP utilised at fatigue is higher when the predetermined force is lower, which indicates that fatigue is not due to depletion of energy stores to any particular critical level.

Other metabolite data from the studies showed that glycogenolytic rate varied from 2.4 to 0.7 $mmol.kg^{-1} \cdot s^{-1}$ of glucose phosphorylated during the contractions in the force interval from 100 to 40% MVC. This means that the glycogenolytic rate is close to $\dot{V}_{max}$ of the phosphorylase enzyme already at start of the maximum contraction, inferring a complete transformation to phosphorylase $\underline{a}$ and a lowering of the K_m for P_i for the enzyme by increased free [AMP], or that both $\underline{a}$ and $\underline{b}$ forms of the enzyme are activated. Also an immediate increase in $[P_i]$ is necessary to explain the glycogenolytic activity. At 66% MVC the mole fraction of phosphorylase $\underline{a}$ was 50% of the total after 25 seconds of contraction and 19% at the end (Chasiotis et al., 1982).

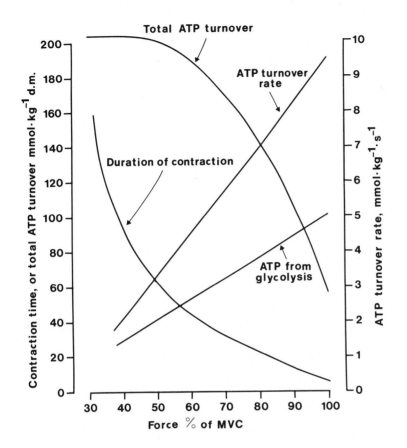

Figure 1. ATP turnover and duration of voluntary isometric contractions sustained to fatigue at varying forces. Total amounts of ATP utilised during the contractions are given, and also the anaerobic ATP turnover rates and the rates of ATP formation from glycolysis.

Hexose-Ps showed a continuous accumulation during the isometric contractions. The glycolytic rates varied between 1.7 and 0.5 mmol.kg^{-1}.s^{-1}. The [PCr]s and [lactate]s at the end of contractions are shown in Fig. 2. The whole PCr store was not utilised during the contraction at maximum force but at or below a force corresponding to 70% of MVC practically all PCr was utilised at fatigue. Lactate accumulation was highest after contraction with the lowest force [ATP] decreased only marginally, 10-15%, during the contractions, with a tendency to slightly larger decreases, i.e. 15% at the lowest contraction forces.

The muscle samples obtained at fatigue, i.e. when pre-determined forces no longer could be sustained showed only marginally decreased [ATP], a [lactate] varying from 20 to 100 mmol.kg^{-1} at different forces and a [PCr] decreased by 90% in the force range 30-75% MVC. When the predetermined force was higher up to 50% of the [PCr] remained in the muscle at fatigue.

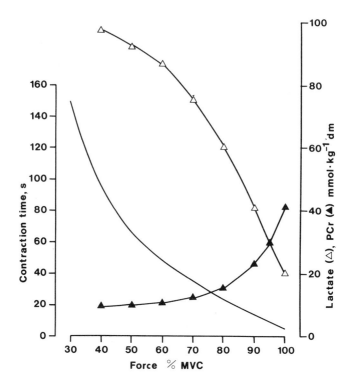

Figure 2. Lactate and PCr concentrations at end of isometric contractions sustained to fatigue at different forces. Also endurance time is given as in Fig. 1.

2.2 Continuous electrical stimulation

During voluntary exercise the frequency of stimulation and the recruitment pattern can be altered by the nervous system during the contraction in order to sustain the force. Also central fatigue can play a role in the endurance time.

Such possible influences can be avoided if the muscle is stimulated electrically which can be done via percutaneous electrodes placed over the muscle. The stimulation frequency determines the power output of the muscle segment stimulated. In most of our studies 20 Hz was used, which gives a contraction force of about 70% of maximum. Continuous stimulation at 20 Hz should consequently have the same metabolic and force patterns as voluntary contraction at 70% MVC. With electrical stimulation activation of the muscle is kept constant and biopsy material can be sampled repeatedly during the contraction enabling measurements of metabolic changes. In a recent study in our laboratory the quadriceps femoris muscle of man was stimulated continuously at 20 Hz during 50 seconds and six biopsy samples were obtained; one before the stimulation and the other five at 10 seconds interval during the contraction (Hultman and Sjöholm, 1983a). The ATP turnover rate during the first 10 seconds was 5.6 mmol.kg^{-1}.s^{-1} and there-after 5.0, 4.6, 4.2, and 4.2 during the following 10 sec periods.

ATP production from PCr during the five periods was 3.3, 2.0, 1.1, 0.7 and 0.4 mmol.kg^{-1}·s^{-1} while glycolytic ADP phosphorylation produced 2.2, 2.9, 3.5, 3.5, and 3.8 mmol ATP.kg^{-1}·s^{-1}. Glycogenolytic activity was highest initially with a rate of 2 mmol glucose units.kg^{-1}.s^{-1} already during the first 10 seconds decreasing to 1.6 mmol in the last period. The glycogenolytic rate was higher than the glycolytic during the whole contraction period resulting in continuous accumulation of hexose-Ps. The increasing glycolytic rate during the first 30 seconds may be due to increased activation of PFK by the accumulation of hexose-Ps, and P_i, decreased [PCr] and a possible decrease in ATP/ADP ratio during the contraction. The force increased slightly during the first 10 seconds and declined significantly in the period 30-50 seconds. At the end of contraction the force was 78% of the initial. The ATP content was unchanged during the first 30 seconds of contraction and thereafter showed a decrease to about 76% of the initial value after 50 seconds. Fig. 3 shows the contraction force and the muscle contents of PCr and lactate during the continuous stimulation. Also in this study the initial force decrease seems to coincide with the depletion of the PCr store. The fall in force generation parallels the decrease in ATP turnover rate.

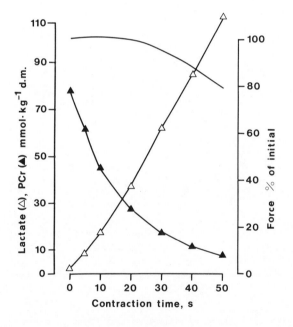

Figure 3. Lactate and PCr concentrations and force generation during 50 seconds electrical stimulation at 20 Hz.

2.3 Prolonged intermittent electrical stimulation
In another series of experiments the electrical stimulation of the quadriceps femoris muscle was continued beyond the 'fatigue point' as defined above, until the force generation was near exhaustion (Hultman and Sjöholm, 1986).

The muscles were stimulated at 20 Hz with a series of tetanic contractions, each lasting 1.6 seconds and separated by 1.6 seconds of rest. The total stimulation time was 160 seconds and the contraction time 80 seconds. The stimulation was done both with open and occluded circulations. Five biopsy samples were obtained during the contraction. The results are shown in Fig. 4. During the initial 30-40 seconds of contraction the metabolic changes were similar with open and closed circulation. As expected the [PCr] decreased rapidly to low values, lactate accumulated and [ATP] fell by about 30%. In the time period 40-80 seconds [ATP] and [PCr] increased in the open circulation leg due to mitochondrial ATP production, which apparently together with glycolytic ATP formation was higher than ATP hydrolysis during the continued stimulation. Lactate accumulation ceased and [lactate] even decreased during the last period of contraction due to escape of lactate from the muscle during the rest period.

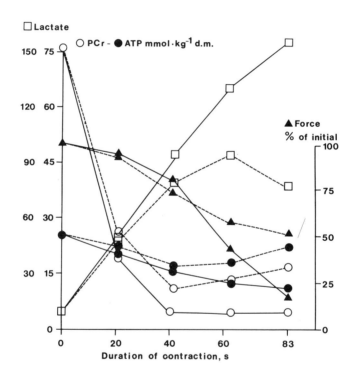

Figure 4. ATP, PCr and lactate contents and force generation in quadriceps femoris muscle during intermittent electrical stimulation at 20 Hz. Stimulation pulses of 1.6 seconds duration were interrupted by 1.6 seconds rest periods. Two series of stimulations were done with the blood flow intact (------) and with occluded circulation (_____).

In the anoxic muscle [PCr] was decreased by 90% after 40 seconds of
contraction and remained at that level. [ATP] continued to
decrease to a final concentration of 50% of the value at rest.
During this period, 40-80 seconds of contraction, there were only
marginal increases in [ADP] and [AMP] but a large formation of IMP
due to the combined activities of adenylate kinase and AMP deaminase.
The force generation decreased in both legs, but less in the leg
with open circulation. The earliest sign of substantial force
decrease was again seen when most of the PCr store had been
utilised, and thereafter the force fell continuously with
contraction time and ATP turnover rate. A detailed discussion of
the metabolic changes during this type of contraction will be
given by Lawrence Spriet in a following paper.

It should be concluded from this study that during intermittent
contraction with high contraction force the metabolism is
predominantly anoxic during the first 30-40 seconds even when the
circulation is open. Furthermore, activating the muscle by
electrical stimulation during anoxia can be continued to the limit
of contraction capacity with larger ATP loss and pH decrease than
during voluntary contraction but without signs of rigor. At the
end of the aerobic contraction the [ATP] was 13 mmol.kg^{-1} [IMP]
13 mmol.kg^{-1}, [PCr] 5.5 mmol.kg^{-1}, [P$_i$] increased by 94 mmol.kg^{-1}
or 31 mmol.l^{-1} i.c. water, and [lactate] was 150 mmol.kg^{-1} (Hultman
and Sjöholm, 1986). In a similar study muscle pH was found to be
6.4 at end of a 100 seconds contraction (Spriet et al., 1986).

3. Mechanisms of fatigue

In a paper by Dawson et al. (1978) studying muscle fatigue by use
of nuclear magnetic resonance technique, it was concluded that
force development is closely correlated with metabolite levels and
is proportional to the rate at which ATP is hydrolysed. In a
symposium on Human Muscle Fatigue (1981), Merton expressed an
opposite opinion and argued that muscle fatigue during isometric
contraction had everything to do with electricity and nothing to do
with chemistry.

According to the first view chemistry will determine the rate
of ATP utilisation - which determines the force. In the second
view the excitation of the muscle is the determining factor
regulating force and secondarily metabolism.

A correlation between ATP hydrolysis and force production is
easy to accept, but is the rate of hydrolysis determined by:

   a) the excitation of muscle membranes and the Ca^{2+}
      release?
   b) the rate of ATP resynthesis by metabolic processes?
   c) changes in metabolite concentrations?

If the ATP hydrolysis rate is higher than the resynthesis rate the
[ATP] will decrease. This was observed during the intermittent
electrical stimulation with a decrease in [ATP] to 50% of the value
at rest mediated via the activities of adenylate kinase and AMP
deaminase when the PCr store was depleted. However, when about 50%
of ATP is lost the force production and ATP hydrolysis cease in

normal muscle. In muscles lacking glycolytic capacity or in rat muscles treated with iodoacetate (Sahlin et al., 1981) this inhibition of ATP hydrolysis is not operative, and the muscles end up in rigor. Apparently the formation of lactic acid inhibits the ATP hydrolysis at this level.

A decrease in force generation and ATP hydrolysis is however seen much earlier in sustained isometric contraction (see Figs 1 and 2). At maximum contraction force practically the whole ATP store is intact and also PCr is available in the muscle when the force starts to fall. The decrease in force generation, i.e. the decrease in ATP hydrolysis during isometric exercise is apparently not due to lack of ATP or decreased metabolic capacity to form ATP, but rather to the level of metabolites in the muscle formed during ATP hydrolysis: ADP, P_i and H^+.

3.1 Fatigue and pH

Decreased intracellular pH as a major factor causing fatigue was suggested as early as 1929 by Hill and Kupalov. Later studies of isolated animal muscle have shown direct inhibition of force generation by increased $[H^+]$ (Hill, 1955; Fretthold and Garg, 1978; Edman and Mattiazzi, 1981; Sahlin et al., 1981). The increase in $[H^+]$ in these studies was produced by incubation of isolated muscle in acid media. In the study by Sahlin et al. (1981) the tetanic tension in rat EDL muscle was decreased by 50% when pH decreased from 7.01 to 6.67. It was, however, also observed that the $[PCr]$ had decreased from 82.9 to 36.6 mmol. kg^{-1} as an effect of the pH change. A series of studies have been performed in isolated muscle fibre preparations showing that the maximum force generation is decreased in the pH interval between 7.0-6.2 (Robertson and Kerrick, 1979) Fabiato and Fabiato, 1978; Donaldson et al., 1978). The effect is most pronounced in fast twitch fibres and is suggested to be due to an inhibition of cross-bridge cycling due to product inhibition of myofibrillar ATP hydrolysis (Donaldson, 1983). It was also shown that acid pH reduces Ca^{2+} sensitivity of the myofilaments (Fabiato and Fabiato, 1978; Donaldson et al., 1978). These studies were done in skinned muscle fibres and the $[Ca^{2+}]$ needed for producing 50% of maximum tension was shown to be increased 2-3 times in the pH range 7.1-6.2. Direct measurements of ATPase activity at pH 7.0-6.2 in rabbit skeletal myofilaments were done by Blanchard et al. (1984). They found decreased Ca^{2+} sensitivity of the ATPase which was due to reduced affinity of Ca^{2+} binding sites on the troponin complex by decreasing pH. An increased binding of Ca^{2+} to the sarcoplasmic reticulum at lower pH was shown by Nakamura and Schwartz (1970), and a depressed Ca^{2+} release in intact fibre in the same situation was suggested in studies by Fabiato and Fabiato (1978). An increased $[H^+]$ would thus both decrease cross-bridge cycling and reduce activation of the contractile system.

3.2 Fatigue and P_i

It has been shown in insect flight muscle (White and Thorson, 1972; Ruegg et al., 1971) that increased $[P_i]$ causes a decrease in the isometric tension. Similar findings have been reported by Herzig et al. (1981) in vertebrate muscle. Recently Cooke and Pate (1985) used chemically skinned psoas muscle fibres from rabbit for analysing the effect of $MgADP^-$, P_i and H^+ on the mechanics of fibre contraction. They could show that an increase of $[P_i]$ from 1-2 to 10-15mmol.l^{-1} significantly decreased isometric tension in the fibres. The tension decrease was proportional to the increase in $[P_i]$ with a maximum of 30% at 20 mmol P_i.l^{-1}. A decrease in pH from 7.0 to 6.5 was shown to have the same effect in this series as described above, and was additive to the P_i effect. The total decrease in isometric tension was 75% in their preparation at a $[P_i]$ of 20 mmol.l^{-1} and pH 6.5. They found no change in isometric tension by a $MgADP^-$ increase in the range 2-4 mmol.l^{-1}. Similar findings were reported by Godt and Nosek (1985). They incubated skinned fibres from rabbit psoas in a solution mimicking the cytoplasm of a fatigued muscle as described by Dawson et al. (1978). The maximum tension was 40% of that of the control fibres incubated in a solution with normal ' at rest composition' and the $[Ca^{2+}]$ needed for producing 50% of maximum tension was increased three times. No effects were seen attributable to changes in $[ATP]$ or $[Cr]$. Lowering of free energy release by ATP hydrolysis appeared according to the authors to have no effect per se.

3.3 Fatigue and Mg^{2+}

The decrease in $[ATP]$ during the contraction also releases Mg^{2+}. The free $[Mg^{2+}]$ at rest is suggested to be 1 mmol.l^{-1} (Veloso et al., 1973) which means that the value at end of the contraction should have increased to 5 mmol.l^{-1} when ATP has decreased by 50% as in the study with intermittent electrical stimulation. Mg^{2+} is known to compete with Ca^{2+} for the binding sites of troponin (Donaldson and Kerrick, 1975) and was shown to depress Ca^{2+} sensitivity of the force generating mechanism in skinned fibres (Donaldson et al., 1978).

3.4 Inhibition of Na^+-K^+ transporting ATPase

The Na^+-K^+ ATPase could similarly be inhibited by product accumulation. In a recent study by Westerblad and Lännergren (1986) isolated fibres from Xenopus were stimulated intermittently via platinium electrodes applied along the isolated muscle fibre. Membrane potential and force were measured during the stimulation. There was a rapid fall in resting membrane potential from -90mV to -60mV. A further decrease in E_m was paralleled by a steep decrease in contraction force. The reason for this fall in tension is suggested to be a progressive blockade of impulse conduction in the T-tubules due to maintained depolarised level. The result is a failure of Ca^{2+} release from the sarcoplasmic reticulum and a lack of activation of myofibrillar ATPase.

4. Combined Effects on Contraction Force

During voluntary isometric contraction at 100% MVC the fatigue point, i.e. the point when the predetermined force no longer could be sustained, was reached when 35 mmol of the PCr store had been broken down (see Fig. 1). The corresponding increase in $[P_i]$ was 7-8mmol.l^{-1} i.c water, a change in $[P_i]$ which according to Cooke and Pate (1985) is sufficient to decrease isometric tension by 20% in isolated rabbit psoas muscle. At isometric contractions with forces lower than 70% MVC the fatigue point occurs after longer contraction times when the whole PCr store is utilised, i.e. when the $[P_i]$ in cell water has increased by 14-15 mmol.l^{-1} and when also the muscle pH is decreased due to lactate accumulation. The combined effects of P_i and H^+ accumulations on the contractile mechanism could explain the inability to sustain also the lower force at the fatigue points at varying % MVC.

During the prolonged intermittent stimulation the P_i accumulates successively to concentrations between 25 and 30 mmol.l^{-1} i.c. water, and pH decreases to 6.4 at the end of contraction. Also free $[Mg^{2+}]$ increases during the later part of contraction. All these changes are shown to inhibit force generation by decreasing cross-bridge cycling directly but also by reducing Ca^{2+} sensitivity and thus the activation of the contractile system. A decreased Ca^{2+} release from the sarcoplasmic reticulum due to lowered pH or to a blockade of impulse conduction in the T-tubules would further decrease activation of myofibrillar ATPase.

5. Conclusion

The creatine kinase reaction has a key role in anaerobic energy release by providing energy for contraction, keeping the ATP to ADP ratio high, releasing P_i necessary for glycogenolysis and stimulating glycolysis.[1] When the PCr store is exhausted force generation in short term heavy exercise is successively inhibited by the accumulation of P_i, H^+ and possibly free Mg^{2+} at the end of contraction. The accumulation of these products will inhibit both cross-bridge cycling and activation of the contractile system. Fatigue is thus due to inhibition of ATP utilisation rather than to insufficient ATP formation.

Acknowledgements

This work was supported by grants from the Swedish Medical Research Council (02647) and the Swedish Sports Research Council. Dr. Spriet was the recipient of a Post-Doctoral Research Fellowship from the Medical Research Council of Canada. The authors wish to thank the entire staff of the Department of Clinical Chemistry II for excellent collaboration in this investigation.

References

Ackerman, J.J.H., Grove, T.H., Wong, G.G., Gadian, D.G and Radda, G.K. (1980). Mappings of metabolites in whole animals by 31P-NMR using surface coils. Nature London 283:167-170.

Ahlborg, B., Bergström, J., Ekelund, L.-G., Guarnieri, B., Harris, R.C., Hultman, E. and Nordesjö, L.-O. (1972). Muscle metabolism during isometric exercise performed at constant force. J. Appl. Physiol. 33:224-228

Aragon, J.J., Tornheim, K. and Lowenstein, J.M. (1980). On a possible role of IMP in the regulation of phosphorylase activity in skeletal muscle. FEBS Letters 117:K56-K64.

Bergström, J., Harris, R.C., Hultman, E. and Nordesjö, L.-O. (1971). Energy rich phosphagens in dynamic and static work. In Advances in Experimental Medicine and Biology II (edited by B. Pernow and B. Saltin), pp. 341-355. Plenum Press, New York - London.

Blanchard, E.M., Pan, B.-S. and Solaro, R.J. (1984). The effect of acidic pH on the ATPase activity and troponin Ca^{2+} binding of rabbit skeletal myofilaments. J. Biological Chemistry 259:3181- 3186.

Bloxham, D.P. and Lardy, H.A. (1956). Phosphofructokinase. In The Enzymes (edited by P.D. Boyer), pp. 239-278, vol.8. New York: Academic.

Boobis, L.H., Williams, C. and Wootton, S.A. (1983). Human muscle metabolism during brief maximal exercise. J. Physiology, 338:21P-22P.

Chasiotis, D. (1983). The regulation of glycogen phosphorylase and glycogen breakdown in human skeletal muscle. Acta Physiol Scand. suppl. 518:1-68.

Chasiotis, D., Sahlin, K. and Hultman, E. (1982). Regulation of glycogenolysis in human muscle at rest and during exercise, J. Appl. Physiol. 53:708-715.

Cheetham, M.E., Boobis, L.H. and Williams, C. (1985). Human muscle metabolism during maximal treadmill sprinting. Clinical Physiol. suppl. 4:154.

Conlee, R.K., McLane, J.A., Rennie, M.J., Winder, W.W. and Holloszy, J.O. (1979). Reversal of phosphorylase activation in muscle despite continued contractile activity. American J. Physiol. 237:R291-R296.

Cooke, R. and Pate, E. (1985). The effects of ADP and phosphate on the contraction of muscle fibres. Biophysical Journal 48: 789-798.

Danforth, W.H. (1965). Activation of glycolytic pathway in muscle in Control of Energy Metabolism (edited by B. Chance and R.W. Estabrook), pp. 287-297. Academic Press, New York.

Davies, C.T.M. (1971). Human power output in exercise of short duration in relation to body size and composition Ergonomics 14: 245-256.

Dawson, M.J., Gadian, D.G. and Wilkie, D.R. (1978). Muscular fatigue investigated by phosphorus nuclear magnetic resonance. Nature 274: 861-866.

Di Prampero, P.E. and Mogoni, P. (1981). Maximal anaerobic power in man, Medicine and Sport 13: 38-44.

Dobson, G.P., Yamamoto, E. and Hochachka, P.W. (1986).
Phosphofructokinase control in muscle: nature and reversal of
pH-dependent ATP inhibition. American J. Physiol.
250:R71-R76.

Donaldson, S.K.B. (1983). Effect of acidosis on maximum force
generation of peeled mammalian skeletal muscle fibres. In
Biochemistry of Exercise (edited by H.G. Knuttgen, J.A. Vogel
and J. Poortmans), pp. 126-133. Human Kinetics Publishers,
Champaign.

Donaldson, S. and Kerrick, W. (1975). Characterisation of the
effects of Mg^{2+} on Ca^{2+}- and Sr^{2+}- activated
tension generation of skinned skeletal muscle fibres.
J. General Physiol. 66:427-444.

Donaldson, S., Best, P. and Kerrick, W. (1978). Characterisation of
the effects of Mg^{2+} on Ca^{2+}- and Sr^{2+}- activated
tension generation of skinned rat cardiac fibres. J. General
Physiol. 71:645-655.

Dudley, G.A. and Terjung, R.L. (1985). Influence of acidosis on AMP
deaminase activity in contracting fast-twitch muscle America
J. Physiol. 248:C43-C50

Edman, K.A.P. and Mattiazzi, A.R. (1981). Effects of fatigue and
altered pH on isometric force and velocity of shortening at
zero load in frog muscle fibres. J. Muscle Research and Cell
Motility 2:321-334

Edwards, R.H.T., Hill, D.K., Jones, D.A. and Merton, P.A. (1977).
Fatigue of long duration in human skeletal muscle after
exercise. J. Physiol. 272:769-778

Fabiato, A. and Fabiato, F. (1978). Effects of pH on the
myofilaments and the sarcoplasmic reticulum of skinned cells
from cardiac and skeletal muscles. J. Physiol. 276:233-255

Fretthold, D.W. and Garg, L.C. (1978). The effect of acidbase
changes on skeletal muscle twitch tension. Canadian J.
Physiol. and Pharmacol. 56:543-549

Godt, R.D. and Nosek, T.M. (1985). The changes in intracellular
millieu accompanying fatigue or hypoxia depress the contractile
machinery of rabbit skeletal and guinea-pig cardiac muscle.
J. Physiol 371:174P

Harris, R.C. (1981). Muscle energy metabolism in man in response
to isometric contraction. A biopsy study. Thesis for the
degree of Magister in Scientia. University of Wales.

Harris, R.C., Essén, B. and Hultman, E. (1976). Glycogen
phosphorylase activity in biopsy samples and single muscle
fibres of musculus quadriceps femoris of man at rest. Scand.
J. Clinical and Laboratory Investigation. 36:521-526

Harris, R.C. Sahlin, K and Hultman, E. (1977). Phosphagen and
lactate contents of m. quadriceps femoris of man after
exercise. J. Appl. Physiol. 43:852-857

Harris, R.C. Edwards, R.H.T., Hultman, E.H., Nordesjö, L.-O.,
Nylind, B. and Sahlin, K. (1976). The time course of
phosphorylcreatine resynthesis during recovery of the
quadriceps muscle in man. Pflugers Archiv. 367:137-142

Harris R.C., Hultman, E., Kaijser, L. and Nordesjö, L.-O. (1975).
The effect of circulatory occlusion on isometric exercise
capacity and energy metabolism of the quadriceps muscle in
man. Scand. J. Clinical and Laboratory Investigation. 35:87-95

Herzig, J.W., Peterson, J.W., Ruegg, J.C. and Solaro, R.J. (1981). Vandata and phosphate ions reduce tension and increase cross-bridge kinetics in chemically skinned heart muscle. Biochimica et Biophysica Acta 672:191-196

Hill, A.V. (1955). The influence of the extended medium of the internal pH of muscle. Proceedings of the Royal Society of London. 144:1-22

Hill, A.V. and Kupalov, P. (1929). Anaerobic and aerobic activity in isolated muscle. Proceedings of the Royal Society of London. Series B: Biological Sciences 105:313-328

Hoffmann, E. (1976). The significance of phosphofructokinase to the regulation of carbohydrate metabolism. Reviews of Physiology, Biochemistry and Pharmacology. 75:1-68

Hultman, E. and Sjöholm, H. (1983a). Energy metabolism and contraction force of human skeletal muscle in situ during electrical stimulation. J. Physiol. 345:525-532

Hultman, E. and Sjöholm, H. (1983b). Substrate availability. In International Series of Sport Sciences vol. 13 (edited by H.G. Knuttgen, J.A. Vogel and J. Poortmans) pp.723-727. Human Kinetics Publishers, Inc. Champaign.

Hultman, E. and Sjöholm, H. (1986). Biochemical causes of fatigue. In Muscle Power: Factors Underlying Maximal Performance. Proc. McMaster Int. Symp. Human Kinetic Publishers Inc. Champaign. In Press.

Hultman, E., Bergström, J. and McLennan Anderson, N. (1967). Breakdown and resynthesis of phosphorylcreatine and adenosine triphosphate in connection with muscular work. Scand. J. Clinical and Laboratory Investigation. 19:56-66

Jones, N.L., McCartney, N., Graham, T., Spriet, L.L., Kowalchuk, J.M., Heigenhauser, G.J.F. and Sutton, J.R. (1985). Muscle performance and metabolism in maximal isokinetic cycling at slow and fast speeds. J. Appl. Physiol. 59:132-136.

Kushmerick, M.J. (1983). Energetics of muscle contraction. In Handbook of Physiology - Skeletal Muscle (edited by L.D. Peachey, R.H. Adrian and S.R. Geiger), pp. 189-236. The Williams & Wilkins Company, Baltimore, American Physiology Society.

Lännergren, J. and Westerblad, H. (1986). Force and membrane potential during and after fatiguing, continuous high frequency stimulation of single Xenopus muscle fibres. Acta physiologica scandinavica. Submitted.

Mansour, T.E. (1972). Phosphofructokinase. In Current Topics in Cellular Regulation (edited by B.L. Horecker and E.R. Stadtman), pp. 1-46. New York: Academic.

Margaria, R., Cerretelli, P., and Mangili, F. (1964). Balance and kinetics of anaerobic energy release during strenous exercise in man. J. Appl. Physiol. 19:623-628

Merton, P. (1981). In Human Muscle Fatigue: Physiological Mechanisms (edited by R. Porter and J. Whelan), p. 152. Pitman Medical.

Meyer, R.A., Brown, T.R and Kushmerick, M.J. (1985). Phosphorus nuclear magnetic resonance of fast- and slow-twitch muscle. American J. Physiol. 248:C279-C287

Nakamura, Y. and Schwartz, A. (1970). Possible control of
intracellular calcium metabolism by H^+: sarcoplasmic
reticulum of skeletal and cardiac muscle. Biochemical and
Biophysical Research Communications. 41:830-836

Robertson, S.P. and Kerrick, W.G.L. (1979). The effects of pH on
Ca^{2+} - activated force in frog skeletal muscle fibres.
Pflugers Archiv. 380:41-45

Rohmert, W. (1960). Ermittlung von Erholungspausen für Statische
Arbeit des Menschen. Internationale Zeitschrift für
Angewandte Physiologie. 18:123-164

Ruegg, J.C., Schadler, M., Steiger, G.J. and Muller, C. (1971).
Effects of inorganic phosphate on the contractile mechanism.
Pflügers Archiv. European J. Physiol. 325:359-364

Sahlin, K., Harris, R.C. and Hultman, E. (1975). Creatine kinase
equilibrium and lactate content compared with muscle pH in
tissue samples obtained after isometric exercise. Biochemical
Journal 152:173-180.

Sahlin, K., Edström, L., Sjöholm, H. and Hultman, E. (1981). Effects
of lactic acid accumulation and ATP decrease on muscle tension
and relaxation. American J. Physiol. 240:C121-C126.

Setlow, B. and Lowestein, J.M. (1967). Adenylate deaminase: II
Purification and some regulatory properties of the enzyme from
calf brain. Journal of Biological Chemistry. 242:607-615.

Spriet, L.L., Söderlund, K. and Hultman, E. (1986). Skeletal muscle
glycogenolysis, glycolysis and pH during electrical stimulation
in man. J. Appl. Physiol. Submitted.

Uyeda, K. (1979). Phosphofructokinase. Advances in Enzymology and
Related Areas of Molecular Biology. 48:193-244

Uyeda, K., Furuya, E. and Luby, L.J. (1981). The effect of natural
and synthetic D-fructose 2.6-bisphosphate and the regulatory
kinetic properties of liver and muscle phosphofructokinases.
J. Biological Chemistry. 256:8394-8399.

Veloso, D., Guynn, R.W., Oskarsson, M., and Veech, R.L. (1973).
The concentration of free and bound magnesium in rat tissue.
Journal of Biological Chemistry. 248:4811-4819.

Westerblad, H. and Lännergren, J. (1986). Force and membrane
potential during and after fatiguing, intermittent tetanic
stimulation of single Xenopus muscle fibres.
Acta physiologica scandinavica. Submitted.

White, D.C.S. and Thorson, J. (1972). Phosphate starvation and the
nonlinear dynamics of insect fibrillar flight muscle.
J. General Physiol. 60:307-336

Discussion

Professor Brooks, California, USA
I would like to ask Professor Hultman if he thinks that in some
cases the production of hydrogen ions might actually be beneficial.
Clearly there is good evidence, which he has shown, that it can be
deleterious. Peter Mitchell who has studied the mechanism of
oxidative phosphorylation, for which he received a Nobel Prize,
described the fact that mitochondria consume oxygen and they make
ATP. What he also did was to block electron transport yet when he

acidified the environment of the mitochondria they were still able to make ATP. So I wonder if anybody had considered that the acidification of the cytoplasm, by glycolysis, might improve the proton motor force for ATP Synthesis.

Professor Hultman, Huddinge, Sweden

Accumulation of H^+ seems to be an important regulator of both force generation and metabolism. Lack of this regulatory mechanism can result in rigor, with destruction of muscle tissue.

The use of H^+ in the mitochondria for ATP resynthesis without oxygen should be possible if an inward-directed electrochemical gradient of H^+ was build up providing the necessary energy. The amount of ATP which could be produced in this way must be very small, as there is a limited capacity in the mitochondria to buffer the H^+.

We have never seen any formation of ATP or PCr in resting anoxic muscle, despite high accumulation of H^+ as occurs after intense contraction combined with occluded blood flow. Immediate resynthesis of PCr is however observed when blood flow is restored (Harris et al., 1976). Similar results were observed experimentally in acidotic biopsy samples taken after anoxic exercise and stored in nitrogen and oxygen atmosphere. No measurable resynthesis of PCr occurred in nitrogen, but rapid resynthesis occurred in oxygen (Sahlin et al., 1979).

Dr Wootton, Southampton, England

Are you suggesing, Professor Hultman, that the apparent fall in the rates of ATP resynthesis are secondary to a fall in utilisation rates?

Professor Hultman

Yes: our studies suggest that inhibition of the contractile mechanism and thus also of ATP hydrolysis is the primary result of continued anoxic contraction and consequently the decreased rate of ATP resynthesis is secondary to inhibited hydrolisis.

The reason for this suggestion is that the initial decrease in force generation during maximal contraction is observed before the whole PCr store is used and ATP content is still close to the resting level. When contraction is continued until exhaustion the ATP store is depleted maximally by only 50% to 60%. Inhibitors of contraction are suggested to be the products formed by the ATP hydrolysis, H^+, P_i and possibly ADP. There is however simultaneously an inhibiting effect of ATP resynthesis via glycolysis due to decreased pH which will be further discussed by Lawrence Spriet.

Dr Spurway, Glasgow, Scotland

I wonder whether it would be appropriate to add another comment on some recent research by Bigland-Ritchie and Lippold? They have shown, in the last few years, that the EMG falls off massively in muscles undergoing the same kind of maximal contraction to fatigue as you have been studying. They demonstrated that EMG declines because motor neurone firing rate declines and they seem to have a nice match of the declined rate of firing with the muscle's changed biochemistry. The biochemistry expresses itself in the slowing

relaxation time. In the fatigued muscle one twitch takes longer
and therefore you don't need such a high firing rate to maintain
just-maximal voluntary contraction. Bigland-Ritchie and Lipold
argue that if you maintained the original firing rate in the
fatigued muscle it would be far supermaximal and the force output
would not be controllable. This work linked in my mind with what
you just said about two different classes of mechanism ATP supply
and ATP utilisation within the cells. Does the third factor,
firing rate, change roughtly in parallel with your two factors?

Professor Hultman

The studies you referred to are voluntary contractions in which the
frequency of neuron firing decreased from 30Hz during the first
10 seconds down to 10-15 Hz after one min contraction. These
changes in motor neuron firing rate were matched to prolongation of
the relaxation time.

During electrical stimulation maximum force generation is
reached at stimulation frequencies of 50-80 Hz, but these
frequencies will result in a loss of force already after 10-20
seconds stimulation apparently due to failure of electrical
propagation, rather than to defects in mechanical contractility
or lack of energy supply. An increase in force and EMG activity
was seen when the frequency of stimulation was changed from 80 Hz
to 20 Hz after 40 seconds of stimulation at the higher frequency
(Bigland-Ritchie, 1981).

In our studies a stimulation frequency of 20 Hz was used, which
produces a force correspondong to 70% of maximum and allows longer
stimulation periods without propagation failure. The relaxation
time increased five times after one minute of electrical stimulation
in anoxia. This prolongation of the twitch time will help to keep
the force constant and decrease energy demand during continuous
isometric contraction.

Constant electrical stimulation at 20Hz could theoretically be
too high for the muscle cells at end of an isometric contraction
and possibly damage the muscle by completely emptying the ATP store
with risk of cell damage. We were in fact afraid of that when we
started this type of study and observed carefully the baseline of
the muscle tension between contractions to exclude tendencies of
rigor formation.

No rigor has ever been observed in our studies with electrical
stimulation and the ATP decrease was about 50% of the basal level.
Similar decreases in ATP have been observed in dynamic exercise in
man by Boobis et al. (1982) and also in the race horse by Snow
et al. (1985). It is however possible that some muscle fibres
could lose more ATP than corresponds to the mean value in the
biopsy sample. I beieve that Roger Harris has some information on
this matter.

Dr Harris, Suffolk, England

Only that when we have been looking at horse muscle, in a
preliminary study, we have been looking at ATP content in
individual muscle fibres. We have found a small group, a very low
proportion of muscle fibres, which are totally devoid of ATP, and
we believed that this may be an artifact of the procedures used,
but we now have some reason to believe that this very small group

of fibres, which even in resting muscle, are devoid of ATP may be
the result of some previous exercise which has occurred. This is
in the race horse, but I believe that even in some of your human
studies, Professor Hultman, you have found something similar.

Professor Hultman

We have some preliminary data on isolated muscle fibres analysed by
Karin Soderlund in our laboratory showing a relatively large
variation in ATP content after the stimulation, ranging from 20-60%
of the initial content. Some fibres also in our study were totally
devoid of ATP. There was no significant difference in ATP
content in different fibre types in our preliminary series.

Professor Saltin, Copenhagen, Denmark

Just to continue the line of thinking suggested as the result of
the work by Biggland-Ritchie and Jones. What I think is critical
in the situation where they saw a drop in force: if they
electrically stimulated the muscle and brought the frequency up to
say 50Hz, they did not have any extra force from that muscle so
obviously there must be an inhibition or block before cross-bridge
stimulation!

Dr Jansson, Stockholm, Sweden

Do you think the myofibrillar ATPase is more sensitive to
phosphocreatine depletion than the sarcoplasmic reticulum ATPase and
the Sodium/Potassium ATPase? If not, if the SR and Sodium/Potasium
ATPase are also inhibited at the same level of phosphocreatine then
I think that the muscles will go into rigor causing calcium
accumulation.

Professor Hultman

We do not know very much about this but it is reasonable to believe
that the function of the creatine kinase bound to the M-band is
important for the ATP formation in direct contact with myofibrillar
ATPase and that a substrate lack in the creatine kinase reaction
also could decrease the ATPase activity. Decreased activity of the
Ca^{2} transporting ATPase could be the reason for the prolongation
of relaxation time, but apparently the decrease in CA - transport
is not sufficient to cause rigor in normal muscle, possible partly
due to inhibited Ca^{2+} binding to troponin in the acidotic muscle.
   Also decreased excitation due to changed membrane potential
caused by inhibited electrolyte transport could add to the lowering
of force production. The relative importance of each of these
processes for fatigue development is not known.

Dr Jansson

As a comment I would like to add that we have measured in single
muscle fibres ATP and IMP concentrations after very exhausting
voluntary exercise and the lowest ATP concentration we have found
in a single fibre is 10 mmol.kg dry weight.

Dr Newsholme, Oxford, England

I am just a little worried in terms of the hypothesis or mechanism
you are proposing, they are no surprise to me, primarily because I
would raise the question do we know which is the primary limiting

factor in the contractile system? Is it for example, the release
of calcium from the SR or is it in fact before that, that is, the
excitation-contraction coupling? Where of course inositol
trisphosphate is now very fashionable and very interesting, is it
perhaps the ability of the troponin to bind calcium which is a
major limiting influence or the controlling factor, or is it
perhaps, as you were suggesting, the actual ATPase itself? It
doesn't seem to me that we have anything like the biochemical
sophistication of the studies of the realm of properties of any of
those systems to be able to interpret your very important data in
relation to which of those might be the more important, if indeed
any of them are.

It seems we are trying to study the control of glycolysis, let
us say, by knowing glucose goes in and lactate comes out of a
muscle and there is something in between. If we were trying to do
that with glycolysis we would raise our hands with horror and say
we cannot do it. I just wonder whether the same situation is not
true of muscle contraction.

Professor Hultman

I agree with you that the detailed mechanisms for limitations of
the contractile system need much more sophisticated methods than
those presented here. This study was focused on the relation
between force generation and rate of ATP utilisation and
resynthesis during intense anaerobic contraction with the aim also
to estimate if the availability of ATP or the change in
intracellular milieu was the controlling factor of force
production. Fatigue mechanisms have been studied during more than
100 years - and probably some years more with extensive studies
will be needed before we understand the intricate mechanism by
which the muscle contraction is controlled.

References

Bigland-Ritchie, B. EMG and fatigue of human voluntary and
    stimulated contractions (1981). Human Muscle Fatigue:
    Physiological Mechanisms. Pitman Medical, London, Ciba
    Foundation symp. 82:pp,130-156.
Boobis, L.H., Williams, C. and Wootton, S.A (1983). Influence of
    sprint training on muscle metabolism during brief maximal
    exercise in man. Journal of Physiology (London), 342:36-37P.
Harris, R.C., Edwards, R.H.T., Hultman, E., Nordesjö, L-O., Nylind,
    B. and Sahlin, K. (1976). The time course of phosphorylcreatine
    resynthesis during recovery of the quadriceps muscle in man.
    Pflügers Arch., 367:137-142.
Sahlin, K., Harris, R.C. and Hultman, R. (1979). Resynthesis of
    creatine phosphate in human muscle after exercise in relation to
    intramuscular pH and availability of oxygen. Scand. J. Clin.
    Lab. Invest., 39:551-558.
Snow, D.H., Harris, R.C. and Gash, S.P. (1985). Metabolic response
    of equine muscle to intermittent maximal exercise. J. Appl.
    Physiol., 58:5,1689-1697.

Muscle pH, glycolytic ATP turnover and the onset of fat

L.L. SPRIET

Muscle ATP turnover, glycogenolytic and glycolytic rates were
estimated and muscle force production and pH (pHm) were measured in
electrically stimulated quadriceps femoris muscles. Leg blood flow
was occluded and muscles were stimulated 64 times at 20Hz, with
contractions lasting 1.6 seconds and separated by pauses of 1.6
seconds. Muscle biopsies were obtained at rest and following 16, 32,
48 and 64 contractions. Glycolytic intermediates and several
modulators of the glycolytic enzyme phosphofructokinase (PFK) were
measured. The respective ATP turnover rates during the four 16
contraction periods were 6.12, 2.56, 2.19 and 0.64 mmol.kg^{-1} dry
muscle.s^{-1} contraction time and force production decreased
correspondingly. Glycogenolytic and glycolytic rates were 1.68 and
1.26 mmol glucosyl units.kg^{-1}.s^{-1} during the initial 16
contractions as pHm decreased from 7.00 $\pm$ 0.01 to 6.70 $\pm$ 0.03.
During the subsequent 32 contractions both rates were maintained at
$\sim$0.70 mmol.kg^{-1}.s^{-1} and pHm decreased to 6.45 $\pm$ 0.04. In the final
16 contractions, glycogenolytic and glycolytic rates were very low
and pHm was unchanged. Continued stimulation during intense
acidosis did not decrease muscle ATP below 60% of the resting
concentration. We conclude that the metabolic production of ATP
did not limit force production as PFK remained active despite
increasing acidity. Increases in the concentrations of several
positive modulators partially reversed pH-dependent ATP inhibition
of PFK in vivo, permitting glycolytic activity to continue
until pHm reached $\sim$6.45.

1. Introduction

The transformation of chemical to mechanical energy in skeletal
muscles enables humans to move about in their environment. In
most instances the chemical energy required for muscular activity
is provided by the oxidation of foodstuffs resulting in the
production of CO_2. The weak acid CO_2 is easily removed
from the muscle and ultimately the body, maintaining the
homeostasis of the muscle cell. However the muscles are
occasionally called upon to perform tasks which require very high
rates of chemical energy production. In these situations the
chemical precursor of mechanical energy production, ATP, must be
provided primarily by anaerobic processes. The majority of

anaerobic ATP regeneration results from phosphocreatine (PCr) degradation and glycolytic activity.

As a consequence of intense glycolytic activity a number of acidic compounds accumulate, the most important of which is lactic acid. Lactic acid is a strong acid (pK 3.8) and is almost totally dissociated to lactate ions (La^-) and hydrogen ions (H^+) at physiological pH. The muscle succeeds in buffering the majority of the released H^+ but intracellular pH can decrease from approximately 7.0 at rest to 6.5 or 6.4 following intense short-term activity. This corresponds to an $[H^+]$ increase from 100 $nmol.l^{-1}$ at rest to 320-400 $nmol.l^{-1}$ following exercise.

Sahlin (1978) reported that muscle pH (pHm) decreased to 6.56 ± 0.07 following a fatiguing contraction at 68% of the maximal voluntary contraction and to 6.60 ± 0.14 after dynamic cycling at a work rate which exhausted the subjects in ~6 min. Calculations based upon the accumulation of muscle La^- and glycolytic intermediates following only 30 seconds of maximal isokinetic cycling revealed that pHm decreased to 6.5 (Jones et al., 1985). In a study where 30 seconds maximal cycling bouts were repeatedly performed, calculated pHm decreased to 6.4 following the fourth bout (McCartney et al., 1986).

It is commonly recognised that increasing H^+ accumulation may adversely affect muscle force production through two main mechanisms: firstly, several of the steps in the excitation-contraction process have been shown to be adversely affected in a variety of muscle preparations and secondly, in vitro and whole body studies suggest that the activity of key glycolytic enzymes are also negatively affected (Hermansen, 1981).

The previous paper by Eric Hultman discussed the possible effects of acidosis at numerous loci in the excitation-contraction coupling process. Therefore, no discussion of these effects is included in this paper except to say that any reduction in actomyosin ATPase activity due to interference with excitation-contraction would reduce ATP utilization by the muscle and decrease force production. On the metabolic side, in vitro studies have demonstrated the extreme pH sensitivity of the key glycolytic enzyme phosphofructokinase (PFK) (Trivedi and Danforth, 1966; Ui, 1966; Uyeda, 1979). Acidosis has also been shown to depress the conversion of phosphorylase b (inactive) to phosphorylase a (active) (Danforth, 1965; Chasiotis et al., 1983). If the primary effect is directly on key glycolytic enzymes a limit could be set for ATP production and therefore force production.

In human studies during short-term intense exercise it is extremely difficult to identify where the primary effect or effects of decreased pH are manifested. The present paper will concentrate on the results of a recent study where we examined muscle pH, glycolytic ATP production and muscle force production during short-term intense muscular activity. In this study the antero-lateral aspect of the quadriceps femoris muscle group was electrically stimulated for ~100 seconds with the blood flow occluded. It was known from previous work that the PCr store would be depleted following ~25 seconds with this model, leaving ATP regeneration solely in the hands of glycolysis during the final 75 seconds (Hultman and Sjöholm, 1986). In this manner it seemed possible to intensify or exaggerate the anaerobic stress and ATP requirement over that possible with volitional isometric or dynamic exercise. With

electrical stimulation the stimulus to activate the muscles is
maintained even when extreme levels of acidosis have been reached.

The aim of the work was to examine how well the production of
ATP and ATP concentration were maintained during progressively
increasing acidosis, to assess the likelihood that ATP regeneration
limited force production. In vivo ATP turnover, glycogenolytic
and glycolytic rates were estimated from the accumulation of
glycolytic intermediates in a closed circulation. This provides
an indirect method for examining the activity of the regulatory
enzymes phosphorylase and PFK. Previous work from this laboratory
has reported constant glycolytic activity in spite of large
increases in muscle La$^-$ accumulation during 40-50 seconds of
continuous isometric contraction (Sahlin et al., 1975; Hultman and
Sjöholm, 1983). Therefore, extending electrical stimulation to 100
seconds in the present work coupled with measurements of several of the
predominate modulators of PFK activity would permit analysis of
the in vivo regulation of this enzyme under conditions of
extreme acidosis.

1.1 Experimental design
The muscles in the antero-lateral region of the thigh (mainly
vastus lateralis) were stimulated to contract via surface
electrodes with square wave pulses of 0.5ms duration at a
frequency of 20Hz as previously described (Hultman et al., 1983).
Electrical stimulation presents the muscles with a constant
contraction stimulus independent of volitional effort. Stimulation
was intermittent with trains lasting 1.6 seconds and separated by rest
pauses of 1.6 seconds for a total of 64 contractions. Total stimulation
time was 204.8 seconds and contraction time was 102.4 seconds. In
this manner approximately 30% of the musculature that extends the
knee was activated. At a frequency of 20Hz the isometric tetanic
force produced by the activated muscle is 70-75% of the maximal
tetanic force. A cuff around the proximal portion of the thigh was
inflated (250mmHg) to occlude blood flow 30 seconds prior to the
onset of stimulation and remained inflated throughout the stimulation.

Muscle biopsies were taken from the vastus lateralis at rest
and following contractions 16, 32, 48 and 64. Isometric force
production by the activated knee extensor muscle was recorded
throughout the stimulation by a strain gauge attached to a strap
around the ankle.

Muscle biopsy samples were immediately frozen in liquid freon.
Two small aliquots (8-20mg each) were removed from each sample
under liquid N$_2$ for the measurement of muscle pH with the
homogenate technique (Spriet et al., 1986). The remainder of the
frozen biopsy samples were freeze-dried and processed as previously
reported from the measurements of muscle metabolites (Harris et
al., 1974).

Throughout the paper metabolite data is reported following 16,
32, 48 and 64 contractions which corresponds to 25.6, 51.2, 76.8
and 102.4 seconds of contraction time. The muscle metabolite results
are presented per kg dry muscle which in the presence of normal
amounts of muscle water corresponds to 4.3 kg wet muscle. In
addition, fatigue is defined here as a decrease in isometric force
production below the force produced during the initial contraction.

1.2. Muscle force production and metabolite results

Isometric force production was well maintained during the initial 16 contractions, averaging 95.6 ± 2.2% of the force produced during the first contraction (Fig.1). Thereafter force production decreased rapidly from 87.6 ± 2.5% of peak force during contraction 16 to 55.6 ± 2.5% and 26.7 ± 2.7% at contractions 32 and 48 respectively. During the final 16 contractions the generated force was extremely low, averaging 20.4 ± 2.3% of the initial.

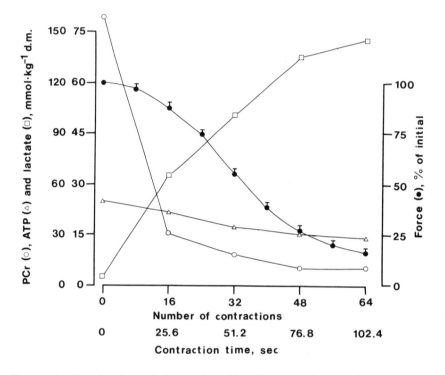

Figure 1. Muscle isometric contraction force and phosphocreatine (PCr), ATP and lactate concentrations during intermittent electrical stimulation with an occluded circulation. Scale for PCr and ATP is 0-75 mmol.kg^{-1} and for lactate is 0-150 mmol.kg^{-1}. Standard errors for PCr, ATP and lactate are not included but appear in Table 1.

Table 1. Muscle metabolite concentrations during intermittent electrical stimulation with an occluded circulation. The quadriceps femoris muscle were stimulated 64 times at 20 Hz with each contraction lasting 1.6 s and followed by 1.6 s of rest.

	Rest	Number of contractions			
		16 (25.6s)	32 (51.2s)	48 (76.8s)	64 (102.4s)
PCr	78.7 ± 2.4	15.7 ± 3.9	9.0 ± 2.7	5.4 ± 1.1	5.5 ± 0.9
ATP	24.81 ± 0.80	21.76 ± 1.23	17.28 ± 1.26	15.48 ± 0.61	14.04 ± 1.19
ADP	2.92 ± 0.06	3.59 ± 0.25	3.71 ± 0.40	3.92 ± 0.19	3.59 ± 0.24
AMP	0.33 ± 0.05	0.44 ± 0.09	0.43 ± 0.04	0.38 ± 0.03	0.45 ± 0.06
TAN	28.06 ± 0.78	25.79 ± 1.47	21.42 ± 1.45	19.78 ± 0.58	18.08 ± 1.25
IMP	0.54 ± 0.08	2.39 ± 1.09	7.90 ± 1.52	10.61 ± 1.90	11.63 ± 1.60
G-1-P	0.08 ± 0.01	0.59 ± 0.10	0.38 ± 0.04	0.48 ± 0.06	0.50 ± 0.04
G-6-P	1.80 ± 0.21	10.35 ± 1.41	8.49 ± 0.78	8.62 ± 1.02	8.08 ± 0.81
F-6-P	0.28 ± 0.04	2.10 ± 0.40	1.75 ± 0.23	1.70 ± 0.29	1.71 ± 0.15
F-1,6-DP	0.15 ± 0.02	0.37 ± 0.09	0.29 ± 0.10	0.27 ± 0.06	0.30 ± 0.08
Glyc-3-P	0.64 ± 0.10	4.51 ± 0.65	7.48 ± 0.79	8.16 ± 0.55	8.24 ± 0.36
pyruvate	0.20 ± 0.06	2.29 ± 0.42	3.42 ± 0.54	2.79 ± 0.40	2.52 ± 0.50
La⁻	5.1 ± 1.0	65.6 ± 7.4	101.7 ± 9.4	135.2 ± 13.5	145.3 ± 9.5

$\bar{X}$ ± SE, $mmol \cdot kg^{-1}$ dm; n=7. For abbrevations, see text. TAN (total adenine nucleotides) = ATP + ADP + AMP.

Approximately 80% of the muscle's PCr store was utilized during the initial 16 contractions (Fig. 1, Table 1). Continued stimulation produced a slight additional decrease such that 93% of the PCr store had been utilized following 48 and 64 contractions. The concentration of ATP in the muscle decreased steadily with continued stimulation from 24.81 ± 0.80 mmol.kg^{-1} dry muscle at rest to 14.04 mmol.kg^{-1} following 64 contractions (Fig. 1, Table 1). Following 32 and 64 contractions ATP had decreased to 70% and 57% of the resting content, respectively. Muscle La$^-$ concentration increased by approximately 60 mmol.kg^{-1} during the initial 16 contractions and 70 mmol.kg^{-1} from contractions 17 to 48. Lactate accumulation during the final 16 contractions was extremely low, in keeping with the low force production.

Concentrations of adenine monophosphate (AMP) and diphosphate (ADP) increased slightly during the initial 16 contractions and remained elevated for the entire stimulation period (Table 1). Increases in inosine monophosphate (IMP) content were stoichiometrically equivalent to decreases in ATP. Therefore following 64 contractions, the decreases in ATP and total adenine content and increase in IMP content were all approximately 10 mmol.kg^{-1}.

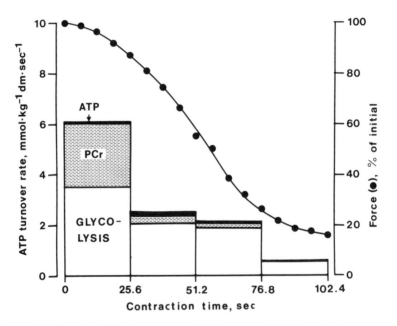

Figure 2. Muscle ATP turnover and force production during intermittent electrical stimulation at 20Hz with an occluded circulation. Energy contributions from PCr and ATP utilisation and glycolysis are indicated.

The concentrations of glucose-1-phosphate (G-1-P), glucose-6-phosphate (G-6-P) and fructose-6-phosphate (F-6-P) increased 6-8 fold and fructose-1,6-diphosphate (F-1,6-DP) increased two fold following 16 contractions and remained constant with continued

stimulation (Table 1). Glycerol-3-phosphate (Glyc-3-P) content
increased seven-fold following 16 contractions and approximately
12 fold following 32, 48 and 64 contractions. Pyruvate content was
12-17 fold greater than rest at all times during the stimulation.

1.2.1 Muscle ATP turnover rate
By occluding muscle blood flow during electrical stimulation, a
closed metabolic system was provided, limiting the majority of ATP
production to anaerobic processes and preventing the escape of
metabolites. The ATP turnover rate could then be calculated for
each 16 contraction period from the accumulated metabolities;
ATP turnover rate (mmol.kg^{-1} dry muscle.s^{-1}) = 1.5(Δ[La$^-$]) +
Δ[PCr] + (2(Δ[ATP]) - Δ[ADP]) divided by 25.6 seconds.
    The ATP turnover rate during the initial 16 contractions was
6.12 $\pm$ 0.56 mmol.kg^{-1}.s^{-1} with 58% of the ATP derived from
glycolysis, 40% from PCr degradation and 2% from partial hydrolysis
of the ATP store (Fig.2). During contractions 17-32 and 33-48 the
respective ATP turnover rates decreased to 2.56 $\pm$ 0.76 and 2.19 $\pm$
0.83 mmol.kg^{-1}.s^{-1} or 42% and 36% of the initial rate.
Glycolysis produced 83-90% of the total ATP during this period even
though glycolytic ATP production decreased to 50-60% of the rate
during the initial 16 contractions. The total ATP turnover rate
during the final 16 contractions was very low (0.64 mmol.kg^{-1}.s^{-1}),
representing only 11% of the initial rate. Glycolysis again
produced nearly all of the generated ATP but the glycolytic rate
was reduced to 17% of the initial rate.

1.2.2 Muscle pH and buffering capacity
The homogenate pH technique was used to estimate the intracellular
pH in muscle biopsy samples. Muscle pH (pHm) at rest averaged 7.00
$\pm$ 0.01 and decreased progressively to 6.70 $\pm$ 0.03, 6.60 $\pm$
0.04 and 6.45 $\pm$ 0.04 following 16, 32 and 48 contractions,
respectively. During the final 16 contractions pHm did not
decrease further (6.43 $\pm$ 0.05). The buffering capacity was
calculated from the estimated production of H$^+$ during the
stimulation period and the measured decrease in pHm and expressed
as slykes (Δ mmol H$^+$.l^{-1} muscle water . ΔpH unit^{-1}) (Table 2).
The changes in the contents of ATP, G-6-P, Glyc-3-P, pyruvate and
La$^-$ during contractions 0-32, 33-64 or 0-64 were expressed per
litre muscle water assuming a normal water content (3.3 l.kg^{-1}
dry muscle). The muscle H$^+$ release (mmol.l^{-1} muscle water)
was then estimated using the appropriate fractions for the
stoichiometric release of H$^+$ for individual metabolites and pH
values as described by Hultman and Sahlin (1980). The buffering
capacity calculated in this manner was 77.5 $\pm$ 4.0 slykes over the
entire 64 contractions (Table 2). When calculated over the initial
and final 32 contractions the respective buffering capacities were
77.6 and 78.2 slykes. These results compare favourably with a
previously reported value, calculated in the same manner following
75 seconds of continuous electrical stimulation (Hultman et al., 1985).

Table 2. The metabolic production of H^+, ΔpHm and buffering capacity during intermittent electrical stimulation of muscle with occluded circulation.

Contraction period	H^+ production (mmol.l^{-1} muscle water)							
	ATP	G-6-P	Glyc-3-P	pyruvate	La^-	total	pHm	$\beta *$
0 - 32 (n=6)	0.46 0.04	0.72 0.08	0.39 0.04	0.98 0.15	28.95 2.92	31.49 3.10	0.406 0.033	77.6 9.8
33 - 64 (n=6)	0.04 0.05	-0.01 0.10	0.05 0.04	-0.20 0.08	14.18 2.79	14.08 2.94	0.180 0.072	78.2 9.3
0 - 64 (n=7)	0.49 0.04	0.76 0.11	0.44 0.02	0.73 0.12	42.02 2.86	44.43 3.00	0.573 0.046	77.5 4.0

$\bar{X} \pm SE$. For abbreviations, see text. * β(buffering capacity) = slykes (mmol $H^+.l^{-1}$ muscle water.pH unit^{-1}).

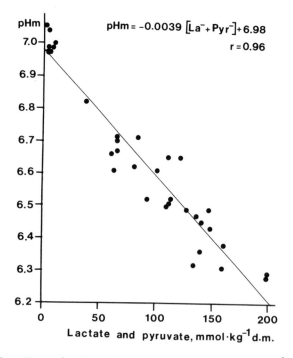

$$pHm = -0.0039 \left[La^- + Pyr^- \right] + 6.98$$

$$r = 0.96$$

Figure 3. The relationship between muscle lactate (La^-) and pyruvate (pyr^-) accumulation and the decrease in muscle pH (pHm) during intermittent electrical stimulation under anaerobic conditions (n=33).

These results demonstrate the tremendous buffering capacity of skeletal muscle. Intermittent stimulation for a total of 102.4 seconds contraction time under anaerobic conditions produced 44.4 mmol $H^+.1^{-1}$ muscle water yet the net change in free $[H^+]$ was limited to an increase from 100 to 372 $nmol.1^{-1}$. This means that 99.9994% of the released H^+ were buffered intracellularly.

During the initial 32 contractions La^- and pyruvate accumulation accounted for 95% of the total H^+ release and in the final 32 contractions La^- alone accounted for all of the H^+ release. Therefore when plotting the accumulation of La^- and pyruvate against the decreases in pHm an inverse linear relationship was obtained (Fig.3). This relationship is similar to the relationships reported by Sahlin (1978) during volitional isometric contraction and intense dynamic cycling in man.

Hydrogen ions are normally buffered in a living cell by three main processes; physiochemical buffering, metabolic consumption of non-volatile acids and transmembrane fluxes of H^+, HCO_3^- and other ions. With a closed circulation, muscle buffering was limited to physiochemical and metabolic processes as transmembrane fluxes were essentially inhibited. In addition, physio-chemical buffering is restricted to phosphate and protein compounds as the CO_2/HCO_3^- system does not function in a closed system. Lastly, metabolic buffering is limited to the consumption of H^+ during PCr utilization and the formation of IMP. From these metabolite changes we calculated that metabolic buffering consumed 16.5 ± 0.7 mmol $H^+.1^{-1}$ muscle water during the 64 contractions (Table 3). PCr degradation contributed 91% and IMP formation 9% of the total metabolic buffering. Since the total H^+ release was 44.4 $mmol.1^{-1}$ muscle water (Table 2), metabolic buffering accounted for 37% of total muscle buffering, leaving 63% to be handled by physiochemical processes. It is also interesting to note that 90% of the metabolic buffering potential was provided during the initial 32 contractions when 70% of the total H^+ release occurred.

Table 3. The metabolic consumption of H^+ during electrical stimulation in muscle.

Contraction period	H^+ consumption (mmol.1^{-1} muscle water)		
	PCr	IMP	total
0 - 32	12.92	0.92	13.83
(n=6)	0.94	0.18	1.02
33 - 64	0.96	0.51	1.49
(n=6)	0.60	0.23	0.80
0 - 64	15.11	1.40	16.51
(n=7)	0.58	0.19	0.72

$\bar{X} \pm$ SE. For abbreviations, see text.

1.2.3 Muscle pH, energy production and fatigue
During the initial 16 contractions a large decrease in pHm
occurred without major decreases in force production (Fig.4).
However, beyond this point, decreases in pHm were accompanied by
decreases in force production. To complicate the picture,
decreases in force production were related to decreases in the
ATP turnover rate (Fig.2). Therefore decreases in energy
production were also related to decreases in pHm. Since decreases
in force production, ATP turnover and pHm were all correlated it is
difficult to determine which factor is cause and which is effect.
One interpretation is that increasing acidity decreased
glycogenolytic and glycolytic activity to such an extent that force
production was reduced due to a limited ability to regenerate ATP.
On the other hand, decreasing pH could reduce force production at a
number of locations in the excitation-contraction process thereby
reducing the demand for ATP and explaining the reduced ATP
turnover.

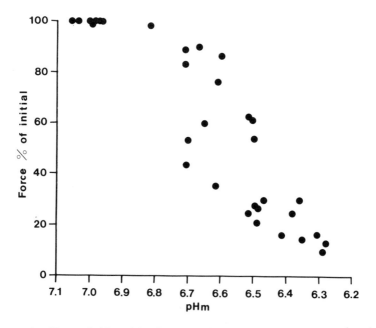

Figure 4. The relationship between decreasing muscle pH (pHm) and
decreasing isometric force production during electrical stimulation.

Total ATP production was decreased during contractions 17-48,
but production representing 36-42% of the initial ATP turnover
rate remained in spite of a pHm decrease from 6.70 to 6.45. We
therefore suggest that the primary effect of increasing $[H^+]$
was not to decrease ATP production to a point where it became
limiting for muscular contraction. During the final 16
contractions the muscle was repeatedly stimulated in a situation
where pHm had already decreased to 6.45. The muscle withstood
this situation, which would not normally occur during intense

volitional muscular activity since the subject would simply stop exercising. Muscle ATP could not be driven down to a concentration consistent with the development of rigor.

Sahlin et al. (1981) electrically stimulated rat muscle poisoned with the glycolytic inhibitor iodoacetatic acid and reported the development of rigor when [ATP] had decreased by 63%. In non-poisoned muscle at fatigue, the [ATP] was reduced by 25% and rigor did not occur, suggesting that ATP shortage produced rigor in the poisoned muscle. In non-poisoned or normal muscle, it appears that extreme acidosis inhibits muscular contraction before ATP can decrease to concentrations consistent with energy shortage and therefore rigor development.

If the above interpretation is correct it remains to be explained why ATP concentration decreases at all during this type of intense work. To do this we must examine the essential equations describing the production and utilization of ATP during muscular contraction;

$$ATP \longrightarrow ADP + P_i + H^+ \tag{1}$$

Equation (1) describes the utilization of ATP in the muscle cell catalyzed by the actomyosin, Ca^{2+} and Na^+-K^+ ATPases. ATP can be regenerated under anaerobic conditions by the processes described in the following reactions;

$$PCr + ADP + H^+ \longrightarrow ATP + Cr \tag{2}$$
$$glycogen + 3ADP + 3P_i \longrightarrow 3ATP + 2La^- + 2H^+ \tag{3}$$
$$2ADP \longrightarrow ATP + AMP \tag{4}$$

During the initial 16 contractions, it seems likely that the activity of equations (2) and (3) were able to regenerate ATP at a rate sufficient to maintain [ATP] at near resting levels and keep the adenylate kinase activity in equation (4) low. During contractions 17-48 the ability to rephosphorylate ADP decreased as PCr was depleted and glycolytic activity was reduced by 50%. Subsequently adenylate kinase activity increased due to the increased [ADP] and the produced AMP was deaminated to IMP through equation (5);

$$AMP + H^+ \longrightarrow IMP + NH_4^+ \tag{5}$$

In this situation it appears the activity of equation (4) increases to maintain a high ATP/ADP ratio, ensuring the maintenance of sufficient free energy liberation during ATP hydrolysis. The apparent cost to the muscle cell for keeping [ADP] low in this manner is reduced total adenine nucleotide and ATP concentrations. However, before [ATP] can decrease to critical levels, muscular contraction is inhibited.

1.2.4 Regulation of muscle glycogenolysis and glycolysis
While decreasing pH was associated with reduced glycolytic ATP
production, significant glycolytic activity was maintained
during contractions 17-48 while pHm decreased from 6.70 to 6.45.
In order to explain this continued activity the accumulation of
glycolytic metabolites reported in Table 1 were used to estimate the
in vivo rates of glycogenolysis and glycolysis (mmol glucosyl
units.kg^{-1}.s^{-1}) during each 16 contraction stimulation period;
Glycogenolysis = $\Delta([G-1-P] + [G-6-P] + [F-6-P]) + \Delta([La^-] + [Glyc-3-P])/2$ divided by 25.6secs.
Glycolysis = $\Delta[La^-] + [Glyc-3-P])/2$ divided by 25.6secs.
These calculations essentially estimate the respective activities
of phosphorylase and PFK, the enzymes thought to regulate
glycogenolytic and glycolytic activity. In addition, several of
the major regulators of PFK were measured throughout the
stimulation period.

The glycogenolytic and glycolytic rates during the initial 16
contractions were 1.68 and 1.26 mmol glucosyl units.kg^{-1}.s^{-1},
respectively (Table 4, Fig. 5). The initial glycogenolysis/
glycolysis ratio was 1.33, glycogenolysis fell to 40% and
glycolysis to 52-60% of the initial rates during contractions 17-48
leaving the glycogenolysis/glycolysis ratio near one. During the
final 16 contractions glycogenolytic and glycolytic activities
were extremely low in keeping with the low force production.

The high glycogenolytic rate relative to glycolytic rate during
the initial 16 contractions produced the large build up of hexose
monophosphates (Table 1). During continued stimulation hexose
monophosphates remained elevated demonstrating that PFK activity
never exceeded phosphorylase activity. At the onset of
contraction we know phosphorylase b to a transformation occurs
rapidly as the result of the increased cytoplasmic [Ca^{2+}]. PCr
degradation increases the concentration of inorganic phosphate
(P$_i$) which coupled with increases in [AMP] enable glycogenolysis
to proceed at a high rate (Chasiotis et al., 1982). Following 30-
60secs of contraction the mole fraction of phosphorylase in the a
form decreases, possibly due in part to H$^+$ accumulation
(Chasiotis et al., 1983). We cannot conclude from our findings
whether the estimated glycogenolytic rate during contractions 17-48
was maintained solely by the decreasing phosphorylase fraction in the
a form or through increased importance of b activity. Elevated
P$_i$ and AMP concentrations would keep the a fraction active
while the increasing [IMP] may have activated the b fraction
(Aragon et al., 1980). The important point here is that
phosphorylase activity was maintained at least as high as PFK
activity.

Phosphofructokinase is believed to be a rate-limiting enzyme in
the glycolytic pathway (Newsholme and Start, 1974). In vitro
kinetic studies with PFK extracted from brain and skeletal muscle
tissues have identified a number of modulators which regulate the
enzyme's activity. Physiological concentrations of ATP strongly
inhibit PFK even though it is a substrate for the reaction (Uyeda,
1979). Several other modulators which enhance the ATP inhibition
or directly inhibit the enzyme include Mg^{2+}, citrate, H$^+$,
PCr and the glycolytic intermediates 3- and 2-phosphoglycerate, 2-3
diphosphoglycerate and phosphoenolpyruvate (Lowry and Passonneau,

1966; Krzankowski and Matschinusky, 1969; Storey and Hochachka, 1974; Trivedi and Danforth, 1966; Uyeda, 1979). Several activators of PFK or deinhibitors of ATP inhibition have also been reported; AMP, ADP, P_i, cyclic AMP, NH_4^+, K^+, F-1,6-DP fructose-2,6-diphosphate (F-2,6-DP), glucose-1,6-DP (G-1,6-DP) and the reaction substrate F-6-P (Beitner, 1979; Dobson et al., 1986; Hue et al., 1982; Lowry and Passonneau, 1966; Uyeda, 1979).

Table 4. Estimated rates of muscle glycogenolysis and glycolysis during intermittent electrical stimulation under anaerobic conditions.

Contraction Number	Glycogenolytic Rate mmol glucosyl units.kg^{-1}.dm per		Glycolytic Rate		Glycogenolysis Glycolysis
	25.6s	1.0s	25.6s	1.0s	
1 - 16	43.1 ± 5.2	1.68	32.2 ± 3.7	1.26	1.33
17 - 32	17.7 ± 6.4	0.69	19.4 ± 5.5	0.76	0.91
33 - 48	17.3 ± 7.9	0.68	17.1 ± 6.8	0.67	1.02
49 - 64	4.6 ± 6.3	0.18	5.1 ± 6.1	0.20	0.90

Calculations based on the mean values in Table 1 as follows; Glycogenolysis = Δ([G-1-P] + [G-6-P] + [F-6-P]) + Δ([La$^-$] + [Glyc-3-P])/2 and Glycolysis = Δ([La$^-$] + [Glyc-3-P])/2.

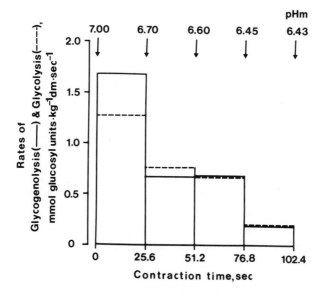

Figure 5. Estimated in vivo rates of muscle glycogenolysis and glycolysis during electrical stimulation with an occluded circulation. Muscle pH (pHm) is also given at points during the stimulation. Calculations are based on the data and formulae reported in Table 4.

Under the conditions of this experiment several of the modulators can be disregarded. Citrate and cyclic AMP are not expected to accumulate during circulatory occlusion. The intracellular $[K^+]$ is unlikely to be affected by 64 contractions as no change occurred following 25 contractions (Hultman and Spriet, unpublished observations). The concentrations of intermediates in the lower half of the glycolytic pathway accumulate to only a minor degree during intense exercise and their inhibiting effects are easily overcome by small increases in $[F\text{-}6\text{-}P]$ (Krzankowski and Matschinusky, 1969). The concentrations of F-2,6-DP and G-1,6-DP were not measured due to their extremely low concentrations in skeletal muscle. However, the potential stimulatory roles of these compounds during muscular activity is uncertain at the present time. While F-2,6-DP and G-1,6-DP are powerful stimulators of mammalian skeletal muscle in vitro (Beitner, 1979; Uyeda et al., 1981), Hue et al., (1982) reported a decrease in $[F\text{-}2,6\text{-}DP]$ following 120secs of electrical stimulation at 10 Hz in rat hindlimb muscle.

During the initial 16 contractions the concentrations of AMP, ADP, F-6-P, F-1,6-DP and P_i increased and ATP and PCr decreased, with all changes favouring increased PFK activity. The most important changes appear to be increased F-6-P, one of the two reaction substrates, and increased AMP which is a potent stimulator of PFK. It has been suggested that the majority of cellular ADP and AMP is not free but bound to proteins (Seraydarian et al., 1962; Sols and Marco, 1970). In this case relatively small increases in measured total ADP and AMP during contraction would translate into large increases in free ADP and AMP, possibly accounting for their important regulatory roles in the control of glycolysis.

Muscle pH decreased to 6.70 following 16 contractions and decreased further to 6.45 during the subsequent 32 contractions. The increased acidity was associated with a reduction in glycolytic and PFK activity to 55% of the rate in the initial 16 contractions. (0.72 mmol glucosyl units.kg^{-1}.s^{-1}). Muscle ATP content decreased by 6.28 mmol.kg^{-1} from contraction 16 to 48 (Table 1), which may have decreased the inhibition of PFK. However, the effect of acidosis on the ionic species of ATP (ATP^{4-}, HATP^{3-}, MgATP^{2-}) is to increase the HATP^{3-} form (Sahlin, 1983), which in brain tissue is a much more potent inhibitor of PFK activity than MgATP^{2-} (Lowry and Passonneau, 1966). Consequently a reduction in the $[ATP]$ may not be associated with reduced inhibition of PFK. A reduced ATP content also releases Mg^{2+}, shown to inhibit PFK in vitro (Lowry and Passonneau, 1966). Lastly, a decreased ATP content will release further amounts of P_i which could assist in stimulating PFK (Sugden and Newsholme, 1975). Therefore the net effect of a decreasing ATP content during this period for PFK activity is difficult to assess quantitatively.

The concentrations of all other measured PFK deinhibitors or activators remained elevated but did not increase during this period (Table 1). However, as muscle ATP and total adenine content decreased, IMP concentration increased in a stoichiometric fashion demonstrating significant AMP deaminase activity (Table 1). The increase in IMP in this situation will be accompanied by an equimolar accumulation of NH$_4^+$ as significant IMP reamination did not occur and significant conversion of NH$_4^+$ and glutamate

to glutamine does not occur during intense anaerobic muscular
activity (Katz et al., 1986).

We suggest that NH_4^+ accummulation assisted in
counteracting the PFK inhibiting effect of increasing $[H^+]$ and
therefore the maintenance of glycolysis during contractions 17-48
(25-78 secs). Sugden and Newsholme (1975) reported no stimulating
effect of NH_4^+ on mouse gastrocnemius PFK in the presence
of non-inhibiting ATP concentrations (1.0 mmol.1^{-1}) in
vitro. However, Dobson et al., (1986) demonstrated a potent
deinhibiting effect of NH_4^+ on rabbit PFK in vitro in
the presence of physiological and inhibiting concentrations of ATP
(5.0 mmol.1^{-1}). As the in vivo ATP concentrations ranged
from 4.7 to 6.6 mmol.1^{-1} during contractions 17-48 it
seems likely that NH_4^+ contributed to the maintenance of PFK
and glycolytic activity. We conclude that in vivo pH-dependent
ATP inhibition of PFK was partially offset during this period by
the decreasing total $[ATP]$, the presence of elevated levels of the
positive modulators ADP, AMP, F-6-P and F-1,6-DP and the continuing
accumulation of P_i and NH_4^+. It appears that positive
modulators release PFK from ATP inhibition at low pH such that the
in vivo or physiological pH profile of PFK is extended beyond
that reported to be inhibitory from in vitro studies.

During the final 16 contractions the inital pHm was 6.45, force
production and glycolytic activity were extremely low and minor
decreases in ATP and increases in IMP occurred while the
concentration of all other modulators were unchanged. Presumably
at this point muscle acidity inhibited muscular contraction (see
above), accounting for the extremely low glycolytic activity. The
present in situ results compare favourably with the work of
Hill (1955), where lactic acid accumulation in electrically
stimulated frog muscle ceased at an intracellular pH of
approximately 6.3. The in vitro work of Danforth (1965) with
frog muscle also demonstrated a complete inhibition of PFK activity
at pH 6.4 when measured at physiological concentrations of F-6-P
and ATP.

2. Conclusion

During intense electrical stimulation extended to $\sim$100 secs under
anaerobic conditions decreases in force production, ATP turnover
rate and pHm were all correlated to each other. The decrease in
muscle ATP concentration was limited to 40% of the resting content.
We suggest that the metabolic production of ATP did not limit
force production as PFK remained active despite increasing acidity.
The decreases in ATP concentration are explained as a consequence
of increased adenylate kinase and AMP deaminase activities and the
resultant decrease in total adenine nucleotide concentration.
Although glycolytic activity decreased as H^+ concentration increased,
approximately 50% of the initial activity remained as pHm decreased
from 6.70 to 6.45. Increases in the concentrations of several
positive modulators partially reversed the pH-dependent ATP
inhibition of PFK in vivo, permitting glycolysis to continue
until pHm reached $\sim$6.45.

Acknowledgements

This work was supported by grants from the Swedish Medical Research
Council (02647) and the Swedish Sports Research Council. Dr Spriet
was the recipient of a Post-Doctoral Research Fellowship from the
Medical Research Council of Canada. The authors wish to thank the
entire staff of the Department of Clinical Chemistry II for their
excellent collaboration in this investigation.

References

Aragon, J.J., Tornheim, K. and Lowenstein, J.M. (1980). On a
    possible role of IMP in the regulation of phosphorylase
    activity in skeletal muscle. FEBS Letters
    117(Suppl.): K56-K64
Beitner, R. (1979). The role of glucose-1,6-bisphosphate in the
    regulation of carbohydrate metabolism in muscle. Trends in
    Biochemical Science 4:228-230
Chasiotis, D., Sahlin, K. and Hultman, E. (1982). Regulation of
    glycogenolysis in human skeletal muscle at rest and during
    exercise. J. Appl. Physiol. 53:708-715
Chasiotis, D., Sahlin, K. and Hultman, E. (1983). Acidotic
    depression of cyclic AMP accumulation and phorphorylase b to
    a transformation in skeletal muscle of man. J. Physiol.
    London 335:197-204
Danforth W.H. (1965). Activation of glycolytic pathway in muscle.
    In Control of Energy Metabolism (edited by B. Chance, R.W.
    Estabrook and J.R. Williamson), pp. 287-297. New York: Academic
    Press.
Dobson, G.F., Yamamoto, E. and Hochachka, P.W. (1986).
    Phosphofructokinase control in muscle: nature and reversal of pH-
    dependent ATP inhibition. American J. Physiol. 250:R71-R76
Harris, R.C., Hultman, E. and Nordesjö, L.-O. (1974). Glycogen,
    glycogenolytic intermediates and high-energy phosphate
    determined in biopsy samples of musculus quadriceps femoris of
    man at rest. Scandinavian J. Clinical and Laboratory
    Investigation 33:109-120
Hermansen, L. (1981). Effect of metabolic changes on force
    generation in skeletal muscle during maximal exercise. In
    Human Muscle Fatigue: Physiological Mechanisms (Ciba
    Foundation Symposium No.82), pp. 75-88. London: Pitman Medical.
Hill, A.V. (1955). The influence of the external medium on the
    internal pH of muscle. Proceedings of the Royal Society of
    London (Biological Sciences) 144:1-22
Hue, L., Blackmore, P.F., Shikama, H., Robinson-Steiner, A. and
    Exton, J.H. (1982). Regulation of fructose-2,6-bisphosphate
    content in rat hepatocytes, perfused hearts, and perfused
    hindlimbs. J. Biological Chemistry 257:4308-4313
Hultman, E. and Sahlin, K. (1980). Acid-base balance during
    exercise. Exercise and Sport Sciences Reviews 8:41-128
Hultman, E. and Sjöholm, H. (1983). Energy metabolism and contraction
    force of human skeletal muscle in situ during electrical
    stimulation. J. Physiol. London 345:525-532

Hultman, E., Sjöholm, H., Jäderholm-Ek, I. and Krynicki, J. (1983). Evaluation of methods for electrical stimulation of human muscle in situ. Pflugers Archiv 398:139-141

Hultman, E., Del Canale, S. and Sjöholm, H. (1985). Effect of induced metabolic acidosis on intracellular pH, buffer capacity and contraction force of human skeletal muscle. Clinical Science 69:505-510

Hultman, E. and Sjöholm, H. (1986). Biochemical causes of fatigue. In Human Muscle Power (edited by N.L. Jones, N. McCartney and A.J. McComes), pp. 215-238 Champaign:Illinois USA Human Kinetic Publishers.

Jones, N.L., McCartney, N., Graham, T., Spriet, L.L., Kowalchuk, J.M., Heigenhauser, G.J.F. and Sutton, J.R. (1985). Muscle performance and metabolism in maximal isokinetic cycling at slow and fast speeds. J. Appl. Physiol. 59:132-136

Katz, A., Sahlin, K. and Henriksson, J. (1986). Muscle ammonia metabolism during isometric contraction in humans. American J. Physiol. 250:In Press

Krzankowski, I. and Matschinusky, F.M. (1969). Regulation of phosphofructokinase by phosphocreatine and phosphorylated glycolytic intermediates. Biochemical and Biophysical Research Communications 34:816-823

Lowry, O.H. and Passonneau, J.V. (1966). Kinetic evidence for multiple binding sites on phosphofructokinase. J. Biological Chemistry 241:2268-2279

McCartney, N., Spriet, L.L. Heigenhauser, G.J.F., Kowalchuk, J.M. Sutton, J.R. and Jones, N.L. (1986). Muscle power and metabolism in maximal intermittent exercise. J. Appl. Physiol 60:1164-1169

Newsholme, E.A. and Start, C. (1974). Regulation in Metabolism New York: Wiley Interscience.

Sahlin, K., Harris, R.C. and Hultman, E. (1975). Creatine kinase equilibrium and lactate content compared with muscle pH in tissue samples obtained after isometric exercise. Biochemical Journal 152:173-180

Sahlin, K. (1978). Intracellular pH and energy metabolism in skeletal muscle of man. Acta Physiologica Scandinavica Suppl. 455:1-56

Sahlin, K. (1983). Effect of acidosis on energy metabolism and force generation in skeletal muscle. In Biochemistry of Exercise (edited by H.G. Knuttgen, J.A. Vogel and J. Poortmans), pp 151-160 Champaign: Human Kinetic Publishers.

Sahlin, K., Edström, L., Sjöholm, H. and Hultman, E. (1981). Effect of lactic acid accumulation and ATP decrease on muscle tension and relaxation. Americal J. Physiol. 240:C121-C126

Seraydarian, K., Mommaerts, W.F.H.M. and Wallner, A. (1962). The amount and compartmentalization of adenosine diphosphate in muscle. Biochimica et Biophysica Acta 65:443-460

Sols, A. and Marco, R. (1970). Concentrations of metabolites and binding sites. Implications in metabolic regulation. Current Topics in Cellular Regulation 2:227-273

Spriet, L.L., Söderlund, K. and Hultman, E. (1986). pH measurement in human skeletal muscle samples; Effect of phosphagen degradation. J. Appl. Physiol 61:In Press

Storey, K.B. and Hochachka, P.W. (1974). Activation of muscle glycolysis: a role for creatine phosphate in phosphofructokinase regulation. FEBS Letters 46:337-339

Sugden, P.H. and Newsholme, E.A. (1975). The effects of ammonia, inorganic phosphate and potassium ions on the activity of phosphofructokinases from muscle and nervous tissues of vertebrates and invertebrates. Biochemical Journal 150:113-122

Trivedi, B. and Danforth, W.H. (1966). Effects of pH on the kinetics of frog muscle phosphofructokinase. J. Biological Chemistry 241:4110-4112

Ui, M. (1966). Role of phosphofructokinase in pH-dependent regulation of glycolysis. Biochimica et Biophysica Acta 124:4110-4112

Uyeda, K. (1979). Phosphofructokinase. Advances in Enzymology and Related Areas of Molecular Biology 48:193-244

Uyeda, K., Furuya, E. and Luby, L.J. (1981). The effect of natural and synthetic D-fructose 2,6-bisphosphate on the regulatory kinetic properties of liver and muscle phosphofructokinases. J. Biological Chemistry 256:8394-8399

Discussion

Dr Jacobs, Ontario, Canada
In light of Dr Sutton's comments regarding arterial blood pressure during leg presses, could you tell us to what pressure you inflated the thigh cuff in your studies?

Dr Spriet, Ontario, Canada
In our studies the thigh cuff was inflated to 250mm Hg to occlude blood flow. I am aware of the work referred to by Dr Sutton where arterial systolic pressures were measured in the 300-400mmHg range during various whole-body weight lifting manoeuvers. What must be remembered is that in our electrical stimulation studies only 1.0-1.5 kg of thigh muscle are actually stimulated and this does not produce a profound whole body effect on heart rate, respiration or blood pressure. In a series of similar experiments where electrical stimulation was coupled with adrenalin infusion, systolic pressures were measured and never increased above 150mm Hg.

While speaking about the practice of occluding blood flow with a cuff it should be mentioned that the muscle is not immediately ischemic as a certain amount of oxygen will be stored in the muscle, bound to myoglobin or to hemoglobin in the trapped blood. The upper limit for this trapped oxygen has been estimated as 2 mmol.kg^{-1}dm, enough to produce 12 mmol ATP.kg^{-1}dm. If all the oxygen was used in the initial 15s, aerobic ATP production would contribute 0.8 mmol.kg^{-1}dm.s^{-1} and subsequent contractions would rely purely on anaerobic metabolism.

Miss M. Cheetham, Leicestershire, England
I was interested to hear that muscle pH was decreased to 6.4 after

electrical stimulation. We have recently measured muscle pH after 30 seconds of maximal treadmill sprinting. The subjects were exhausted and power output was decreased by 50% but muscle pH had only fallen to 6.7. Would you be prepared to hypothesise as to the possible causes of fatigue during electrical stimulation and if such ideas can also be applied to dynamic exercise where the pH at exhaustion is somewhat higher?

Dr Spriet
In our work muscle pH decreased to 6.4 but only following 102.4 seconds of electrical stimulation. After 25.6 seconds muscle pH was 6.70, similar to your finding following 30 seconds of maximal treadmill running. However, power output was reduced by 50% in your work and in our studies, isometric force production was only marginally reduced at a pH of 6.7. In explaining the fatigue which occurred in our work beyond 25 seconds of stimulation, I believe that muscle acidosis inhibited muscular contraction at some point or points in the excitation-contraction coupling process. This is based on the finding that muscle [ATP] could not be driven below ~50% of resting even when stimulation was continued under extremely acidotic conditions (76.8-102.4 seconds). The presence of H+ appears to inhibit contractions before ATP decreases to concentrations consistent with rigor development while the absence of H+ permitted [ATP] to decrease further with subsequent rigor development in rat muscle. As muscles are pushed to the limits of their anaerobic potential the accumulation of H+ acts as a built-in protective mechanism.

In dynamic whole-body exercise the situation may be very different. Obvious differences between our work are isometric vs isotonic contractions and the presence of the central nervous system in dynamic exercise. Motivation must be maintained and the presence of involuntary muscle reflex induced or local central inhibition always exists. Also, treadmill sprinting must be maximal, while we know that force production with electrical stimulation at 20H is only 70% of that at 50-80 H or during a maximal voluntary contraction. Accordingly, rates of energy production and by-product accumulation must be faster in the dynamic situation bringing up the possibility that an inability to maintain ATP turnover rates or inhibition through by-products other than H+ (Pi, Mg^{2+}) may contribute to fatigue. Lastly, we have also heard that O_2 uptake increases rapidly in dynamic sprinting which means muscle citrate levels will be elevated. Citrate is a potent inhibitor of the enzyme phosphofructokinase in vitro and I have often wondered if citrate alone or interaction with the increasing [H+] could be responsible for the earlier onset of fatigue in dynamic versus intense isometric exercise at a given pH.

Influence of carbohydrate stores on maximal human power output

I. JACOBS

There is a well established relationship between endurance exercise
performance and muscle glycogen availability. This paper describes
the results of recent studies which examined the effects of
skeletal muscle glycogen depletion on performance of a one minute
maximal intensity muscle fatigue test (MFT). When acute glycogen
depletion of both main muscle fibre types was induced by exercise,
subsequent muscle strength and power during the MFT were impaired.
Subjects with muscle rich in FT fibers demonstrated a greater
impairment than those rich in ST fibers. If exercise-induced
glycogen depletion was limited to the ST muscle fibers, no
significant impairment of muscle force was observed, but the muscle
was more susceptible to fatigue during repeated maximal
contractions. If muscle glycogen levels were very low prior to
exercise, impairments of force production were accompanied by
significantly reduced muscle lactate accumulation during the MFT,
suggesting that glycogenolytic flux was reduced. Although muscle
weakness observed after prolonged exercise may be a function of the
exercise used to induce glycogen depletion, the weakness is greater
when glycogen levels in the exercising muscles are low.

1. Introduction

The relationship between the ability to perform prolonged heavy
exercise and muscle glycogen concentration is well documented and
it has been repeatedly shown that when exercise intensity is 65-85%
of maximal aerobic power ($\dot{V}O_2max$), exhaustion occurs when the
glycogen stores in the exercising muscles are very low or totally
depleted (Bergström et al., 1967; Saltin and Karlsson, 1971).
Combinations of exercise and dietary procedures have been developed
which enable the athlete to maintain high muscle glycogen
concentrations thereby delaying glycogen exhaustion and the
concomitant fatigue (for review see Costill and Miller, 1980).
Research pertaining to the relevance of skeletal muscle glycogen
availability to exercise performance has, until recently, focused
entirely on endurance exercise. Many competitive sports, however,
are characterized by short bursts of maximal power demanding energy
derivation from non-oxidative energy metabolism pathways. The
importance of glycogenolysis during such high intensity exercise
was first suggested in the work of Saltin and Karlsson (1971) who
showed that the rate of glycogen utilization in exercising muscle

increased exponentially as a function of exercise intensity,
expressed relative to $\dot{V}O_2$max. They reported utilization rates
of about 40 mmol glucose units.kg^{-1} dry muscle min^{-1} at
an intensity of 150% $\dot{V}O_2$max. More recent studies have
demonstrated that glycogenolysis leading to lactate production is
probably a very significant source of energy to fuel the
contractile process during such high intensity exercise lasting
only a few seconds. Supramaximal cycle exercise lasting only 30
seconds has been reported to elicit changes in muscle glycogen
concentrations at a rate of 101-175 mmol glucose units.kg^{-1}.min^{-1}
(Saltin et al., 1971; Jacobs et al., 1982a; Boobis et al., 1983).
In addition, marked increases in muscle lactate concentrations
after 5-10 seconds of voluntary supramaximal exercise (Jacobs et
al., 1983) or electrical stimulation (Sjöholm et al., 1983) suggest
that the rate of skeletal muscle glycogenolysis is increased almost
immediately with the onset of muscle contraction during such high
intensity exercise. The question therefore arises as to the
relevance of studies examining the relationship between glycogen
content and endurance performance, when considering short term,
high intensity exercise. The remainder of this paper will describe
studies which have evaluated the effects of skeletal muscle
glycogen availability and depletion on muscle strength during
single maximal contractions and muscular endurance during exercise
of about 60 seconds in duration.

2. Changes in muscle strength and fatigue after glycogen
   depletion

The established relationship between glycogen depletion and
fatigue during submaximal exercise stimulated our study of the
effects of depletion on performance of short term activities such
as single, maximal muscular contractions, and repeated maximal
contractions (Jacobs, 1981a). A criterion muscle strength and
fatigue test (MFT) was administered on an isokinetic dynamometer
according to a procedure described by Thorstensson (1976) and
Tesch (1980). Briefly, the subjects were seated with the lower
leg attached to the lever arm of the dynamometer and were
instructed to perform 50 maximal extensions of the knee at a
controlled angular velocity of 180°/s. The variables of
interest were the peak torque (i.e. the maximal torque produced
during the strongest contraction), and the torque decline during
the 50 contractions, which served as a fatigue index. This MFT
was performed before and one hour after a standardized exercise
program which included the following activities to induce glycogen
depletion: running at the maximal velocity that could be maintained
for 75 minutes; cycling for 30 minutes at approximately 70%
$\dot{V}O_2$max; three bouts of isokinetic maximal contractions of the
quadriceps (one bout = 50 repetitions at 180°/s); cycling five
times for one minute each time at a maximal load. Short periods of
rest (15 minutes) intervened between different activities. Biopsies
were taken from the vastus lateralis after this protocol for fiber
type determination and for histochemical staining for glycogen
content. These stainings demonstrated that both the type I or
slow twitch (ST) and the type II or fast twitch (FT) fibers were

equally well depleted of glycogen.

Maximal strength, expressed as peak torque, was significantly reduced following the exercise program (Fig. 1). Based upon the myofibrillar ATPase stainings of their muscle biopsy samples the subjects were divided into two groups: those with greater than 50% FT fibers (FT group) in the vastus lateralis, and those with greater than 50% ST fibers (ST group). Both FT and ST groups experienced a significant decrease in peak torque following the exercise program, but it was most pronounced in the FT group (Fig.1). Prior to the glycogen depletion protocol the FT group demonstrated a higher peak torque than the ST group, however this difference was not maintained following the exercise program. A greater torque decline in the FT group during the MFT prior to glycogen depletion was evidence of greater fatiguability than in the ST group. This torque decline was not as pronounced in the FT group when the MFT was performed after glycogen depletion ($p<0.05$) (Fig. 1). In contrast, the ST group exhibited similar levels of fatigue during the MFT both before and after the glycogen depletion inducing exercise.

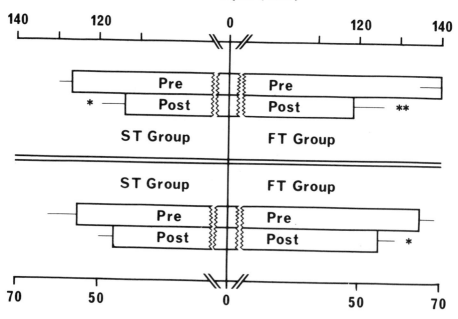

Figure 1. Peak torque and torque decline during 50 consecutive, maximal muscle contractions before (pre) and after (post) prolonged exercise. Values are means and SE for those subjects with >50% fast twitch fibers (FT group) and those with >50% slow twitch fibers (ST group) in the vastus lateralis muscle. (Reproduced with permission from Acta Physiologica Scandinavica Supplementum 495).

This study demonstrated that there was a reduced maximal voluntary force production following glycogen depletion, and that this impairment was more pronounced in subjects rich in FT fibers in the affected musculature than in those subjects rich in ST fibers. The work of Thorstensson (1976), Coyle et al., (1979), and Tesch (1980) demonstrated that a large FT fiber distribution in the vastus lateralis facilitates force production during maximal muscle contractions (180°/s). Another characteristic of FT fibers is the potential for glycogenolysis, which is inherently greater than for ST fibers (for review see Saltin and Gollnick, 1983). Therefore, it is tempting to speculate that depleted intramuscular glycogen stores are more likely to impair those fibers which are better suited to metabolize glycogen, i.e. the FT fiber. Consequently, it is not surprising that MFT performance impairments are more pronounced in those subjects with a greater percentage of FT fibers.

2.1 Performance after selective fiber type glycogen depletion
In an attempt to confirm our interpretation of the results described above, changes in strength performance were examined in two groups of subjects with approximately equal fiber type distribution in the vastus lateralis (Jacobs et al., 1981). One group performed the prolonged exercise protocol described earlier to deplete glycogen; histochemical stains again confirmed that depletion occurred equally in both main fiber types. The other group participated in a running marathon, and post race biopsies revealed that only 20% of the FT fibers were glycogen depleted, in contrast to the depletion of about 70% of the ST fibers.

If the alterations in strength performance observed in the previous study were mainly due to an impairment of the FT fibers, then the predominantly ST fiber glycogen depletion in the marathon group should not cause a pronounced impairment of strength performance, contrasting with an expected impairment in the group of subjects where both fiber types were depleted. The results, shown in Fig.2, confirm this hypothesis because peak torque was significantly reduced only in the group where both FT and ST fibers were glycogen depleted. It should be noted that when glycogen depletion was induced selectively in the ST fibers, no impairment was observed in peak torque generation but the fatigue during the MFT was significantly increased (Fig. 2). Since an established characteristic of FT fibers is their relatively rapid fatiguability, maintenance of force during the repeated maximal contractions of the MFT can be attributed in large part to the fatigue resistant ST fibers. An attractive explanation for the greater fatigue exhibited by the marathon group after glycogen depletion is that this fatigue resistance was impaired because of the continuous recruitment of ST motor units during the marathon.

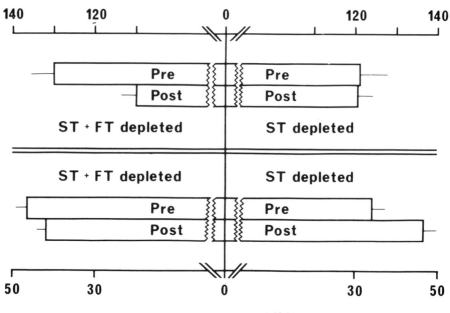

Peak Torque (Nm)

Torque Decline (%)

Figure 2. Peak torque and torque decline during 50 consecutive, maximal muscle contractions before (pre) and after (post) either a marathon run inducing glycogen depletion in mainly slow twitch muscle fibers (ST depleted), or after an exercise program inducing glycogen depletion in both fast and slow twitch fibers (ST+FT depleted). (Reproduced with permission from Acta Physiologica Scandinavica Supplementum 495).

2.2 Lactate accumulation after exercise at various glycogen levels

Tesch (1980) has suggested that lactate accumulation or associated pH changes occurring primarily in FT fibers could be one factor responsible for muscle fatigue as represented by the torque decline during the MFT. Since the relative contribution of FT motor unit recruitment to force production at the angular velocity employed is critical, low FT fiber glycogen concentrations, such as were induced in the studies described above, may affect lactate production thereby reducing the strength of the 'lactate-fatigue' relationship described by Tesch (1980).

   In order to investigate this possibility a study was designed to evaluate the effects of changes in glycogen concentrations on lactate accumulation in human skeletal muscle during the MFT (Jacobs 1981b). All subjects first performed the MFT during a control experiment. Four subjects then performed the test again one hour after prolonged exercise designed to deplete glycogen from both muscle fiber types as previously desbribed. These subjects

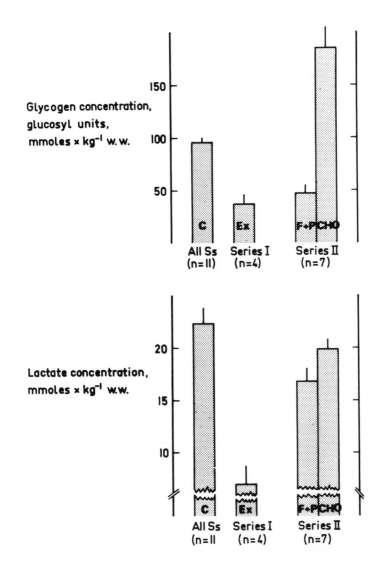

Figure 3. Mean values and SE are shown for glycogen levels prior to
performance of the muscle fatigue test, and lactate levels in
muscles sampled immediately after the test. Abbreviations refer to
the control experiment (C); when the test was done after the
glycogen depletion inducing exercise (Ex); when the test was done
after the fat and protein rich (F+P) and the carbohydrate rich
(CHO) diets. (Reproduced with permission from Acta Physiologica
Scandinavica 111:465-469, 1981).

and seven other subjects performed the test again after a three-day
carbohydrate-poor diet, and again after four additional days of a
carbohydrate-rich diet. The vastus lateralis was biopsied before
(for glycogen determinations) and after (for lactate

determinations) each performance of the MFT. High, but similar, lactate concentrations were observed after the MFT when pre-exercise glycogen concentrations were either normal or super compensated (Fig.3). Lactate was significantly reduced when the MFT was performed both after the prolonged glycogen depletion inducing exercise, and after the carbohydrate-poor diet (Fig.3). These results could be explained on the basis of an increased lactate uptake within the exercising muscle, without an alteration in glycogenolytic flux and lactate production. The short duration of exercise, however, makes it seem implausible that the high lactate levels observed after exercise in the control condition could be metabolized so rapidly. The alternative explanation presented by Klausen and Sjøgaard (1980), who reported similar results, is that the potential for energy derivation via anaerobic glycogenolysis is reduced, perhaps because of insufficient substrate (i.e. glycogen) to saturate the enzymatic potential for glycogenolysis to proceed at a maximal rate. Although the Km of glycogen for phosphorylase in vitro is much lower (Gollnick et al., 1978) than the low glycogen concentrations reported here, the in vivo relationship has not been thoroughly established.

In summary of the studies described above, muscle performance during intense, short time exercise including single, maximal muscle contractions is impaired in association with severe glycogen depletion of the musculature involved. The extent of this impairment is related to FT fiber distribution and to the degree of glycogen depletion within the FT fiber population. Concomitant with this impairment of strength performance, an impaired ability to produce and/or accumulate lactate during such exercise is also noted.

3. Impairments in association with or caused by glycogen depletion?

Our observations of a temporal association between glycogen depletion and impairments of short term, high intensity exercise performance cannot be interpreted as being conclusive evidence for a causal relationship. Sherman et al. (1984) pointed out that the effects of the exercise used to induce glycogen depletion cannot be separated from the effects of the lack of intramuscular glycogen per se because of the design of earlier experiments (Jacobs et al., 1981). Young and Davies (1984), however, developed an improved experimental design by having subjects perform glycogen depletion exercise on two occasions; the depletion exercise was followed by a carbohydrate-poor diet on the first occasion, and by a carbohydrate-rich diet on the second occasion. Changes in electrically evoked muscle forces and maximal voluntary forces were evaluated after each dietary manipulation, thereby focusing on the effects of glycogen, while controlling the effects of previous exercise. Although no biopsies were taken to measure glycogen, these investigators did find evidence that the exercise used to induce glycogen depletion resulted in an impairment of the isometric force generating capacity of muscle under both dietary conditions. They also found that the 'exercise- induced muscle weakness' was significantly greater following the carbohydrate-poor diet when muscle glycogen was assumed to be low (Young and Davies, 1984).

Sherman and colleagues (1984) demonstrated a dissociation of impaired muscle strength from glycogen depletion following a marathon. The results of repeated muscle biopsies and isokinetic strength tests for one week after the marathon showed that maximal force generation was still reduced seven days after a marathon, in spite of normal muscle glycogen levels. This study is, however, open to the criticism that glycogen concentrations were assayed in biopsy samples obtained from the lateral gastrocnemius muscle, but muscle strength of the quadriceps was evaluated during sitting knee extension. In addition, glycogen depletion induced by the marathon in these subjects was reported to occur primarily in the ST fibers (Sherman et al., 1983) which would probably cause a less marked strength impairment than would glycogen depletion from both the FT and ST fibers (Jacobs et al., 1981).

The results of earlier studies suggest that muscle lactate accumulation after supramaximal exercise is markedly reduced when glycogen concentrations prior to exercise are less than about 220 mmol glucosyl units$\cdot$kg^{-1} dry muscle, or about 50% of normal resting levels in sedentary subjects (Jacobs, 1981b). To determine if there are accompanying impairments of muscular strength at these glycogen levels recent experiments (Jacobs and Symons, unpublished observations) have been conducted in an attempt to have subjects perform the MFT on two occasions: when glycogen levels were normal, and when they were reduced to levels of 220 mmol.kg^{-1} dm. The effects of prior exercise were controlled by having the subjects perform a glycogen depletion inducing exercise protocol, similar to that described earlier, on two occasions separated by a week. The MFT was performed prior to the depletion and again three days after the depletion. Half of the subjects consumed a carbohydrate-rich diet during the intervening three days while the remaining subjects consumed a carbohydrate-poor diet. The same procedures were carried out the following week with the diets being reversed among subjects. Table 1 shows that the desired glycogen concentrations were attained in the three subjects for whom preliminary results are available, i.e. glycogen concentrations averaged only 224 mmol.kg^{-1} dm before the MFT after the carbohydrate-poor diet, in contrast to the 539 mmol.kg^{-1} dm after the carbohydrate-rich diet. The total work performed during the 50 maximal contractions comprising the MFT was lower in each subject three days after the prolonged exerise under both dietary conditions. The three subjects all exhibited more marked decreases in total work in the low glycogen condition, supporting the conclusion of Young and Davies (1984) that exercise-induced weakness is greater when muscle glycogen levels are very low.

4. Practical considerations

Endurance athletes, such as cyclists, runners and cross-country skiers, are well aware of the established relationship between intramuscular glycogen levels and their exercise performance. These athletes have probably found it relatively easy to relate to the classical laboratory experiments which have employed treadmill or cycle exercise and demonstrated increased time to fatigue during exercise (Bergström et al., 1967) or a more rapid time required to run a certain distance (Karlsson and Saltin, 1971) when glycogen exhaustion of the exercising muscle is delayed.

Although the endurance component is an integral part of many other sports, individual as well as team, many of these sports also involve critical aspects which demand short term supramaximal exertion. Examples include explosive sprints during soccer, North American Football, and ice-hockey. Changes in muscle glycogen concentration during actual competition conditions have been reported for such sports demonstrating decreases during competition to between 30-60% of pre-competition glycogen values (Saltin, 1973; Green et al., 1978; Zapiec and Taylor, 1979; Jacobs et al., 1982b). These results indicate that glycogenolysis is an important source of fuel during such high intensity exercise. Training for such sports usually involves 3-5 training sessions per week in addition to actual competitions, so that the cumulative effects of consecutive exercise days on glycogen concentrations could potentially result in an athlete commencing each day of exercise with a progressively decreasing glycogen level in the muscles to be exercised (Costill et al., 1971). The endurance performance impairments could be as much as 50% (Bergström et al., 1967), and the studies summarized in this paper indicate that a 10-20% decrease in the explosive power component of exercise performance can also be expected.

The implications should be brought to the attention of not only the classical endurance athlete, but also other athletic groups and even military combat personnel, so that proper nutritional counselling can be instituted to avoid commencing exercise in a glycogen depleted state.

References

Bergström, J., Hermansen, L., Hultman, E. and Saltin, B. (1967) Diet, muscle glycogen and physical performance. Acta physiologica Scandinavica. 71:140-150

Boobis, L.H., Williams, C. and Wooton, S.A. (1983) Influence of sprint training on muscle metabolism during brief maximal exercise in man. J. Physiol. (London). 342:36-37P.

Costill, D.L., Bowers, R., Granam, G. and Sparks, K. (1971) Muscle glycogen utilization during prolonged exercise on successive days. J. Appl. Physiol. 31:834-838.

Costill, D.L. and Miller, J. (1980) Nutrition for endurance sport: carbohydrate and fluid balance. International Journal of Sports Medicine. 1:2-14.

Coyle, E., Costill, D. and Lesmes, G. (1979) Leg extension power and muscle fiber composition. Medicine and Science in Sports. 11:12-15.

Gollnick, P.D., Karlsson, J., Piehl, K. and Saltin, B. (1978) Phosphorylase a in human skeletal muscle during exercise and electrical stimulation. J. Appl. Physiol. 45:852-857.

Green, H.J., Daub, B.D., Painter, D.C. and Thomson, J.A. (1978) Glycogen depletion patterns during ice hockey performance. Medicine and Science in Sports. 10:289-293.

Jacobs, I. (1981a)   Lactate, muscle glycogen and exercise performance in man. Acta Physiologica Scandinavica, Supplementum 495.

Jacobs, I. (1981b)   Lactate concentrations after short, maximal exercise at various glycogen levels. Acta Physiologica Scandinavica. 111:465-469.

Jacobs, I., Bar-Or, O., Karlsson, J., Dotan, R., Tesch, P., Kaiser, P. and Inbar, P. (1982a)   Changes in muscle metabolites in females with 30 seconds exhaustive exercise. Medicine and Science in Sports and Exercise. 14:457-460.

Jacobs, I., Kaiser, P and Tesch, P. (1981)   Muscle strength after selective glycogen depletion in human skeletal muscle fibers. European J. Appl. Physiuol. 46:47-53.

Jacobs, I., Tesch, P., Bar-Or, O., Karlsson, J. and Dotan, R. (1983). Lactate in human skeletal muscle after 10 and 30 seconds of supramaximal exercise. J. Appl. Physiol. 55:3653-367.

Jacobs, I., Weslin, N., Karlsson, J., Rasmusson, M. and Houghton,B. (1982b)   Muscle glycogen depletion and diet in elite soccer players. European J. Appl. Physiol. 48:297-302.

Karlsson, J. and Saltin, B. (1971)   Diet, muscle glycogen and endurance performance. J. Appl. Physiol. 31:203-206.

Klausen, K. and Sjøgaard, G. (1980)   Glycogen stores and lactate accumulation in skeletal muscle of man during intense bicycle exercise. Scandinavian J. Sports Sciences. 2:7-12.

Saltin, B. (1973)   Metabolic fundamentals in exercise. Medicine and Science in Sports. 5:137-146.

Saltin, B and Gollnick, P.D. (1983)   Skeletal muscle adaptability: significance for metabolism and performance. In Skeletal Muscle (edited by L.E. Peachey), pp. 555-631. Bethesda, Maryland: American Physiological Society.

Saltin, B., P.D., Eriksson, B.O. and Piehl, K.(1971)   Metabolic and circulatory adjustments at onset of exercise. In Onset of Exercise (edited by A. Gillbert and P. Guille), pp. 63-76. Toulouse: University of Toulouse.

Saltin, B., and Karlsson, J. (1971)   Muscle glycogen utilization during work of different intensities. In Muscle Metabolism During Exercise (edited by B. Pernow and B. Saltin), pp. 289-299. New York: Plenum Press.

Sherman, W.M., Armstrong, L.E., Murray, T.M., Hagerman, F.C., Costill, D.L., Staron, R.C. and Ivy, J.L. (1984)   Effect of a 42.2 km footrace and subsequent rest or exercise on muscular strength and work capacity. J. Appl. Physiol. 57:1668-1673.

Sherman, W.M., Costill, D.L., Fink, W.J., Hagerman, F.C., Armstrong, L.E and Murray, T.M. (1983)   Effect of a 42.2 km footrace and subsequent rest or exercise on muscle glycogen and enzymes. J. Appl. Physiol. 55:1219-1224.

Sjöholm, H. Sahlin, K., Edstrom, L. and Hultman, E. (1983) Quantitative estimation of anaerobic and oxidative energy metabolism and contraction characteristics in intact human skeletal muscle in response to electrical stimulation. Clinical Physiology. 3:2276-239.

Tesch, P. (1980)   Muscle fatigue in man with special reference to lactate accumulation during short term intense exercise. Acta Physiologica Scandinavica, Supplementum 480.

Thorstensson, A. (1976) Muscle strength, fibre types and enzyme
    activities in man. Acta Physiologica Scandinavica,
    Supplementum 443.
Young, K. and Davies, C.T.M. (1984) Effect of diet on human muscle
    weakness following prolonged exercise. European J. Appl.
    Physiol. 53:81-85
Zapiec, C. and Taylor, A.W. (1979) Muscle fiber composition and
    energy utilization in CFL football players. Canadian J. Appl.
    Sports Sciences 4:140-142.

Discussions

Dr Maughan, Aberdeen, Scotland

There is substantial evidence that alterations in dietary protein
intake can alter blood acid-base status. We have been concerned
with CHO intake in dietary manipulation such as that which you have
used, but a high CHO diet can normally only be achieved if protein
intake is higher than normal. Do you think that this has
significant implications for the performance of brief high
intensity exercise and may indeed be more important than CHO
intake?

Dr Jacobs, Ontario, Canada

I am somewhat doubtful that the alterations would be all that
marked in light of the short duration, i.e. 2-3 days, of dietary
manipulations. Dr Eva Jansson has reported that arterial pH is not
affected by a much longer period of five consecutive days of either
a carbohydrate-rich or carbohydrate-poor diet (Jansson, E. (1982)
On the significance of the respiratory exchange ratio after
different diets during exercise in man. Acta Physiol. Scand.
114:103-110). In addition, you Dr Maughan, have also recently
published a paper demonstrating that marked alterations in blood pH
do not significantly change MVC isometric force nor muscular
endurance at 80% MVC (Maughan, R.J., Leiper, J.B., and Litchfield,
P.E. The effects of induced acidosis and alkalosis on isometric
endurance capacity in man, Exercise Physiology, Vol. 2, New York:
AMS Press Inc., 1986, pp. 73-82). These results suggest to me that
the dietary manipulations we employed would not affect circulating
pH to the extent that there would be a direct effect on the kind of
exercise performance we have examined.

Dr N. Mutrie, Glasgow, Scotland

Given that motivation is a part of maximal voluntary contraction,
do you think that:
(a) your subjects were knowledgeable about effects of low and
high carbohydrate diets? and therefore
(b) did they guess the Ho: and thus change motivation to maximal
voluntary contraction?

Dr Jacobs

Our subjects were knowledgeable physical education and physiology students and I therefore agree that they were susceptible to motivational factors that may confound interpretation of their performance.

Metabolic aspects of fatigue during sprinting

L.H. BOOBIS

During high intensity sprinting on both a cycle ergometer and a non-motorised treadmill a characteristic fatigue profile was generated with peak power output being reached within 2 seconds and then declining by 50% by the end of 30 seconds. Plasma catecholamines rose by 400% and β-endorphins by a similar magnitude. Muscle metabolism studied on needle biopsies of quadriceps revealed that initial anaerobic energy supply was provided equally by glycolysis and phosphocreatine breakdown. Total ATP turnover fell by the same amount as power output by the end of the sprint but by then glycolysis contributed 80% of the energy required. The glycogenolytic rate was initially twice the rate of glycolysis and although it declined more rapidly than the latter it always exceeded it. Substrate depletion did not occur but ATP levels dropped by 42% and calculated muscle pH fell to 6.68. Hexose monophosphates and lactate concentrations increased 16.5 and 13 fold respectively. Training increased the amount of work performed without an appreciable increase in ATP turnover even though 50% more glycogen was mobilised, of which only 74% could be accounted for. At exhaustion, force had decreased probably due to a diminishing energy supply, which may have been aggrevated by a fall in energy from ATP hydrolysis and a reduction in cross-bridge tension, these factors occurring as a result of enzyme inhibition by metabolite accumulation and electrolyte changes and alterations in cellular energetics.

1. Introduction

1.1 Fatigue

Edwards (1983) has defined fatigue as the failure to maintain the required or expected force or power output. In the early studies of muscular fatigue the central nervous system was considered the culprit (Waller, 1891, Setchenov, 1903) but as early as 1914 Weber had suggested that fatigue was local in origin with the brain simply modifying local events (from Karlsson, 1979 and Edwards, 1981). Since then fatigue has been considered to comprise of central and peripheral components which Edwards has elegantly classified on the basis of failure of each of the various events leading from the volition of initiating a muscular contraction to the eventual force or power output. For the purpose of our exercise model we can consider a simplified version of this scheme

(Fig. 1). Central fatigue can be influenced by motivation, pain, perceived severity of exercise, dysnoea and the central effects of systemic metabolic changes. Peripheral fatigue can be considered to comprise of three main components; impaired activation/excitation of the motor units, impaired energy supply and impaired actin-myosin cross bridge coupling.

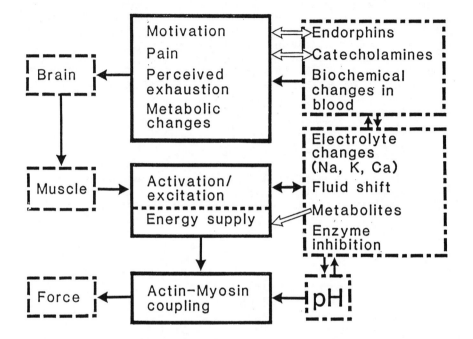

Figure 1. Pathways to fatigue (after Edwards, 1978).

1.2 Anaerobic muscle metabolism - a historical introduction
The events arising from anaerobic glycolysis were first described by Hill and Meyerhof (who shared the Nobel prize in physiology) in the early 1920's, namely that:

1. glycogen disappears,
2. lactic acid appears in equivalent amounts,
3. the hydrogen ion concentration rises.

About the same time Embden found that phosphate was liberated on the production of lactate the precursor of which he attributed to hexose diphosphate. A few years later phosphocreatine (PCr), which was found to decrease during exercise and increase with recovery was discovered independently by Eggleton and Eggleton and Fiske and Subbarow (from Asmussen, 1971). In 1930, Lundsgaard found that if glycolysis was inhibited by mono-iodo acetic acid anaerobic contractions could still take place by the breakdown of PCr, and the splitting of PCr into inorganic phosphate (Pi) and free creatine (Cr) was presumed to be the basis for mechanical

work, lactic acid (La) being formed as a secondary event to
rebuild PCr. However within a short time adenosine triphosphate
(ATP) was discovered by Fiske and Subbarow, and Lohmann who found
that adenosine diphosphate (ADP) was necessary for the conversion
of PCr into its components, and the importance of ATP as the
immediate energy source was realised. In 1933 the concept of the
alactacid oxygen debt was raised as relating to the resynthesis of
phosphogens (from Asmussen, 1971). However it was not until the
reintroduction of the muscle biopsy needle by Bergström in 1962
that studies on metabolism of working human muscle could be made.
In 1969 Margaria postulated that the initial provision of the
first few seconds of anaerobic energy was by PCr breakdown (his
alactacid interval) but in 1971 Saltin et al., were able to
demonstrate the initiation of glycolysis within 10 seconds of
exercise and surmised that it occured the instant muscular
contraction began and 10 years later Jacobs et al., (1983)
confirmed this finding.

2. Supramaximal exercise

We now believe that under conditions of supramaximal exercise at
least, energy for muscular contraction is provided simultaneously
by PCr breakdown and glycolysis. Under these conditions using two

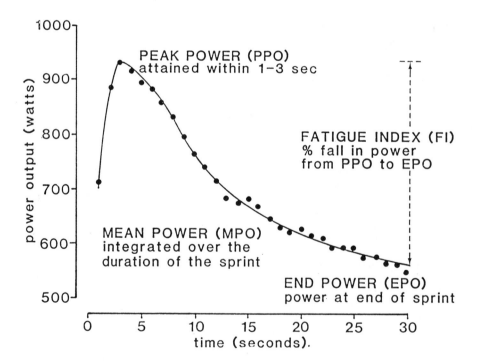

Figure 2. Power output and fatigue profile generated during cycle
ergometer sprints (after Wootton, 1984).

exercise models developed in the sports science laboratory at
Loughborough University, namely a modification of the Wingate cycle
ergometer test and sprint running test on a free running friction
driven treadmill, we have been able to demonstrate a characteristic
fatigue profile for extreme dynamic muscular exertion (Fig. 2 and
Fig. 3). The work described comprises three studies; the exercise
protocol for studies A and B were the same, and the biopsy
technique and analytical methods were uniform throughout.

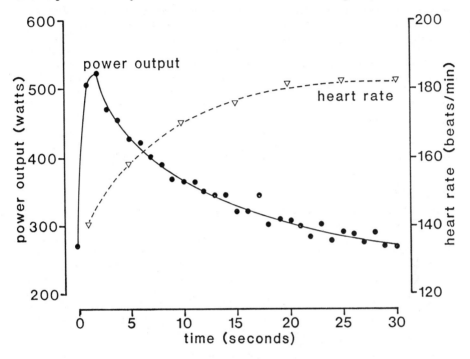

Figure 3. Power output and fatigue profile generated during
treadmill sprint (after Cheetham et al., 1986).

2.1 Study A
The changes in power output during a 6 second and 30 second maximal
work test on a cycle ergometer and the concomitant changes in
muscle metabolism and blood lactate (4 male subjects; age 21-40
years; weight 71.2±8.3kg) (Boobis et al., 1982; Wooton, 1984).

2.2 Study B
The effects of high intensity interval training on performance,
muscle metabolism and blood lactate with the 30 second maximal
cycle ergometer test (7 male subjects; age 21-31 years; weight
72.4±12.2kg) (Boobis et al., 1983; Wooton, 1984).

2.3 Study C
The changes in power output, muscle metabolism, blood pH and lactate,
and blood catecholamines as a result of a 30 second maximal sprint

treadmill test (8 female subjects; age 21-33 years; weight 59.6±8.2kg) (Cheetham et al., 1986).

3. Methods

3.1 Study A (6 and 30 second maximal cycle sprint)
3.1.1 Exercise test
Four male subjects performed a 6 second and 30 second maximal work test on a cycle ergometer (Monark), the tests being randomly allocated and separated by a period of 7 days. The load on the cycle ergometer was selected (after a period of familiarisation) to give the highest mean power output over the 30 second sprint and was the same for the two tests. The power output generated was some three times greater than that which elicited the subjects' $\bar{V}O_2$max. Power output was monitored continuously throughout the test using an optical counter of flywheel revolutions and the fatigue profile derived from 1 second sampling intervals (Wootton, 1984). About five minutes after a 30 second standardised warm-up the subjects performed their maximal exercise test which was maintained for either 6 or 30 seconds.

3.1.2 Muscle biopsies
The resting muscle biopsy was taken 5 minutes after the warm-up from the vastus lateralis muscle and the post-exercise biopsy was taken immediately on cessation of exercise. The delay in obtaining the post-exercise biopsies was between 2 and 4 seconds and the time from removal of the biopsy from the leg until freezing averaged 500 milliseconds. The biopsies were freeze dried, and metabolites assayed on a perchloric acid extract prepared from fat free muscle powder from which all connective tissue and blood had been removed. Acid insoluble glycogen was determined in the precipitated muscle pellet. All metabolite assays were performed by fluorimetric analysis using principles as described by Lowry and Passeneau (1973). Glycogen was assayed as described by Jansson (1981).

3.1.3 Blood samples
Capillary blood samples were taken at the same time as the muscle biopsies and 5 minutes post exercise for the determination of lactate and glucose (Maughan, 1982).

3.2 Study B (30 second maximal cycle sprint before and
        after interval training)
Seven male subjects performed the 30 second maximal work test as outlined above before and after 8 weeks of intensive interval training. Power output for this study was recorded by means of analogue to digital conversion of the current generated by a DC motor linked to the cycle fly wheel and fed directly to a micro-computer (Lakomy, 1986). Muscle biopsies and blood samples were taken as in study A.

3.3 Study C (30 second maximal treadmill sprint)
3.3.1 Exercise test
Eight female subjects undertook a 30 second maximal sprint on a non-motorized treadmill preceded by a warm-up of two 30 second

submaximal runs. The horizontal component of the power output
generated during the test was continuously monitored being
calculated from the instantaneous product of restraint force and
treadmill belt velocity. The latter was determined by a method
similar to that used in Study B and the former from the output of a
force transducer fixed to a rear crossbar of the treadmill to which
was attached a non-elastic belt passing round the subjects' waist
(Lakomy, 1984).

3.3.2 Muscle biopsies
Muscle biopsies were again obtained from vastus lateralis at rest
(before any warm-up) and immediately on cessation of the sprint.
The average time taken from the end of the sprint until obtaining
the biopsy was 7 seconds with a delay of 600 milliseconds before it
was frozen. Metabolites were again assayed on the freeze dried,
fat free muscle samples.

3.3.3 Blood samples
Venous blood samples were obtained at 4 minutes post warm-up and at
3 minutes after the sprint and capillary blood samples at 4 minutes
after warm-up and 5 minutes following the sprint for determination
of blood pH and catecholamines (Davies et al., 1981) and blood
lactate and glucose respectively.

4. Results

4.1 Study A
4.1.1 Power output
The peak power output (PPO) and mean power output (MPO) over the
first 6 seconds of the exercise test was the same for the 30 second
sprint (922w and 837w) and the truncated 6 second sprint (914w and
847w) confirming that the short sprint reflected an accurate
sample of the initial six seconds of the test. Within this period
26% of the total work performed had been done.

4.1.2 Change in muscle metabolites
Biopsy samples were not obtained in two subjects prior to the 6
second sprint and the mean for all resting biopsies are given as
our results compared favourably with published data and there was
no obvious difference between pre-exercise values for the two
tests. Resting muscle metabolite concentrations expressed as
mmoles kg^{-1} dry wt were as follows: glycogen 261.2; PCr 84.3; ATP
24.3; ADP 3.8; AMP 0.2; glucose 1.9; gluc-1-P 0.1; gluc-6-P 1.3:
fruc-6-P).2; FBP 0.1; TP 0.3; pyruvate 0.2; lactate 8.4. After 6
seconds there was as expected an appreciable fall in PCr (35%)
whereas ATP, ADP and AMP levels remained constant. Despite the
extreme fatigue after the 30 second sprint, PCr levels were still
34% of the resting values but there was now a 44% fall in ATP
concentration but still no change in ADP or AMP (Fig.4). More
dramatic, however, was the fall in glycogen and the marked increase
in hexose monophosphates (HMP). At 6 seconds glycogen had fallen
by 43 mmol glucosyl units kg^{-1} dry wt and HMP increased by 850%
with a 330% increase in La. There was a much more modest increase
in those metabolites below phosphofructokinase (PFK) in the Embden-

Myerhof pathway (210%). After the 30 second sprint HMP had
increased to 15 times the pre-exercise levels and La was now 10
times greater with a corresponding fall in glycogen of 79 mmol
glucosyl units kg^{-1} dry wt (30%). Fructose bisphosphate (FBP) and
the triose phosphates (TP) had risen to 9 times their basal levels
(Fig.5). Interestingly, 85% of the glycogen utilised during the 30
second sprint could be accounted for by the accumulation of
glycolytic intermediates and La but during the 6 second test only
56% of the glycogen used could be accounted for in this way. The
significance of this finding is unclear.

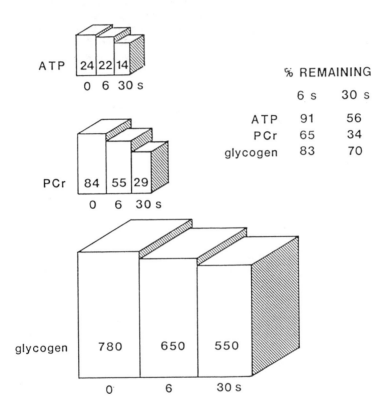

% REMAINING

	6 s	30 s
ATP	91	56
PCr	65	34
glycogen	83	70

Figure 4. Study A: anaerobic energy supply before and after 6 and
30 seconds of high intensity sprinting as mmoles high energy
phosphate (ATP) kg^{-1} dry wt. The volumes of the boxes are
proportional to the concentration of the metabolite.

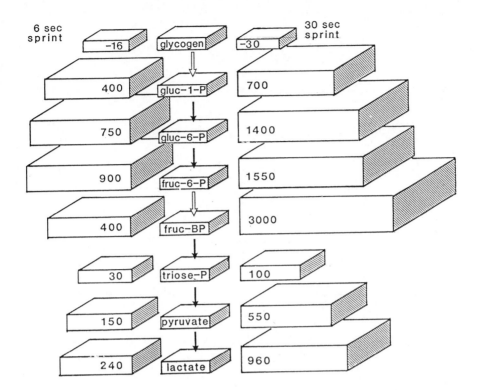

Figure 5. Study A: pathways chart demonstrating kpercentage change
in glycolytic intermediates after the 6 and 30 second sprint. The
open arrows indicate the regulatory enzymes of phosphorylase and
PFK and the volumes of the boxes are proportional to the change in
metabolite concentration.

4.1.3 Changes in blood lactate
Blood La increased from 1.39 mmol.l^{-1} at rest to 1.83 mmol.l^{-1}
at the end of the 6 second sprint and after 5 minutes this had
risen to 5.01 mmol.l^{-1} whereas after the 30 second sprint the values
were 4.49 mmol.l^{-1} and 12.41 mmol.l^{-1} .

4.2 Study B
4.2.1 Power output
After eight weeks of training PPO had increased by 7.5%, end power
output (EPO) by 5.5% and MPO by 8.1% but the fatigue index (the
percentage drop from peak to end power output) was unchanged (Fig.6).

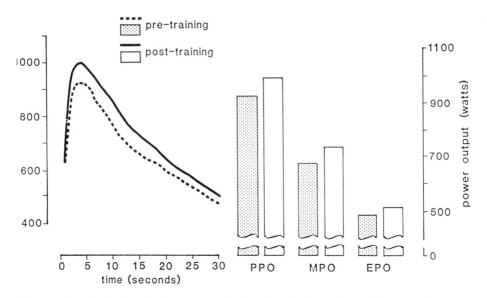

Figure 6. Study B: influence of intensive interval training on the fatigue profile and power output produced by 30 seconds of cycle ergometer sprinting.

4.2.2 Changes in muscle metabolism

Pre-training resting muscle metabolite concentrations were similar to those in Studay A. Muscle glycogen increased 36% with training but there was no change in ATP levels. There was a small fall in post-training resting PCr which was accompanied by a significant drop in total Cr concentration which may merely reflect a sampling error (Fig.7). No attempt however was made to correct for a constant total Cr level to compensate for this change in the reference base. Values for the other metabolites were the same before and after training.

The pre-training metabolic changes after the 30 second sprint were almost identical to those in study A, with a 28% fall in glycogen (74 mmoles of glucosyl units), a 65% fall in PCr and a 44% drop in ATP. The HMP concentration increased 16 fold, La increased 11 fold but FBP and TP only increased 5 times. After training 111 mmol kg^{-1} dry wt of glycogen were utilised representing a 31% drop from, it should be noted, the much higher resting concentration. Phosphocreatine and ATP decreased by the same amounts (67% and 56% respectively) whereas there was a 2300% increase in HMP and 1250% rise in La but no change in the rise in FBP and TP (Fig.8). Before training 97% of the glucosyl residues from glycogen could be accounted for but this fell to only 74% after training.

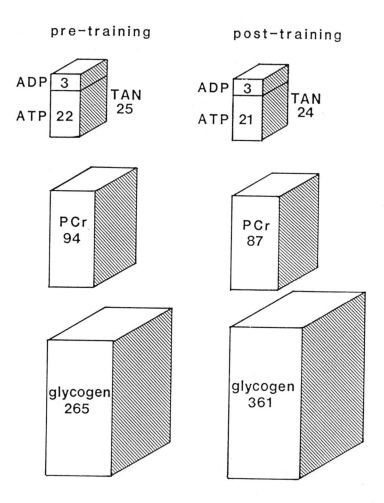

pre-training   post-training

Figure 7. Study B: effect of intensive interval training on muscle glycogen and phosphogen stores. Concentrations are shown as mmoles kg^{-1} dry wt and the boxes are proportional to the amount of metabolite. (Total adenine nucleotide pool) TAN=ATP+ADP+AMP.

4.2.3 Changes in blood lactate

Blood La values were very similar to those obtained in study A and were unchanged by training with resting values of 1.59 and 1.61 mmol l^{-1}, immediate post-exercise levels of 4.40 and 3.95 mmol l^{-1} and 5 minute post-exercise concentrations of 13.30 and 12.50 mmol l^{-1} pre- and post-training respectively.

4.3 Study C
4.3.1 Power output

Treadmill sprinting although using a completely different exercise model, produced a similar fatigue profile and power output over 30 seconds as obtained in the cycling sprints discussed in studies A and B (Fig. 2). The PPO of 534 W was reached within 1.63 s of the

start of the sprint and decreased by 50% at the end with an overall
MPO of 347 W. Although these figures seem much lower than those
generated by the males during the cycling ergometer tests, when
corrected for body weight the values of 9.2 W kg^{-1} (PPO) and
6.00 W kg^{-1} (MPO) bear comparison with those of 12.8 W kg^{-1}
and 12.9 W kg^{-1} (PPO) and 9.1 W kg^{-1} and 9.4 W kg^{-1} (MPO)
for studies A and B respectively when the difference in measuring
the work done and the nature of the two tests are considered.

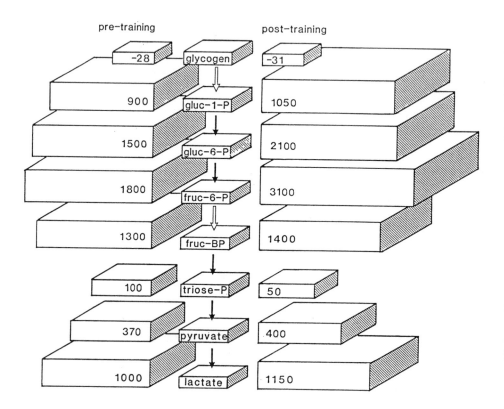

pre-training   post-training

pre	intermediate	post
-28	glycogen	-31
900	gluc-1-P	1050
1500	gluc-6-P	2100
1800	fruc-6-P	3100
1300	fruc-BP	1400
100	triose-P	50
370	pyruvate	400
1000	lactate	1150

Figure 8. Study B: pathways chart showing percentage change in
glycolytic intermediates after 30 second cycle ergometer sprint
before and after 8 weeks of intensive interval training.

4.3.2 Changes in muscle metabolism
Again, resting metabolite concentrations and post-exercise changes
in muscle metabolites closely mirrored those seen in the cycle
ergometer sprint. Muscle glycogen fell by 69 mmol of glucosyl
units kg^{-1} dry wt (25%) and PCr and ATP by 64% and 37%
respectively. The HMP concentration increased by 13 fold and La
increased 29 times. The apparent greater percentage increase in La
over studies A and B is explained by the fact that in the first
two studies the 'resting' biopsy was taken after the standardised
warm-up and in this study the subjects rested completely prior to

the first biopsy and undertook their warm-up afterwards.   There was
again only a modest rise in FBP and TP of 2 fold (Fig.9).   Overall
92% of the glycogen utilised could be accounted for by the
products of glycogenolysis and glycolysis.

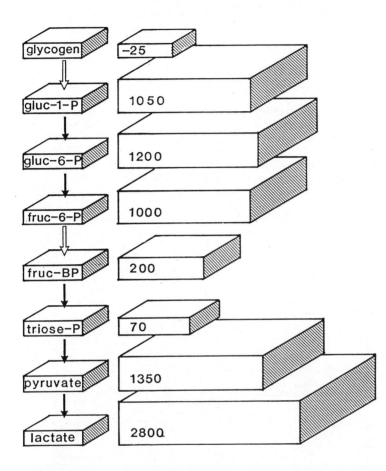

Figure 9. Study C: pathways chart showing percentage change in
glycolytic intermediates after 30 seconds of treadmill sprinting.

4.3.3 Changes in blood biochemistry
(a) Lactate and glucose
Blood La concentrations were similar to the cycle ergometer studies
with a resting level of 0.73 mmol.1^{-1} rising to 1.96 mmol.1^{-1} after
the warm-up and then increasing to 11.57 mmol.1^{-1} and 13.06 mmol. 1^{-1}
at 3 minutes and 5 minutes after the sprint.   Blood glucose was 40%
higher 5 minutes after the sprint than at rest.

(b) Catecholamines and pH
Total plasma catecholamine concentration (adrenaline plus
noradrenaline) increased from a resting concentration of 3.0 nmol l^{-1}
to 13.0 nmol l^{-1} at 3 minutes after the sprint. Blood pH sampled
at the same times fell from 7.40 to 7.16.

4.4 Muscle pH
Muscle pH was calculated using the formula

$$pH = 7.06-0.00413(lactate+pyruvate) \qquad (4.1)$$
(Sahlin et al., 1976)

Thus in study A, the derived pH was 7.02 at rest and fell to
6.94 after 6 seconds and 6.69 after 30 seconds. The resting values
for study B were the same and again pH fell to 6.64 after the 30
second cycle sprint before training and 6.63 afterwards. On the
treadmill sprint resting pH was a little higher (7.05) and reflects
the lower lactate level in the true basal state. After the
exercise test calculated pH was found to be 6.73.

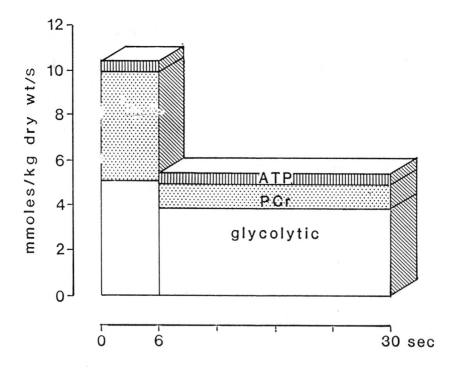

Figure 10. Study A: ATP turnover rates expressed as mmoles kg^{-1} dry
wt s^{-1} during cycle ergometer sprinting calculated for 0 to 6 and 6
to 30 seconds. ATP = ATP from ATP decline; PCr = ATP from PCr
breakdown; glycolytic = ATP from glycolysis.

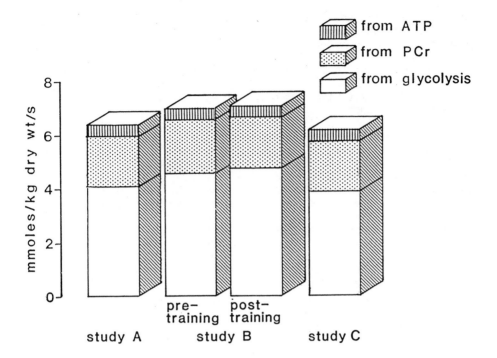

Figure 11. ATP turnover rates for all three studies expressed as mmoles kg^{-1} dry wt s^{-1} averaged over the full 30 second sprint.

4.5 ATP turnover
Anaerobic ATP turnover was calculated using the formulae

total ATP turnover = $-\Delta PCr-\Delta ATP+1.5 \times \Delta lactate+1.5 \times \Delta pyruvate$ (4.2)

glycolytic ATP turnover = $1.5 \times \Delta lactate+1.5 \times \Delta pyruvate$ (4.3)
(Sahlin and Henrikssen, 1984)

Total ATP turnover from anaerobic sources during the six second sprint was 10.4 mmol kg^{-1} dry wt s^{-1} to which glycolysis contributed 49% (5.1 mmol kg^{-1} dry wt s^{-1}). Between 6 and 30 seconds the ATP turnover had fallen to 5.4 mmol kg^{-1} dry wt s^{-1} of which glycolysis provided 80% (Fig.10). Training did not significantly alter either total ATP utilisation or the percentage contribution from PCr and ATP the values being 7.0 and 7.1 mmol kg^{-1} dry wt s^{-1} and 35% and 32% before and after training respectively (Fig.11). On the treadmill sprint total turnover was a little lower (6.2 mmol kg^{-1} dry wt s^{-1}) but glycolysis still provided 63% of the energy supply (Fig.11).

4.6 Glycogenolytic and glycolytic rates
Glycogenolytic and glycolytic rates were calculated using the
formulae

glycogenolysis = $\Delta G6P + 0.33x\,\Delta G6P + 1/2\,(\Delta lactate + 0.1x\Delta lactate)$ (4.4)

Glycolysis = $1/2(\Delta lactate + 0.1x\,\Delta lactate)$ (4.5)
(Hultman and Sjöholm, 1983)

Within 6 seconds of exercise glycogenolysis had reached a rate
of 4.0 mmol kg^{-1} dry wt s^{-1} exceeding glycolysis by more
than 100%. After 30 seconds the rate of glycogen breakdown had
fallen by 43% (2.3 mmol kg^{-1} dry wt s^{-1}) whereas glycolysis
had only fallen by 20% (from 1.8 to 1.5 mmol kg^{-1} dry wt s^{-1}) (Fig.12).
In the training study, the pre-training values were very similar to
the first experiment with results of 2.4 and 1.6 mmol kg^{-1} dry wt s^{-1}
for glycogenolysis and glycolysis respectively. With training
glycogen breakdown increased to 2.8 mmol kg^{-1} dry wt s^{-1} surpassing
the rate of glycolysis by nearly 160% compared with the pre-training
excess of 150%. In study C the glycogenolytic rate was a little
lower at 2.1 mmol kg^{-1} dry wt s^{-1} but again, as was uniformly
found, exceeded glycolysis, in this case by 1.5 times (Fig.13).

Calculated values for muscle pH, rates of ATP turnover and
glycogenolytic and glycolytic rates are summarised in Table 4.1.

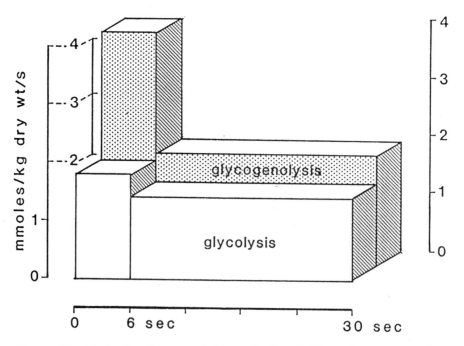

Figure 12. Study A: glycogenolytic and glycolytic rates expressed
as mmoles kg^{-1} s^{-1} calculated for 0 to 6 and 6 to 30 seconds.

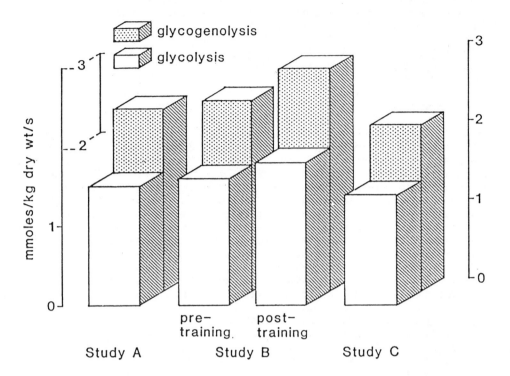

Figure 13. Glycogenolytic and glycolytic rates for all three studies expressed as mmoles kg^{-1} s^{-1} averaged over the full 30 second sprint.

Table 4.1 Calculated values for muscle pH, glycogenolytic rate, glycolytic rate, total anaerobic ATP turnover, ATP turnover from glycolysis, and ATP turnover from PCr. Turnover rates are given as mmoles kg^{-1} dry weight s^{-1}.

	Study A			Study B		Study C
	0-6s	0-30s	6-30s	pre	post	
pH before sprint	7.02	7.02		7.02	7.02	7.05
pH after sprint	6.94	6.69		6.64	6.63	6.73
glycogenolytic rate	4.0	2.3	1.9	2.4	2.8	2.1
glycolytic rate	1.8	1.5	1.4	1.6	1.8	1.4
total ATP turnover	10.4	6.4	5.4	7.0	7.1	6.2
ATP glycolytic	5.1	4.1	3.9	4.6	4.8	3.9
ATP from PCr	4.9	1.9	1.1	2.0	1.9	1.9

ATP = adenosine triphosphate; PCr = phosphocreatine
pre and post = pre- and post-training values are computed for
0 to 30 seconds for sprints B and C.

(Calculated from data in Boobis et al., 1982; Boobis et al., 1983;
Wootton, 1984; Cheetham et al., 1986).

5. Discussion

5.1 Central fatigue

Our subjects studied comprised extremely well motivated individuals
- a mixture of recreational games players and runners (who usually
had a vested interest in the study!) and international level games
players - so psychological drive and motivation was invariably
high. As we are able to account for almost all of the products of
glycolysis (for the 30 second test at least) we feel that we are
justified in considering our models as representing 'closed
systems' with there being very little interchange between the
muscle cell and its immediate extracellular environment and the
circulation. It is very unlikely therefore that there occurred
sufficient circulating biochemical changes from muscle metabolites
in the course of the sprint to modulate central fatigue.

5.2 Catecholamines and muscle metabolism

After the treadmill test noradrenaline concentration increased 4
fold (from 2.7 to 11.7 nmol l^{-1}) and adrenaline rose from 0.3
to 1.3 nmol l^{-1}. There was significant correlation between
both the rate of glycolysis and blood glucose concentration and the
rises in catecholamines. Although there may have been some
increased sympathetic drive in anticipation of the sprint the
normal resting values do not support this. MacDonald et al. (1983)
have shown that the peak catecholamine concentration occurs
immediately on cessation of a maximal anaerobic work test, plateaus
for 3 minutes and then declines, whereas peak concentrations of
lactate and glucose are not reached for 5 minutes. It is unlikely
then that even if adrenaline and noradrenaline increase hepatic
glucose production, either by a direct effect on liver glycogen or
indirectly by stimulating pancreatic glucagon production (Naveri et
al., 1985), that the exercising muscle during such brief high
intensity exercise will benefit from this late availability of blood
glucose. The exact mechanism for this early rise in catecholamines
is unclear but it is probable that the initial control, at least, is
peripheral (see Galbo, 1983 for review). The likely local benefit
therefore of this rapid rise in catecholamines is to initiate the
transformation of phosphorylase b to a in readiness for rapid
mobilisation of glycogen (Chasiotis et al., 1983).

5.3 Influence of β-endorphins on fatigue

Little information is available on the changes in β-endorphins in
anaerobic exercise but our group have recently shown that they
exhibit a rise of the same magnitude as the catecholamines after a
30 second cycle ergometer sprint (Brooks et al., 1986). It would
be interesting to conjecture that this rise in endogenous opioids

could alter cortical appreciation of pain and decrease central
fatigue in addition to any effect that they may have at the neuromuscular junction (Haynes et al., 1983).

5.4 Peripheral fatigue - a protective mechanism
Although fatigue is undesirable from the sportman's point of view
it is an important protective mechanism for the organism. Using
our maximum rate of glycolysis of 1.8 mmol kg^{-1} dry wt s^{-1}
and a glycogen content of 300 mmol kg^{-1} dry wt, if the body's
entire skeletal muscle mass were to produce La at that rate the
muscle glycogen stores would be depleted in under three minutes and
death would ensue from profound acidosis. Even with a buffering
capacity of 60 Slykes (Sahlin and Henriksson, 1984) complete breakdown of all glycogen to lactate would generate 140 mmol hydrogen
ions kg^{-1} wet wt and cellular pH would fall to less than 5!

5.5 Glycogenolysis and phosphorylase activity
A glycogenolytic rate of 4.0 mmol kg^{-1} dry wt s^{-1} would require
a total phosphorylase activity of 240 mmol glucosyl units kg^{-1} dry
wt m^{-1} which is 1.6 times the maximum activity reported by
Chasiotis (1983) during either dynamic or isometric exercise, and
if we consider the measured fall in muscle glycogen during the
6 second sprint instead, this would require an activity of 430
falling to 160 mmol kg^{-1} dry wt m^{-1} after 30 seconds, the
latter value now in keeping with Chasiotis' measured activity.
As 40% of glycogen mobilised occurred within the first 20% of the
sprint it is likely that there is a very early and rapid increase
in phosphorylase activity followed by an exponential fall. By
6 seconds there has already been suffcient Pi release by PCr
breakdown to allow a saturating concentration for phosphorylase b
and a. This is in contradiction to Hultman et al.'s (1983) findings
that phosphorylase activity increased during the first 30 seconds
of exercise and then declined.
    These high glycogenolytic rates can be confirmed by calculation
of the data presented by Jones et al. in 1985. Their study using a
constant velocity cycle ergometer at two pedal frequencies, 60 and
140 rmp gives a computed rate of 3.2 and 3.0 mmol glucosyl units
kg^{-1} dry wt s^{-1} over a thirty second sprint and in two subjects
in whom they measured metabolites at 10 seconds of exercise the
rates were 4.4 and 4.9 mmol kg^{-1} dry wt s^{-1} at the slower and
faster cycling speeds. We do not support their finding however that
FBP decreases after an early peak.

5.6 Glycolytic rates and the relationship between
    glucose-6-phosphate and lactate
Phosphofructokinase is accepted as the control enzyme of
glycolysis, as phosphorylase is the rate limiting enzyme for
glycogen degradation (Newsholme and Start, 1973) and the 'stacking
up' of the HMP above PFK certainly lends weight to the regulatory
role of PFK. Our initial glycolytic rate of 1.8 mmol kg^{-1} dry wt s^{-1}
falls to 1.5 after 30 seconds this 20% fall being much less than
the 33% fall in glycogenolysis. Again our findings and the
calculated glycolytic rates from Jones et al.'s (1985) data (3.2 at
10 seconds and 2.2 at 30) revealed that the rate of glycolysis
decreased during the exercise test in contradiction to Hultman and

Sjöholm's (1983) finding although as in their case it always exceeded glycogenolysis. Plotting glucose-6-phosphate (G6P) concentration against La (Fig.14) does not give such a clearly linear relationship as Hultman and Sjöholm (1983) found. The graph seems to be curvilinear with an initial rapid rise in G6P and then flattening off at the highest concentrations of La and G6P and this would be in keeping with our finding of the very high initial glycogenolytic rate declining much more rapidly than glycolysis.

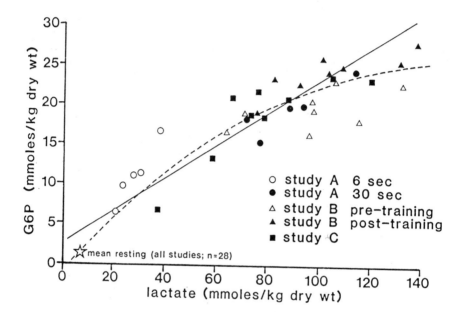

Figure 14. Plot of muscle lactate against glucose-6-phosphate (G6P) with best fit curve and regression line.
(r=0.97, n=58, lactate=0.89+4.41XG6P)

5.7 ATP turnover and power output
There is an equal contribution to ATP from PCr and glycolysis to the initial turnover rate of 10.4 mmol kg^{-1} dry wt s^{-1} which is close to the maximum rate calculated by McGilvery (1973) (11 to 17 mmol kg^{-1} dry wt s^{-1}) and this had fallen to 6.7 after 30 seconds (mean of studies A and pre-training B) of which PCr contributed 35% and ATP itself 5%. The fall in ATP turnover (46% of the peak value at 6 sec when measured between 6 and 30 sec) was due primarily to the 78% drop in its contribution from PCr. Over this period glycolysis declined by just 22% and it would appear that despite their initial shared contribution to energy supply, ATP from PCr decays more than three times as fast as the rate of glycolysis.
    Using McGilvery's (1975) figures, who calculated ATP energy provision at 100kJ mole and applying this figure to our values for power output, we can derive estimated ATP turnover rates necessary to sustain the work done. Assuming 25% efficiency, a water content of 77% and a maximally exercising muscle mass of 50% of a total of 30kg (upper leg muscle mass is approximately 30% of the body's

total (Wootton, 1984)), the calculated ATP turnover in the first 6 seconds of the sprint in study A would be 9.8 mmol ATP kg^{-1} dry wt s^{-1} the mean over 30 seconds would be 7.5, and the terminal turnover rate would be 5.3 mmol s^{-1}. These values are remarkably close to those derived from equation (4.2). For the treadmill sprint these estimated values would be 8.8, 5.7 and 4.4 and again these theoretical values are close to those derived from equation (4.2) (total muscle mass in female subjects estimated at 21kg).

Although we can derive mean theoretical values close to our calculated ones, plotting MPO against ATP turnover gives reasonable correlation for the cycle ergometer sprints but poor correlation for the treadmill sprint but this may be a reflection of the different experimental models (Fig.15). From these figures it is extremely likely that the biopsy technique gives an accurate picture of the profound biochemical changes occurring within the muscle.

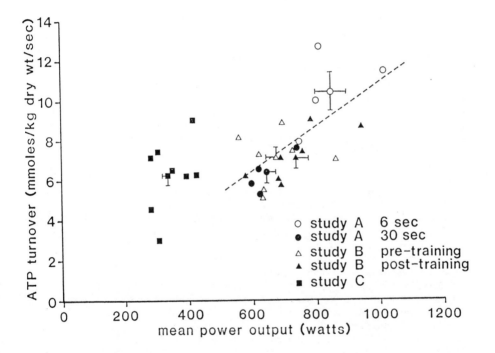

Figure 15. Plot of mean power output against total anaerobic ATP turnover with regression line for cycle ergometer sprints. (r=0.66, n=22, ATP=-0.261+0.011Xwatts)

5.8 Fall in muscle ATP concentration
The dramatic reduction in ATP concentration found after the sprints is not seen with isometric exercise or electrical stimulation (Hultman and Sjöholm, 1983) but has been demonstrated by Jacobs et al. (1982) and Jones et al. (1985) using a cycle ergometer test of a similar work intensity as in studies A and B. A few years earlier Sahlin et al. (1978b) described a more modest

decrease in ATP using a less strenuous exercise model and found
that they could account for the fall in adenine nucleotides by an
increase in inosine monophosphate (IMP). Harris and Hultman (1985)
were able to reproduce this more pronounced fall in ATP with
repeated stimulation of quadriceps with an occluded blood flow
(they were able to produce a 63% fall with La concentrations
reaching 170 mmol kg^{-1} dry wt) and found that the decrease in
ATP was accompanied by a stochiometric increase in IMP. As
neither ourselves nor the other workers were able to demonstrate a
concommitant change in ADP or AMP, the result of these changes
would be to cause a build-up of Pi from both PCr and ATP breakdown.

5.9 Muscle pH
Muscle pH has been shown to be linearly related to lactate
concentration (Sahlin et al., 1976) and as we have previously
discussed our results suggest that pH falls to about 6.6 after the
30 seconds of exercise described in the first two studies, a value
which is widely reported as occurring at exhaustion (Sahlin, 1978;
Costill et al., 1983; Sahlin and Henriksson, 1984).

5.10 Changes in potassium concentration
Although Sahlin et al. (1978a) demonstrated a fall in both plasma
and muscle potassium concetrations immediately after exhaustive
exercise, Sejersted et al. (1984) reported a doubling of femoral
arterial potassium after one minute of maximal exercise (treadmill
sprint to exhaustion) and in one subject recorded similar
elevations of K$^+$ during five repeated sprints with complete
recovery to normal concentrations in the four minute rests between
sprints.

5.11 Aerobic contribution to high intensity exercise
The role of aerobic metabolism in exercise of this nature is
uncertain. It is certain, however, that some oxidative
phosphorylation occurs and our finding that we can only account for
a little over half the products of glycolysis after the six
second sprint may reflect the greater percentage contribution from
oxygen utilisation in the initial stages of exercise or
alternatively loss of lactate from the working muscle. If the
initial part of the G6P/La curve is due to the loss of La from the
muscle then taking this into account would restore linearity to
the relationship that Hultman and Sjöholm (1983) found in their
study which used an occluded circulation and electrical
stimulation.

5.12 Effects of training
During the 30 second exercise period after training 50% more
glucosyl units were mobilised than before training but only 74%
could be accounted for by glycolytic intermediates. As was seen
there was an apparent greater increase in glycogenolysis than
glycolysis with a resultant significant increase in HMP but no
change in the total anaerobic ATP turnover rate. Parkhouse and
McKenzie (1984) in their excellent review on anaerobic performance
conclude, in keeping with these findings, that although an
improvement in glycolytic enzyme activity occurs with sprint-

training the resultant increases in power output are greater than the enhanced ability to produce ATP. An improvement in muscle buffering capacity has therefore been postulated as being a possible method by which the anaerobically trained muscle can resist pH changes over a greater hydrogen ion concentration. In addition, if our metabolite results are correct, it is possible that some lactate has been lost from the muscle either to the circulation or by aerobic metabolism and we are underestimating the rates of glycolysis and ATP turnover and the increased power output could be accounted for by this 'lost' lactate.

6. Conclusions

The consequence of these metabolic changes is fatigue in the working muscle. Substrate depletion does not occur; there are still ample PCr and glycogen stores at the end of the sprint but ATP levels have falen dramatically despite Wilkie's (1981) comments that contraction fails before any significant fall in ATP concentration occurs. Accumulation of Pi and H^+ and a fall in the ATP/ADP ratio will decrease the free energy charge from further ATP hydrolysis to values that may be too low for maintenance of electrolyte concentrations across the cell (Newsholme and Start, 1973; Sahlin et al., 1978b) (this might be the explanation for the high arterial potassium concentrations which may be even higher in the interstitial fluid and which may further contribute to fatigue by causing a depolarising block). The fall in ATP and increase in H^+ activates AMP deaminase and increases IMP formation. High hydrogen ion concentration itself may inhibit actomysin ATPase and lower cross bridge tension (Donaldson, 1983) and will in addition reduce the activity of phosphorylase by affecting its transformation from b to a (Chasiotis et al., 1982). Further inhibition of PFK occurs as a result of the fall in pH and the fall in the rate of glycolysis in excess of glycogenolysis, in the latter part of the sprint, would suggest that the rise in fructose-6-phosphate was insufficient to overcome this inhibition which is contrary to the findings of Hultman and Sjöholm (1983). The considerable rise in G6P would further inhibit phosphorylase (Newsholme and Start, 1973). A low pH will alter the creatine kinase equilibrium which itself will determine the relative concentrations of PCr and ATP for a given hydrogen ion concentration (Sahlin et al., 1975).

The overall effect of these changes will be to decrease the rate of glycogenolysis and glycolysis, decrease the rate of ATP turnover both by glycolysis and from PCr, and decrease the force that the muscle is able to generate thereby inducing a sensation of muscular exhaustion. As can be seen our studies provide evidence which clearly demonstrates the existence of this chain of events.

Acknowledgements

This work was supported by grants from The Sports Council. Leslie Boobis is a Royal College of Surgeons of England Porritt Fellow, the award for which provided additional financial support. The authors would like to thank the other members of their Sports Science Research Group for their contribution to these studies, and especially Mr Stephen Brooks and Mr Henry K.A. Lakomy.

References

Asmussen, E. (1971). Muscle metabolism during exercise in man: a historical survey. In Muscle metabolism during exercise (edited by B. Pernow and B. Saltin), pp 1-12. New York: Plenum Press.

Bergström, J. (1962). Muscle electrolytes in man. Scandinavian Journal of Clinical and Laboratory Investigation supplement 68.

Boobis, L., Williams, C. and Wootton, S.A. (1982). Human muscle metabolism during brief maximal exercise. J. Physiol. 338:21-22P.

Boobis, L.H., Williams, C. and Wootton, S.A. (1983). Influence of sprint training on muscle metabolism during brief maximal exercise in man. J. Physiol. 342:36-37P.

Brooks, S., Burrin, J., Cheetham, M.E., Hall, G., Williams, C. and Yeo, T. (1986). The β-endorphin response to brief maximal exercise in man. J. Physiol. 377:106P.

Chasiotis, D. (1983). The regulation of glycogen phosphorylase and glycogen breakdown in human skeletal muscle. Acta Physiologica Scandinavica supplementum 518.

Chasiotis, D., Hultman, E. and Sahlin, K. (1982). Acidotic depression of cyclic AMP accumulation and phosphorylase b to a transformation in skeletal muscle of man. J. Physiol. 335:197-204.

Chasiotis, D., Sahlin, K. and Hultman, E. (1983). Regulation of glycogenolysis in human muscle in response to epinephrine infusion. J. Appl. Physiol. 54:45-50.

Cheetham, M.E., Boobis, L.H., Brooks, S. and Williams, C. (1986). Human muscle metabolism during sprint running. J. Appl. Physiol. 61:54-60.

Costill, D.L., Barnett, A., Sharp, R., Fink, W.J. and Katz, A. (1983). Leg muscle pH following sprint running. Medicine and Science in Sports and Exercise 15:325-329.

Davies, C.L., Kissinger, P.T. and Shoup, R.E. (1981). Strategies for the determination of serum or plasma norepinephrine by reverse phase liquid chromatography. Annals of Chemistry 53:156-159.

Donaldson, S.K.B. (1983). Effect of acidosis on maximal force generation of peeled mammalian skeletal muscle fibres. In Biochemistry of Exercise (edited by H.G. Knuttgen, J.A. Vogel and J. Poortmans), pp. 126-133. Champaign, IL: Human Kinetic Publishers, Inc.

Edwards, R.H.T. (1978). Physiological analysis of skeletal muscle weakness and fatigue. Clinical Science and Molecular Medicine 54:463-470.

Edwards, R.H.T. (1981). Human muscle function and fatigue. In Human muscle fatigue: physiological mechanisms (Ciba Foundation Symposium 82) (Edited by R. Porter and J. Whelan), pp 1-18. London: Pitman Medical.

Edwards, R.H.T. (1983). Biochemical bases of fatigue in exercise performance: catastrophe theory of muscular fatigue. In Biochemistry of Exercise (edited by H.G. Knuttgen, J.A. Vogel and J. Poortmans), pp. 3-28. Champaign, IL: Human Kinetics Publishers, Inc.

Galbo, H. (1983). Hormonal and metabolic adaptation to exercise Stuttgart/New York: Georg Thieme Verlag/Thieme-Stratton, Inc.

Harris, R.C. and Hultman, E. (1985). Adenine nucleotide depletion in human muscle in response to intermittent stimulation in situ. J. Physiol. 365:73P.

Haynes, L.W., Harborne, A.J. and Smith, M.E. (1983). Augmentation of acetylcholine response in denervated skeletal muscle by endorphins and spinal cord-conditioned culture media. European J. Pharmacology 86:415-425.

Hultman, E., Chasiotis, D. and Sjöholm, H. (1983). Energy metabolism in muscle in hypoxia, exercise, and altitude: Proceedings of the Third Banff International Hypoxia Symposium, pp. 257-272. New York: Alan R. Liss, Inc.

Hultman, E. and Sjöholm, H. (1983). Energy metabolism and contraction force of human skeletal muscle in situ during electrical stimulation. J. Physiol. 345:525-532.

Jacobs, I., Bar-Or, O., Karlsson, J., Dotan, R., Tesch, P., Kaiser, P. and Inbar, O. (1982). Changes in muscle metabolites in females with 30-s exhaustive exercise. Medicine and Science in Sports and Exercise 14:457-460.

Jacobs, I., Tesch, P.A., Bar-Or. O., Karlsson, J. and Dotan, R. (1983). Lactate in human skeletal muscle after 10 and 30 s of supramaximal exercise. J. Appl. Physiol. 55:365-367.

Jansson, E. (1981). Acid soluble and insoluble glycogen in human skeletal muscle. Acta Physiologica Scandinavica 113:337-340.

Jones, N.L., McCartney, N., Graham, T., Spriet, L.L., Kowalchuk, J.M., Heigenhauser, G.J.F. and Sutton, J.R. (1985). Muscle performance and metabolism in maximal isokinetic cycling at slow and fast speeds. J. Appl. Physiol. 59:132-136.

Karlsson, J. (1979). Localized muscular fatigue: role of muscle metabolism and substrate depletion. Exercise and Sports Sciences Reviews 7:1-42.

Lakomy, H.K.A. (1984). An ergometer for measuring the power, generated during sprinting. J. Physiol. 354:33P.

Lakomy, H.K.A. (1986). Measurement of work and power output using friction-loaded cycle ergometers. Ergonomics 29:509-517.

Lowry, D.H. and Passoneau, J.V. (1973). A flexible system of enzymatic analysis. New York: Academic Press.

MacDonald, I.A., Wootton, S.A., Muñoz, B., Fentem, P.H. and Williams, C. (1983). Catecholamine response to maximal anaerobic exercise. In Biochemistry of Exercise (edited by H.G. Knuttgen, J.A. Vogel and J. Poortmans), pp. 749-754. Champaign, IL: Human Kinetic Publishers, Inc.

McGilvery, R.W. (1975). The use of fuels for muscular work. In Metabolic adaptation to prolonged physical exercise (edited by H. Howald and J.R. Poortmans), pp. 12-31. Basel: Birkhauser, Verlag.

Margaria, R., Olivia, R.D., DiPrampero, P.E. and Cerretelli, P. (1969). Energy utilization in intermittent exercise of supramaximal intensity. J. Appl. Physiol. 26:752-756.

Maughan, R.J. (1982). A simple rapid method for the determination of glucose, lactate, pyruvate, alanine, β-hydroxybutyrate and acetoacetate on a single 20μℓ blood sample. Clinica Chimica Acta 122:231-240.

Näveri, H., Kuoppasalmi, K. and Härkönen, M.. (1985). Plasma glucagon and catecholamines during exhaustive short-term exercise. European J. Appl. Physiol. 53:308-311.

Newsholme, E.A. and Start, C. (1973). Regulation in Metabolism. Chichester: John Wiley & Sons.

Parkhouse, W.S. and McKenzie, D.C. (1984). Possible contribution of skeletal muscle buffers to enhanced anaerobic performance: a brief review. Medicine and Science in Sports and Exercise 16:328-338.

Sahlin, K. (1978). Intracellular pH and energy metabolism in skeletal muscle of man. Acta Physiologica Scandinavica supplementum 455.

Sahlin, K., Alvestrand, A., Brandt, R. and Hultman, E. (1978a). Intracellular pH and bicarbonate concentration in human muscle during recovery from exercise. J. Appl. Physiol. 45:474-480.

Sahlin, K., Harris, R.C. and Hultman, E. (1975). Creatine kinase equilibrium and lactate content compared with muscle pH in tissue samples obtained after isometric exercise. Biochemical Journal 152:173-180.

Sahlin, K., Harris, R.C., Nylind, B. and Hultman E. (1976). Lactate content and pH in muscle samples obtained after dynamic exercise. Pflügers Archiv 367:143-149.

Sahlin, K. and Henriksson, J. (1984). Buffer capacity and lactate accumulation in skeletal muscle of trained and untrained men. Acta Physiologica Scandinavica 122:331-339.

Sahlin, K., Palmskog, G. and Hultman, E. (1978b). Adenine nucleotide and IMP contents of the quadriceps muscle in man after exercise. Pflügers Archiv 374:193-198.

Saltin, B.P., Gollnick, P.D., Eriksson, B.-O. and Piehl, K. (1971). Metabolic and circulatory adjustments at onset of maximal work. In Onset of Exercise (edited by A. Gilbert and P. Guille), pp 63-76. Toulouse: University of Toulouse Press.

Sejersted, O.M., Medbø, J.O., Orheim, A. and Hermansen, L. (1984). Relationship between acid-base status and electrolyte balance after maximal work of short duration. Medicine and Sports Science 17:40-55.

Wilkie, D. (1981). Shortage of chemical fuel as a cause of fatigue: Studies by nuclear magnetic resonance and bicycle ergometry. In Human muscle fatigue: physiological mechanisms (Ciba Foundation Symposium 82) (edited by R. Porter and J. Whelan), pp. 102-114. London: Pitman Medical.

Wootton, S.A. (1984). Influence of diet and training on the metabolic responses to maximal exercise in man. Ph.D. Thesis, Loughborough University of Technology.

Discussion

Dr Spriet, Ontario, Canada
Could you postulate why in your training study that so few of the
glucose molecules could be accounted for in the glycolytic
metabolites relative to the untrained study?

Mr Boobis, Leicester, England
We found a similar situation after the 6 second as opposed to the
30 second sprint. It is certain that there is some aerobic
component to exercise of this nature, despite its intensity, but
the magnitude of its contribution is uncertain. In our most recent
study we have tried to measure oxygen utilisation during this type
of exercise test but we have not yet worked out the results. After
training, therefore, lactate may have been 'lost' from the muscle
by aerobic metabolism with the result that we are underestimating
both the rates of glycolysis and ATP turnover.

Dr Jacobs, Ontario, Canada
The values you report for resting ATP and PCr concentrations are
relatively high compared to what is usually reported. Why?

Mr Boobis
As our total creatine concentrations are similar to those reported
by other authors, we feel that the values that we have measured are
true values. We take great care to ensure that our freeze dried
muscle powder is as free from all blood and connective tissue as
possible. In addition all assays are carried out on fat free
muscle, fat being extracted from the muscle powder by ether which
has the additional benefit of allowing the removal of any blood
admixed with the powder, as blood remains in suspension after
mixing much longer than the particles of muscle, allowing it to be
discarded with the ether. This is combined with a 'snap-freezing'
technique wherein the time from taking the biopsy to its immersion
in liquid nitrogen is in the order of 500 milliseconds.

Dr Jacobs
In the training study you reported, the resting glycogen levels
were higher after training than before training. Since glycogen
concentration before exercise is directly related to subsequent
glycogen utilisation, perhaps the increased rate of glycogenolysis
and increased lactate accumulation after training were a function
of the higher pre-exercise glycogen levels and not a direct
function of the training.
    In addition, how can you be certain that the improved
performance is not a function of an enhanced aerobic contribution
to exercise, in contrast to an increased anaerobic energy
metabolism?

Mr Boobis
We fully accept that our increased rate of glycogenolysis with
training may have been, in part at least, related to the higher

resting muscle glycogen. However while there is evidence to support the importance of the initial concentation of glycogen in determining its eventual utilisation, I am unaware of any work that shows that the rates of glycolysis and lactate accumulation are similarly dependent. It would be nice, though, to think that we could all improve our maximal anaerobic capacity by 'simple glycogen loading'!

In affirming my reply to Dr Spriet's question, we have already accepted that there is an unknown contribution from aerobic metabolism in this type of exercise. However, in our most recent study we have been able to demonstrate both an increase in power output and in glycolytic ATP turnover with training using our treadmill sprint exercise test. It would appear therefore that the improved performance with training is associated with some enhanced anaerobic metabolism.

Dr R. Maughan, Aberdeen, Scotland

Your results indicate they glycogen utilisation is 50% higher in the trained that the untrained condition without any apparent increase in lactate or glycolytic intermediates.

Do you have any idea where this glycogen is going to?

Is the increased capillarity observed after training likely to increase lactate clearance from muscle?

Mr Boobis

Although glycogen utilisation was 50% higher after training based on changes in glycogen concentration, calculated glycolytic activity was in fact only 12.5% higher. This was associated with a 34% increase in HMP (a 25% increase in G6P, a 68% increase in F6P and a 100% increase in G1P) over the pre-training post-exercise values and in addition lactate increased 7%. Despite this we could only account for 74% of the glycolytic intermediates after training compared with 94% before. In addition to any contribution from aerobic metabolism to account for these 'lost' glucosyl units it is possible that there was an improved lactate clearance from the muscle in keeping with an increased capillarity. However the finding that blood lactate levels were unchanged with training does not support this (although it does not actually preclude it, as I am sure Professor Brooks will agree).

Dr Frederick, New Hampshire, USA

You stated 'for measurement of mean power output' that you 'integrated the area under the power output curve'. Is this correct?

Mr Boobis

I meant to say 'calculated the area under the curve'.

Dr Frederick

In your graph of power output against total ATP turnover you expressed power output per kilogram leg muscle. How did you calculate leg muscle content?

Mr Boobis

Lean leg volume was determined by anthropometric techniques as described by Jones and Pearson, (1969) (J. Physiol. Lond. 204:63-64P). Dr Jones validated this method by comparing it to radiographic determination of lean leg volume and leg muscle volume (Jones P.R.M. (1969) J. Physiol. Lond. 207:1-3P).

Lactate production during exercise: oxidizable substrate versus fatigue agent

G.A. BROOKS

Recent studies utilizing isotopic tracer techniques have
demonstrated that during sustained exercise lactate provides a
major source of oxidizable substrate. As part of the 'Lactate
Shuttle' mechanism, lactate formed in active muscle cells
undergoing high rates of glycogenolysis and glycolysis can enter the
interstitium and vasculature and reach tissues with high capacities
for cellular respiration. During exercise, lactate represents a fuel
source which is quantitatively more important than blood glucose.
At intensities ranging from 40-75% of $\dot{V}O_2$max, 70-90% of lactate
formed is oxidized, while only approximately 15% undergoes
gluconeogenesis. Approximately half the lactate is removed by
oxidation within active muscle tissue, either immediately or on
reperfusion. Heart and inactive skeletal muscle account for the
remainder of lactate removal by oxidation. For each subject,
however, there can occur an exercise intensity where the mechanisms
of lactate removal cannot keep pace with the mechanisms of lactate
production. Increased capacity for lactate clearance in trained
individuals prevents, or minimizes lactate accumulation and lactic
acidosis during high exercise power outputs. There is very good
evidence that muscle lactic acidosis which causes intramuscular pH
to decline to approximately 6.4 will interfere with excitation-
contraction coupling and lead to muscle fatigue in very strenuous
exercise.

1. Statement of problems and historical context

The great physiologists and biochemists who studied muscle
energetics and chemistry during an earlier part of this century
(Bang, 1936; Hill and Lupton, 1923; Margaria, et al., 1933;
Meyerhof, 1920; Smith, 1922) recognized that exercise was supported
by both oxidative (aerobic) and nonoxidative (anaerobic)
mechanisms. Although the precise pathways, constituents, and
control mechanisms were then unknown, these earlier workers framed
much of what we know about the energetics of locomotion and were
able to define many of the problems to which we seek solutions
today.

The engenderer scientists realized that during sustained submaximal intensity exercise (i.e. steady-state exercise) the
immediate energy requirements could be met by oxidative mechanisms
of energy transduction. However, maximal exercise efforts resulted

in large accumulations of lactic acid which were removed during the post-exercise period. Consequently, it was recognized that non-oxidative energy mechanisms were activated during exercise and that evaluation of the disturbances to homeostasis elicited by exercise required consideration of the post-exercise recovery period.

Because of the research published during the first third of this century, several impressions about lactic acid appearance and O_2 supply, lactate removal during exercise and recovery, and lactate as a cause of muscle fatigue have become prevalent. Some of these are that:

(1) lactic acid formation in muscle is the result of O_2 limited metabolism;
(2) during sustained submaximal exercise, lactic acid is formed only during the initial, 'O_2 deficit' period, prior to the attainment of a steady rate of O_2 consumption;
(3) lactate removal is accomplished only during the post-exercise, 'O_2 debt' period; and,
(4) lactic acid accumulation leads to fatigue.

Today, we know some things about metabolism and its regulation that the engenderer scientists could not because of the advent of isotope tracer, nuclear magnetic resonance (NMR), muscle biopsy, and other techniques. For instance, we recognize that lactic acid is formed continuously, during rest as well as sub-maximal exercise. Additionally, lactic acid is formed in contracting muscles under fully aerobic conditions. Further, lactic acid is an indirect product of carbohydrate digestion and is a means of shuttling oxidizable substrate and gluconeogenic and glycogenic precursors between cells, tissues and organs.

Before proceeding, it must be mentioned that for the first part of this discussion, the terms lactic acid and lactate will be used interchangeably. Later on, we will need to distinguish between them.

2. Renewed appreciation of lactic acid metabolism during rest

During the 1930s the Coris recognized that lactate released into the blood as the result of epinephrine-stimulated muscle glycogenolysis could support hepatic glycogen synthesis (Cori, 1931). Thus, lactate became recognized as a major glycogenic and gluconeogenic precursor, and the 'Cori Cycle' was established as an important means by which blood glucose homeostasis is achieved. In the contemporary literature, McGarry and associates (Katz and McGarry, 1984; Foster, 1984; Newgard, et al., 1983) have again demonstrated the importance of lactate as a precursor for hepatic glycogenolysis. In studies on a variety of systems in vitro and in vivo, McGarry and associates have observed that lactate can be a far more effective precursor to hepatic glycogen synthesis than is glucose. According to them, in rats refed after fasting, much of the glucose from dietary carbohydrate bypasses the liver and reaches peripheral tissues (assumed to be muscle). In the periphery, glucose if first cleaved to lactate then released into the venous circulation. [We shall return to this point later.]

Arterial lactate then becomes the precursor for liver glycogen synthesis. Because liver glycogen is paradoxically formed from systemic lactate, rather then portal glucose, the process is referred to as the 'Glucose Paradox'. In the paradox paradigm, lactate is an indirect product of carbohydrate digestion and an essential intermediate in liver glycogen synthesis.

Under circumstances of both fasting and glucagon stimulation Davis, et al. (1985) have observed significant hepatic lactate release in dogs. The presence of an extrahepatic site, or sites, of lactate catabolism are indicated because the levels of lactate in arterial blood were consistently lower than those in the hapatic vein.

2.1 Oxidation as the major means of lactate catabolism
The rates of lactate turnover (Rt) and oxidation (Rox) have been studied in resting rats (Brooks and Donovan, 1983; Freminet, et al., 1974; White and Brooks, 1981), dogs (Depocas, et al., 1969; Eldridge, 1975; Issekutz, et al., 1976), and humans (Kreisberg, et al., 1970; Mazzeo, et al., 1986; Stanley, et al., 1985, 1986; Searle and Cavalieri, 1972). As reviewed recently (Brooks, 1985, 1986) each of the studies which has reported on lactate oxidation in resting mammals has demonstrated active lactate turnover, with approximately 50% removed through oxidation. Further, under resting, post-absorptive conditions, the quantity of lactate oxidized represents approximately 50% of the total CHO combusted (Brooks, 1985b). This latter estimate is based on a comparison of the lactate Rox and the total CHO oxidation as determined from the carbon dioxide production ($\dot{V}CO_2$) and the respiratory exchange ratio. Clearly, even under resting conditions when, compared to exercise, lactate production is relatively low, lactate oxidation makes a meaningful contribution to the total supply of oxidizable substrate. As recognized in the Cori Cycle and Glucose Paradox, lactate fills an important role as a gluconeogenic and glycogenic precursor in liver. However, as recognized in the Lactate Shuttle, lactate is equally important, or perhaps more important, as an oxidizable substrate. As we will see this is especially true during sustained exercise, when rates of lactate turnover (Rt), and oxidation (Rox), and fractional removal through oxidation are elevated compared to rest.

3. Lactic acid formation during sustained exercise

Lactate turnover has been studied during sustained, sub-maximal exercise in rats (Donovan and Brooks, 1983), dogs (Depocas, et al., 1969; Issekutz, et al., 1976, 1984) and humans (Mazzeo, et al., 1986; Stanley, et al., 1985, 1986). Every study which has determined lactate turnover during exercise has reported direct relationships between lactate turnover and metabolic rate as given by the rate of oxygen consumption ($\dot{V}O_2$). Those studies which have determined lactate oxidation rate during exercise have reported also that the rate of lactate oxidation is also related to $\dot{V}O_2$, and, further, that the relative removal through oxidation increased during exercise. Perhaps most revealing in these studies of metabolite kinetics during exercise is that lactate turnover and oxidation (Donovan and Brooks, 1983) exceed glucose turnover and oxidation (Brooks and Donovan, 1983; Brooks, 1985).

In Fig.1 data are reported on 6 males studied at rest and during continuous exercise at 50 and 75% of $\dot{V}O_2$max. At rest, approximately 50% of the lactate disposal (turnover) was removed by direct oxidation. During exercise at 50% of $\dot{V}O_2$max, lactate turnover and oxidation increased compared to rest but the relative removal through oxidation increased to approximately 90%.

Under conditions of sustained moderate intensity exercise, arterial lactate levels may increase slightly, remain the same, or decrease compared to rest (Issekutz, et al., 1976; Stanley, et al., 1985). During exercise for a given blood lactate level, the rate of lactate production may exceed that during rest by 3 to 5 fold (Issekutz, et al., 1976). This is due to the fact that the lactate metabolic clearance rate (MCR=Rt/[lact]) increases tremendously in the transition from rest to exercise. Consequently, it is impossible to derive lactate production rates during exercise from measurements of blood lactate levels.

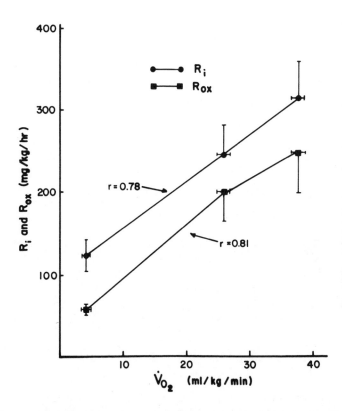

Figure 1. Lactate irreversible disposal (turnover measured with carbon labelled tracer) in six males during rest, easy (50% $\dot{V}O_2$max), and hard (75% $\dot{V}O_2$max) exercise studied with bolus injections of [1-^{13}C]lactate. Reproduced with permission, Mazzeo, et al. (1986).

3.1 Effect of training on lactate production

At present it is not possible to make a definitive statement on the
effect of training on lactate production because lactate kinetics
have not been studied in humans before and after training. The
single published study available is that of Donovan and Brooks
(1983) who utilized primed-continuous infusions of $[U-^{14}C]$ lactate
in trained and untrained rats during rest and two intensities of
sustained exercise. The results (Fig.2) indicate no significant
differences in blood lactate turnover between the trained and
untrained animals. However, during the harder exercise bouts,
arterial blood lactate levels were 4.62±0.57 mM in untrained rats,

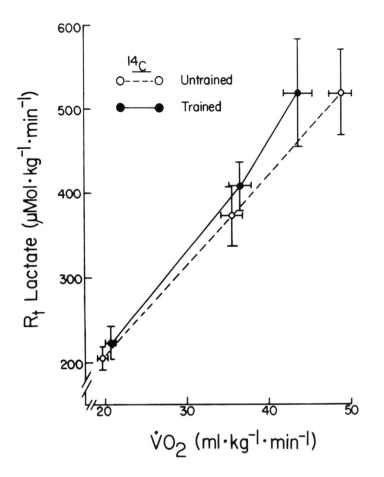

Figure 2. Lactate turnover rate based on continuous infusions of
$[U-^{14}C]$lactate in trained and untrained rats at rest and during two
intensities of exercise. Turnover values plotted as a function of
the metabolic rate ($\dot{V}O_2$). There were no significant
differences between trained and untrained rats at any work load.
Reproduced with permission, Donovan and Brooks (1983).

whereas in trained animals levels were only 2.66±0.38 mM. Due to the lack of difference in turnover rates, but with large differences in arterial concentrations, Donovan and Brooks concluded that the major effect of training was on lactate metabolic clearance rate (MCR=Rt/[lactate]), not production.

Although a definitive study on the effects of training on lactate kinetics in humans has yet to be done, Stanley, et al. (1985) have observed very tight relationships between lactate appearance rates (Ra) and metabolic rate ($\dot{V}O_2$) during exercise, but wide differences in lactate MCR. These differences appeared to be related to the level of fitness in the subjects, with the most fit subjects having greater MCRs than those who were less fit. In Fig. 3 the relationship between lactate disappearance rate (Rd) and blood lactate level is given for the most, and least fit subjects.

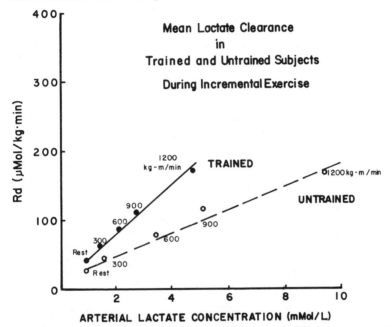

Figure 3. Rate of blood lactate disappearance (Rd) as a function of arterial blood level in trained and untrained males studied using primed-continuous infusions of [1-^{14}C]lactate during continuous progressive intensity exercise. The slope of the line is the metabolic clearance rate (MCR) and it is clearly greater in the trained subject. Modified from Stanley, et al., (1985).

3.2 Skeletal muscle as the major site of lactate removal
      during exercise
Both contracting and inactive skeletal muscle beds extract lactate from the arterial circulation (Stanley, et al., 1986). Perhaps the first observation that this might be the case was the report of Stainsby and Welch (1966) on dog muscle contracting in situ. Initially, after the onset of electrically stimulated contractions, the gastrocnemius muscles released lactate on a net basis.

Subsequently, continued contractions resulted in a net uptake of lactate from the arterial circulation.

That contracting human skeletal muscle is capable of simultaneous lactate extraction and release was demonstrated by Jorfeldt (1970). In those experiments $[U-^{14}C]$ lactate was infused into the brachial artery and venous blood was collected. The results indicated that a significant portion of the tracer dose was taken up and combusted to CO_2 within the contracting skeletal muscle. Most recently, Stanley, et al., (1986) measured tracer and cold lactate exchange across active (leg) and inactive (arm) muscle beds during supine cycling exercise. During rest, both arm and leg muscle beds released lactate on net basis. However, significant tracer uptake by active muscles was observed during exercise while there occurred a net release of lactate. In contrast, during exercise when arterial lactate levels were elevated, the arm muscles took up lactate (Fig. 4).

On the basis of the results of Stanley, et al., (1986) it can be estimated that during cycling exercise, the legs account for approximately 50% of the lactate removal, while the heart, liver, and inactive muscles each account for approximately 15% of the total removal.

3.3 Muscle lactate production under fully aerobic conditions
Fairly recently, Connett et al. (1984) studied lactate accumulation in dog gracilis muscles contracting in situ. In these muscle preparations which contain 100% oxidative fibers, Connett et al. (1984) always observed significant lactate accumulation even if muscle blood flow was increased by administration of the vasodilator adenosine. Further, myoglobin cryomicroscopy determinations of muscle pO_2 failed to reveal the presence of anoxic areas. These workers concluded that lactate production occurs in fully aerobic working muscle.

4. The lactate shuttle hypothesis

It is possible to form a new hypothesis (the 'Lactate Shuttle') about the role of lactate in the overall distribution of oxidizable substrate during rest and exercise based on the observations reported above. According to the lactate shuttle hypothesis (Brooks, 1985, 1986), the formation and distribution of fuel in the form of lactate provides a central means by which the coordination of intermediary metabolism in diverse tissues and different cells within the tissues is accomplished. Lactate formed in some muscle cells with high rates of glycogenolysis and glycolysis becomes an energy source not only in adjacent cells with high cellular respiratory rates, but also in anatomicaly distributed tissues with high respiratory rates [e.g. heart (Gertz, et al., 1981), and inactive skeletal muscle (Stanley, et al., 1986)]. The production and release of lactate also provide for distribution of the major gluconeogenic precursor.

Recognition of the above observations is the key to the lactate shuttle hypothesis and provides a basis upon which to answer three of the four questions of classic interest identified above.

(1) Lactic acid can be formed under fully aerobic conditions [e.g., at rest as an indirect product of digestion in the Glucose Paradox] or as part of the Cori cycle mechanism.

(2) Lactic acid is actively and continuously formed during sustained, sub-maximal exercise.

(3) Lactic acid formed during exercise can be removed during exercise. In fact, even during steady-state exercise bouts of sufficient intensity to elevate blood lactate levels several-fold compared to rest, almost all of the lactate formed will be removed by direct oxidation and the lactate shuttle mechanism during the exercise itself. In recovery then, only a small amount of the lactate formed remains to be removed. As during exercise, most of the lactate removed during recovery is oxidized (Brooks, et al., 1973; Brooks and Gaesser, 1980).

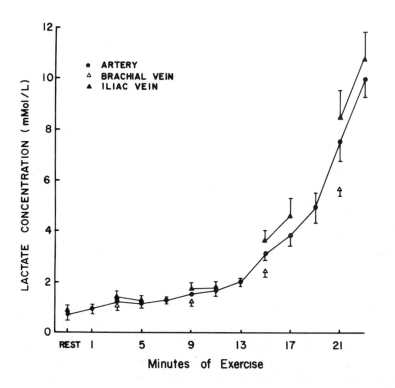

Figure 4. Lactate levels in arterial, iliac venous, and brachial venous blood as a function of time in 6 males during rest and continuous progressive intensity supine leg cycling. During rest, venous blood lactate levels are higher than arterial, indicating net lactate release from leg and arm muscle beds. However, during exercise there occurs an increase in net release from the legs (iliac vein while the arms switch to a net extraction of lactate as indicated by lower levels of lactate in brachial vein than in arterial blood. Reproduced with permission, Stanley, et al. (1986).

5. Lactic acid accumulation and fatigue

Our fourth question of discussion, the issue of lactate as a fatigue agent, is unfortunately little helped by isotope tracer techniques for they require the presence of a steady, or near steady state. Such exercise tasks do not lead to enormous lactic acid accumulations or decrements in tissue pH, as encountered with maximal exercise bouts. Therefore, other measurement strategies, such as muscle biopsy and NMR spectroscopy, are required. Before proceeding to those arguments, several preliminary items need to be reviewed.

The lactic acid theory of muscle fatigue originated at a time when lactic acid was thought to be involved in the excitation-contraction coupling process in muscle (Fletcher and Hopkins, 1907). The removal of lactic acid was thought to be essential for muscle relaxation to occur. The use of iodoacetic acid by Lundsgaard (1934) to block glycolysis revealed that muscles could contract and become fatigued without formation and accumulation of lactic acid. Since then, the occurrences of muscle fatigue and lactate accumulation have been disassociated in diverse circumstances. These include fatigue during hyperthermia, and prolonged exercise leading to dehydration, glycogen depletion, and hypoglycemia (Brooks and Fahey, 1984). Therefore, our discussion is not that lactic acid accumulation is universally the cause of fatigue, but rather that it can be one of the causes of fatigue.

At this point we need also to distinguish among the components of lactic acid dissociation. Because of the low pK of lactic acid, at physiological pHs it will be almost completely dissociated. Therefore, it is the resulting hydrogen ion (H^+) and its effect on pH, rather than the lactate anion, which is considered to be detrimental to muscular function.

During maximal exercise exertion, there occurs a metabolic acidosis which is due to lactate accumulation. Sahlin, et al., (1976, 1978) have demonstrated that both during exercise and recovery, muscle biopsy pH is well correlated with lactate content. During exercise as well as at rest, the concentration of lactate in muscle is higher than in blood (Diamant, et al., 1968; Sacks and Sacks, 1937; Stanley, et al., 1986). Consequently, when exercise stops, lactate levels in the blood rise due to an efflux from the muscles (Bang, 1936; Hermansen and Osnes, 1972). These results suggest an intramuscular compartmentation of lactate which appears to enter blood by a mechanism of facilitated transport (Deuticke, et al., 1982). Symport, antiport, and non-ionic exchange mechanisms have been proposed.

Perhaps the strongest indication that intra-muscular rather than blood lactate accumulation imposes a greater impediment to the performance during maximal work is the report of Hermansen and Osnes (1972). In their experiment, the authors measured arterialized (capillary) and muscle biopsy pH during exhausting continuous and intermittent exercise. By means of maximal intermittent exercise bouts of 40-60 secs duration with 5 mins rest periods, Hermansen and Osnes were able to cause blood pH levels to decline to 6.94 which were significantly less than 7.11 achieved

after a single 2 mins bout of exhausting exercise. After both
continuous and intermittent exercise, however, muscle pH
declined to the same level, 6.40. These results seem to indicate
that low muscle pH, rather than blood pH, is a limiting factor
during maximal exercise of short duration.

In recent years there has been considerable interest in
improving exercise performance through oral administration of
bicarbonates and several groups of investigators have reported
these to be beneficial (Jones, et al., 1977; Mainwood, et al.,
1972). That administration of bicarbonate (a weak buffer) would
improve performance whereas Tris (a very effective buffer) would
not improve performance (Kinderman, et al., 1977) might be related
to the mechanism of lactate exchange. The efflux of muscle lactate
might be accomplished through a facilitated exchange of muscle cell
lactic acid for plasma sodium bicarbonate.

6. Low intramuscular pH and fatigue

Two debilitating effects of low pH on muscle function have been
proposed. These are: 1. inhibition of the rate limiting enzyme of
glycolysis, phosphofructokinase (PFK) (Danforth, 1965), and
2. inhibition of excitation-contraction coupling through
interference of protons with Ca^{++} binding to troponin (Fuchs et
al., 1970), or interference with the Ca^{++} - ATPase of
sarcoplasmic reticulum (Fabiato and Fabiato, 1978; Sahlin, et al.,
1981). Additionally, the effects of decreased pH on feelings of
well-being and other psychological parameters.

6.1 Inhibition of muscle PFK
It has been recognized that muscle PFK (EC2.7.1.11) is inhibited
in vitro at pH values which would be low for muscle pH in
vivo. Consequently it has been suggested that the cessation of
glycolysis through inhibition of its rate limiting enzyme is a
cause of muscle fatigue. For several reasons, however, this
explanation has been less than satisfying. Sometimes, the best
sprint performances were associated with the highest lactate
levels, and not vice-versa (Ohkuwa and Miyamura, 1984).
Moreover, from the perspective of the comparative physiologist, the
argument that glycolysis can be limited by the accumulation of one
of its products was not compelling. In freely swimming tuna, blood
lactates in the range of 20-30 mM are usual and do not appear to
limit these animals from performing either extensive migrations or
remarkable sprints (Webber, et al., 1986).

Very recently Dobson, et al. (1986) showed very nicely that the
inhibitory effect of low pH on PFK could be almost completely
abolished by the presence of a very small amount (10 μM of
fructose 2,6-bisphosphate (F 2,6-P_2). Thus, these authors
concluded, PFK could adequately supply muscle with glycolytic
substrate as pH falls during contraction. For the present,
therefore, we are advised to concentrate on another mechanism of
muscle fatigue induced by lactic acidosis.

6.2 Interference with excitation-contraction coupling

The mass of evidence is that muscle lactic acid accumulation and low pH during maximal exercise bouts can lead to fatigue. With the recent results of Dobson, et al. in the modulation of muscle PFK by $F_{+}2,6-P_2$, interference of excitation-contraction coupling by H^+ accumulation emerges as a candidate for the cause of muscle fatigue under these circumstances. As noted above, there is very good evidence to suspect interference with excitation-contraction coupling by protons as a cause of muscle fatigue during maximal exercise.

7. Conclusion

We have seen that the production and removal of lactic acid is one of the major metabolic strategies for supplying oxidizable and glyconeogenic substrates in the animal kingdom. Separate hypotheses of a 'Glucose Paradox' (Foster, 1984) and a 'Lactate Shuttle' (Brooks, 1985) may, in fact, represent descriptions of the role of lactate under conditions of rest and exercise, respectively. However, as is often the case, too much of a good thing may be deleterious. In the case of extremely difficult exercise tasks, the failure to remove lactic acid at a rate comparable to the production rate may lead to the cessation of exercise. A review of some of the pertinent literature seems to indicate that the fall of intramuscular pH to levels of 6.4 can interfere with excitation-contraction coupling. Some of the adaptations to endurance training seem to be aimed at reducing lactate accumulation through decreased production (Holloszy and Coyle, 1984), increased clearance (Donovan and Brooks, 1983), and increased intramuscular buffering capacity (Parkhouse and McKenzie, 1984).

References

Bang, O. (1936). The lactate content of the blood during and after muscular exercise in man. Scand. Arch. Physiol. 74 (suppl.10):49-82.

Brooks, G.A. (1985). Lactate: Glycolytic end product and oxidative substrate during exercise in mammals - 'The lactate shuttle'. In, Comparative Physiology and Biochemistry-Current Topics and Trends, Volume A. 'Respiration - Metabolism - Circulation,' (edited by R. Gilles), pp. 208-218. Springer-Verlag: Berlin.

Brooks, G.A. (1985). 'Anaerobic threshold': Review of the concept and directions for future research. Med. Sci. Sports Exercise 17:22-31.

Brooks, G.A. (1986). The lactate shuttle during exercise and recovery. Med. Sci. Sports Exercise.

Brooks, G.A., Brauner, K.E. and Cassens, R.G. (1973). Glycogen synthesis and metabolism of lactic acid after exercise. Am. J. Physiol. 224:1162-1166.

Brooks, G.A., and Donovan, C.M. (1983). Effect of endurance training on glucose kinetics during exercise. Am. J. Physiol. (Endocrinol. Metab. 7), E505-E512.

Brooks, G.A. and Fahey, T.D. (1984). Exercise Physiology: Human
Bioenergetics and its Applications. Macmillan, Publishers:
New York.

Brooks, G.A. and Gaesser, G.A. (1980). End points of lactate and
glucose metabolism after exhausting exercise. J. Appl. Physiol:
Respirat. Environ. Exercise Physiol. 49:1057-1069.

Connett, R.J., Gaueski, T.E.J. and Honig, G.R. (1984). Lactate
accumulation in fully aerobic, working dog gracilis muscle.
Am. J. Physiol. 246:H120-H128.

Cori, C.F. (1931). Mammalian carbohydrate metabolism. Physiol.
Rev. 11:143-275.

Danforth, W.H. (1965). Activation of glycolytic pathway in muscle.
In Control of Energy Metabolism (edited by B. Chance and R.W.
Estabrook), pp. 287-297. Academic Press: New York.

Davis, M.A., Williams, P.E. and Cherrington, A.D. (1985). Effect
of glucagon on hepatic lactate metabolism in the conscious dog.
Am. J. Physiol. 248 (Endocrinol. Metab. 11):E463-E470.

Depocas, R., Minaire, Y. and Chatonnet, J. (1969). Rates of
formation and oxidation of lactic acid in dogs at rest and
during moderate exercise. Can. J. Physiol. Pharmacol.
47:603-610.

Deuticke, B., Beyer, E. and Forst, B. (1982). Discrimination of
three parallel pathways of lactate in human erythrocyte
membranes by inhibitors and kinetic properties. Biochem.
Biophys. Acta. 6894:96-110.

Diamant, B., Karlsson, J. and Saltin, B. (1968). Muscle tissue
lactate after maximal exercise in man. Acta. Physiol. Scand.
72:383-384.

Dobson, G.P., Yamamoto, E. and Hochachka, P.W. (1986).
Phosphofuncto-kinase control in muscle: Nature and reversal of
pH-dependent ATP inhibition. Am. J. Physiol. 250 (Regulatory
Integrative Comp. Physiol. 19):R71-R76.

Donovan, C.M. and Brooks, C.M. (1983). Training affects lactate
clearance, not lactate production. Am. J. Physiol.
244(Endocrinol. Metab. 7):E83-E92.

Eldridge, F.L. (1975). Relationship between turnover and blood
concentration of lactate in exercising dogs. J. Appl. Physiol.
d39:231-234.

Fabiato, A. and Fabiato, F. (1978). Effects of pH on the
myofilaments and the sarcoplasmic reticulum of skinned cells
from cardiac and skeletal muscles. J. Physiol. London.
276:233-255.

Fletcher, W.M. and Hopkins, F.G. (1907). Lactic acid in amphibian
muscle. J. Physiol. 35:247-309.

Foster, D.W. (1984). From glycogen to ketones - and back.
Diabetes. 33:1188-1199.

Freminet, A., Bursaux, E. and Poyart, C.F. (1974). Effect of
elevated lactataemia in the rates of lactate turnover and
oxidation in rats. Pflügers Arch. 346:75-86.

Fuchs, F., Reddy, V. and Briggs, F.N. (1970). The interaction of
cations with the calcium-binding site of troponin. Biochim.
Biophys. Acta. 221:407-409.

Gertz, E.W., Wisneski, J.A., Neese, R., Bristow, J.D., Searle, G.L. and Hanlon, J.T. (1981). Myocardial lactate metabolism: evidence of lactate release during net chemical extraction in man. Circulation:1273-1279.

Hermansen, L. and Osnes J.B. (1972). Blood and muscle pH after maximal exercise in man. J. Appl. Physiol. 32:304-308.

Hill, A.V. and Lupton, H. (1923). Muscular exercise, lactic acid and the supply and utilization of oxygen. Quart. J. Med. 16:135-171.

Holloszy, J.V. and Coyle, E.F. (1984). Adaptations of skeletal muscle to endurance exercise and their metabolic consequences. J. Appl. Physiol. 56:831-838.

Issekutz, B., Shaw, W.A.S. and Issekutz, A.C. (1976). Lactate metabolism in resting and exercising dogs. J. Appl. Physiol. 40:312-319.

Issekutz, B. (1984). Effect of B-adrenergic blockade on lactate turnover in exercising dogs. J. Appl. Physiol. 57:1754-1759.

Jones, N.L., Sutton, J.R., Taylor, R. and Toews, C.J. (1977). Effect of pH on cardiorespiratory and metabolic responses to exercise. J. Appl. Physiol. 43:959-964.

Jorfeldt, L. (1970). Metabolism of L(+)-lactate in human skeletal muscle during exercise. Acta. Physiol. Scand. Suppl. 338.

Katz, J. and McGarry, J.D. (1984). The glucose paradox: is glucose a substrate for liver metabolism? J. Clin. Invest. 74:1901-1909, 1984.

Kinderman, W., Keul, J., and Haber, G. (1977). Physical exercise after induced alkalosis (Bicarbonate of Tris-buffer). Europ, J. Appl. Physiol. 37:197-204.

Kreisberg, R.A., Pennington, L.F., and Boshell, B.R. (1970). Lactate turnover and gluconeogenesis in normal and obese humans. Diabetes. 19:53-63.

Lundsgaard, E. (1934). Phosphageund pyrophosphatumsatz in Eidoessigsaurevergiften Muskeln. Biochem. 2. 269:308-328.

Mainwood, G.W., and Lucier, G.E. (1972). Fatigue and recovery in isolated frog sartorius muscles: The effects of bicarbonate concentration and associated potassium loss. Can. J. Physiol. Pharmacol. 50:132-142.

Margaria, R., Edwards, H.T., Dill, D.B. (1933). Possible mechanisms of contracting and paying oxygen debt and the role of lactic acid in muscular contraction. Amer. J. Physiol. 106:689-715.

Mazzeo, R.S., Brooks, G.A., Schoeller, D.A., and Budinger, T.F. (1986). Disposal of blood [1-^{13}C]lactate in humans during rest and exercise. J. Appl. Physiol. 60:232-241.

Meyerhof, O. (1920). Die Energie umwandlungeri im Muskel. Uber die Beziehungen der Milchsaure zur Warmebildung und Arbeitsleistung des Muskels in der Anaerobiose. Pflügers Arch. ges. Physiol 182:232-283.

Newgard, C.B., Hirsch, L.J., Foster, D.W., McGarry, J.D. (1983). Studies on the mechanism by which exogenous glucose is converted into liver glycogen in the rat: a direct or indirect pathway. J. Biol. Chem. 258:8046-8052.

Ohkuwa, T., and Miyamura, M. (1984). Peak blood lactate after 400 m sprinting in sprinters and long-distance runners. Jap. J. Physiol. 34:553-556.

Parkhouse, W.S., and McKenzie, D.C. (1984). Possible contribution of skeletal muscle buffers to enhanced anaerobic performance: a brief review. Med. Sci. Sports Exerc. 16:328-338.

Sacks, J., and Sacks, W.C. (1937). Blood and muscle lactic acid in the steady state. Am. J. Physiol. 118:697-702.

Sahlin, K., Harris, R.C., Nylind, B., and Hultman, E. (1976). Lactate content and pH in muscle samples obtained after dynamic exercise. Pflügers Archiv. 367:163-149.

Sahlin, K., Alvestrand, A., Brandt, R., and Hultman, E. (1978). Intracellular pH and bicarbonate concentration in human muscle during recovery from exercise. J. Appl. Physiol. 45:474-480.

Sahlin, K., Edstrom, L., Sjöholm, H., and Hultman, E. (1981). Effects of lactic acid accumulation and ATP decrease on muscle tension and relaxation. Am. J. Physiol. 240(Cell Physiol. (9):C121-C126.

Searle, G.l., and Cavalieri, R.R. (1972). Determination of lactate kinetics in the human. Analysis of data from single injection vs continuous infusion. Proc. Soc. Expl. Biol. and Med. 139:1002-1006.

Smith, H.M. (1922). Gaseous exchange and physiological requirements for level and grade walking. Carnegie Inst. Washington Publ. 309.

Stainsby, W.N., and Welch, H.G. (1966). Lactate metabolism of contracting dog skeletal muscle in situ. Amer. J. Physiol. 211:177-183.

Stanley, W.C., Gertz, E.W., Wisneski, J.A., Morris, D.L., Neese, R.A., and Brooks, G.A. (1985). Systemic lactate kinetics during graded exercise in man. Amer. J. Physiol. 249 (Endocrinol. Metab. 12):E595-E602.

Stanley, W.C., Gertz, E.W., Wisneski, J.A., Neese, R.A., Morris, D.L., and Brooks, G.A. (1986). Lactate extraction during net lactate release by the exercising legs of man. J. Appl. Physiol. 60(4).

Weber, J.-M., Brill, R.W., and Hochachka, P.W. (1986). Mammalian metabolite flux rates in a teleost: lactate and glucose turnover in tuna. Amer. J. Physiol. 250(Regulatory Integrative Comp. Physiol. 19), R452-R458.

White, T.P., and Brooks, G.A. (1981). $[U-^{14}C]$glucose, -alanine, and - leucine oxidation in rats at rest and two intensities of running. Amer. J. Physiol. (Endocrinol. Metabl.) E155-E165

Discussion

Dr Jacobs, Ontario, Canada

How much of the reduced arterial blood lactate and muscle lactate accumulation seen after endurance training is due to reduced lactate production and how much is due to increased rate of disappearance or clearance?

Professor Brooks, California, USA

As you know Donovan and I were unable to demonstrate a decreased lactate production in trained rats during moderate intensity exercise. It was our observation that the large reduction in arterial lactate concentration of trained rats during exercise was due to increased clearance. As for the human condition, unfortunately I cannot as yet answer your question. We have performed only a modest number of trials on humans. However if one compares the most highly trained subjects with the least trained, we again see approximately the same rate of blood lactate appearance in the trained subjects. Again the lower arterial lactate levels in the trained human subjects is largely due to improved clearance. On this basis we believe that the major difference in blood lactate levels in trained humans is due to improved clearance and also perhaps, in part, to a slightly decreased production.

Dr J. Poortmans, Brussels, Belgium
You pointed out that humans may derive during exercise up to 10% of its energy from amino acids. Do you not think this problem is yet to be solved since one has to be more cautious on the influence of stable protein intake for several days?

Professor Brooks
Dr Poortmans' point is well taken that metabolic adaptions to any condition, such as exercise, need to be made against the background of a stable metabolic baseline. In particular, wholebody nitrogen balance studies require this equilibration period. It is well known that amino acid and protein metabolism are affected by a variety of conditions. Some of these include: malnutrition, dietary manipulation, injury, and surgery. During exercise, the situation is complicated because both the intensity and duration of effort likely change the response.

My estimation of up to 10% of energy needs stemming from protein is based on the results obtained from a number of sources. Our work on rats (White and Brooks, Am. J. Physiol. 1981; Henderson et al., Am. J. Physiol., 1985) support the contention that during sustained exercise approximately one percent of the fuel is derived from leucine. Then, depending on how representative leucine (an essential and purely ketogenic amino acid) is of body protein, the total role of protein must be expanded upward from the minimal value of one percent. In this context, an estimate of from 5 to 10% of the energy coming from amino acid and protein derivatives seems appropriate. In the report of Henderson et al., I should point out that the results were obtained using two independent isotopic tracer techniques (i.e., steady-state isotopic dilution, and occupancy).

Isotope tracer studies on humans are in agreement with the work on rats, which shows leucine oxidation to be increased by exercise and training. In particular, the work of C.T.M. Davies, et al. (J. Physiol., 1982), Hagg et al., (Am. J. Physiol., 1982), and Robert Wolfe et al. (Am. J. Physiol., 1982 and 1984) are of note.

In their experiments on humans, Lemon and Mullin (J. Appl. Physiol., 1980) used nitrogen balance measurements to study the interactive effects of exercise and substate availability on protein utilization. Their estimates also support the conclusion that approximately 10% of the fuel utilized during sustained submaximal intensity exercise comes from protein.

PART III ENDURANCE:
A MULTI-DISCIPLINARY PERSPECTIVE

This whole section is concerned with endurance, a term that denotes
prolonged, sustained or repetitive activity. The topic is
addressed from different disciplinary viewpoints - physiology,
biochemistry, biomechanics and orthopaedic medicine. Thus a unique
opportunity was presented of bringing these specialisms together so
that an interdisciplinary perspective on endurance might emerge
from the discussions. In addition this conference of minds allowed
the possibilities for cross-fertilisation between the sciences and
medicine to be highlighted.

Endurance exercise taxes the aerobic power and the aerobic
capacity and so is dependent on the integrity of the oxygen
transport system. The physiological factors that limit the
maximum ability to consume oxygen during strenuous exercise, known
as $\dot{V}O_2$max, has long been a prominent theme in the research of
exercise physiologists. The work of Bengt Saltin has made
enormous contributions to our understanding of these limits and
how it is not possible to single out one factor as limiting. The
conventional line of doctrine, notably from Scandinavian
authorities, was that the upper limit depended on the amount of
oxygen actually offered to the active tissues. The firm
implication was that the limitation was central, the determinant
being the pumping capacity of the heart. An alternative viewpoint
was possible when studies were considered that used one limb as a
control while the other was subjected to a training programme.
Both $\dot{V}O_2$max and peripheral changes were evident only in the trained
limb. The conclusion was that local factors must have hitherto
provided the limitation. The muscle biopsy studies that
demonstrated huge metabolic adaptations to endurance training in
skeletal muscle added to the argument about the relative
importance of central and peripheral factors.

The recent work of Saltin and his Scandinavian colleagues has
demonstrated convincingly how various factors within the
circulatory system can limit $\dot{V}O_2$max, how important it is to
consider the active muscle mass and requirement to maintain blood
pressure in determining the limit. For the future it is envisaged
that ventilatory factors, such as airway resistance and pulmonary
vasculature, may be limiting in some elite athletes with
extraordinarily high values of $\dot{V}O_2$max.

Exercise cannot be sustained for very long at a level corresponding to $\dot{V}O_2$max. Top marathon runners, for example, race at about 75% $\dot{V}O_2$max during their event. The ability to utilise a high fraction of the $\dot{V}O_2$max is therefore important. At this exercise intensity, performance can be limited by the magnitude of the carbohydrate stored within the body before the start of exercise. Recognition of this has led to the practice of specific training and dietary regimes among marathon runners in the week preceding competition. An understanding of the biochemical basis and repercussions of these manipulations can help practitioners in enhancing their race preparations and eschewing detrimental practices.

The metabolic limitations to endurance are evident when we consider the energy stores in the body and how these are used. The application of metabolic logic to endurance sports and the reminders about the relevant biochemical control mechanisms that operate within biological systems are hallmarks of the work of Eric Newsholme at the University of Oxford. The extent and the limitations of biochemical manipulations, the mechanisms involved in subtle changes in the choice of substrate for exercising muscles and the subsequent impact on performance are all pertinent considerations. These are integrated with an interpretation of the biochemical basis of central fatigue, which is linked to changes in the availability of substrate for neurotransmitter substance. Central fatigue is arguably too often neglected when the limits of endurance are considered: here the notion that, though the flesh is willing the spirit may be weak, still applies.

The energy cost of exercising at a given level may be influenced by a host of factors. Besides the choice of fuel as substrate for the muscles, biochemical alterations, dietary and training effects, these include inherent variations, skill and biomechanical elements. Muscular efficiency during prolonged exercise can be important in that a lowered metabolic cost for a given level of power output will reduce the fractional utilisation of $\dot{V}O_2$max and hence the degree of physiological strain. As efficiency is difficult to measure accurately in most sports activities, the simpler concept of 'economy' is frequently adopted. This refers to the energy consumed for a given task performance. There is now a recognition among sports scientists that the economy of running is an important determinant of performance in distance racing and is a consequence of endurance training. Small changes in economy can be crucial where finely honed endurance athletes are concerned, as these can make the difference between failure and success in competition.

The factors which affect the economy of physical activity have been examined in depth by Ned Frederick and co-workers at the Nike Sport Research Laboratory. Their endeavours have been directed towards fundamental experimental work, running economy being a particular focus of attention. Their studies are helping to clarify the extent to which mechanical constraints on the sports performer can be offset. Mechanical ergogenic aids operate by improving the economy of activity. The effects of sports equipment, clothing and shoes are all pertinent ergonomic considerations. Within an ergonomics framework, safety as well as efficiency or effectiveness is an important criterion.

It is at this ergonomics interface that the worlds of
biomechanics and orthopaedic medicine meet. Biomechanicians have
made enormous contributions to the evaluation of injury risk by
the calculations of forces and strain on the human during
different sports activities. Their role in designing and
validating protective equipment has also to be recognised. The
repetitive strain on anatomical structures frequently limits
performance of endurance athletes. Though the effect is mostly
insidious, the point is not lost on the many athletes who break
down in training as a result of adopting programmes that are too
arduous.

The articular structures at risk during strenuous training and
competition are described by David Muckle. His experience in
treating the injured athletes and prescribing preventative
practices is coupled to research work which embraces the study of
meniscal damage and repair as well as use of anti-inflammitant
agents in treatment. Mechanisms of injury differ widely between
sports and this makes generalisations difficult to make. Progress
in the understanding of the mechanisms and the reactions to trauma
may hasten the day when the line between positively beneficial
effects of exercise on the joints and the occupational hazard of
professional sport can be drawn more distinctively.

Collectively the four disciplinary perspectives on endurance
suggest that in striving for excellence, the limits of tolerance
of musculoskeletal structures may be surpassed and injury results.
The adaptations to endurance training can be outlined in
physiological, biochemical and biomechanical terms. The benefits
will be personal, depending on the goals, aspirations and needs of
the individual to realise potential.

Dr Thomas Reilly

Central cardiovascular factors as limits to endurance; with a note on the distinction between maximal oxygen uptake and endurance fitness

G. SAVARD, B. KIENS and B. SALTIN

Through the years the issue of what sets the limit for endurance performance in man has been widely discussed. It has been known for a long time that high values of maximal oxygen uptake are found among successful athletes in endurance events (Saltin and Åstrand, 1967). However, it was soon equally clear that among individuals with similar high aerobic capacities, work output and fatigue could vary considerably (Saltin, 1973; Costill et al., 1971).

This paper will deal with these two problems: what limits maximal oxygen uptake in man and what is its relation to endurance performance.

1. What factors limit maximal oxygen uptake?

Longitudinal studies with training and detraining have revealed a close relationship between changes in the stroke volume of the heart and maximal oxygen uptake (Table 1) suggesting a central haemodynamic limitation of maximal oxygen uptake in man. A similar conclusion was reached by Ekblom and associates (1972, 1976) based on results from studies showing that reinfusion of red cells temporarily increased maximal oxygen uptake, a finding similar to the one observed when oxygen-enriched gas mixtures are inhaled during maximal exercise (Margaria et al., 1961).

This concept was challenged in the early 1970s. Kaijser (1970) was unable to demonstrate an increase in maximal oxygen uptake in subjects breathing air at 10 atmospheres. He concluded that the extra oxygen delivered to the skeletal muscles could not be utilised because of a limitation in the muscle, that is, the capacity of the respiratory chain was saturated. Further work by Holloszy (1967), and later by others (for reference see: Saltin and Gollnick, 1983), confirmed that the mitochondrial enzyme activity of skeletal muscle increased during training. Chronic and enhanced use of muscles for many months results in a 2- to 3-fold increase in mitochondrial enzyme activities, and it was believed by some that this elevation had significant importance for the rate at which oxygen could be utilised by the human body during exercise (Weibel, 1979; Hoppeler et al., 1985).

The strongest support for a peripheral (circulatory and metabolic) limitation was obtained when one-legged training studies revealed that, when exercised, the trained leg could reach a peak oxygen consumption rate that could not be attained when the

untrained leg was used (Saltin et al., 1976; Klausen et al., 1982).
In the trained leg, in contrast to the non-trained leg, capillaries
had proliferated and mitochondrial enzymes had increased (Table 2).

To pinpoint one single factor limiting maximal aerobic power on
a cellular, subcellular, or molecular level can hardly be done
today. The question is, however, whether or not data are available
on an organ level to support the concept that central (lungs -
heart) rather than peripheral (vascular tree, muscle aerobic
potential) factors are limiting.

Table 1. Cardiovascular and pulmonary functional capacities
determined during maximal execise in college students and Olympic
athletes.

	STUDENTS			
	Control	After Bedrest	After Training	Olympic Athletes
Maximal oxygen uptake,$(1.min^{-1})$	3.30	2.43	3.91	5.38
Maximal voluntary ventilation, $(1.min^{-1})$	191	201	197	219
Transfer coefficient for O_2, $(ml.min^{-1})/(mmHg)$:	96	83	86	95
Arterial O_2 capacity, Vol%:	21.9	20.5	20.8	22.4
Maximal cardiac output,$(1.min^{-1})$:	20.0	14.8	22.8	30.4
Stroke volume, ml:	104	74	120	167
Maximal heart rate, beats.min^{-1}):	192	197	190	182
Systemic arteriovenous O_2 difference, Vol%:	16.2	16.5	17.1	18.0

In the past the lungs have been excluded as a limiting factor
for maximal oxygen uptake at sea level as oxygen saturation, with
few exceptions, has always been found to be above 90% during peak
exercise in sedentary subjects as well as in champion endurance
athletes (Åstrand et al., 1964; Ekblom and Hermansen, 1968). Recent
reports however, have convincingly shown that, in some endurance
athletes, desaturation of arterial blood may occur during exercise
at sea level (Dempsey, 1986; Dempsey et al., 1984; Terrados et al.,
1985). This is in part due to a reduced ventilatory drive, but it
is also most likely a demonstration of less adaptability of the
lungs, including its diffusing capacity, to endurance training as
compared to the plasticity of the cardiovascular system or the
skeletal muscles. In untrained man and in most endurance-trained
individuals, however, the maximal capacity of the lung to transfer
oxygen is far from taxed during exhaustive exercise eliciting
maximal oxygen uptake. What is presently lacking to better
elucidate the most likely candidate limiting maximal oxygen uptake
in man is knowledge of the true perfusion capacity of the skeletal
muscle and its capacity to consume oxygen.

To obtain such data an exercise model had to be established in
which the muscle mass performing the contraction was well defined

and the weight of which could be estimated. This was accomplished using the knee-extensors of one leg for the exercise, and measuring flow in the femoral (iliac) vein with a cuff inflated just below the knee (Anderson and Saltin, 1985). In contrast to earlier reports on muscle blood flow and exercise, blood flow in the femoral vein increased linearly with work intensity, reaching values of 6-10 l.min^{-1} in sedentary and trained subjects, at work loads which exhausted the knee-extensors of the exercising limb within 5-6 minutes of work (Fig.1). Oxygen uptake by the knee-extensors also increased linearly with work load and, at exhaustion, was 0.7-1.6 l.min^{-1} depending upon the magnitude of the work load. The muscle perfusion at this point was 200-300 ml.min^{-1} based on a knee-extensor mass of 2-3kg and allowing for the fact that 10% of the observed blood flow may come from parts other than the knee-extensors. This value surpasses all earlier estimates in man by a factor of 2 or more (for reference see: Mellander, 1981).

These data indicate that, if most of the muscle mass of the body was intensely engaged in the exercise, had the same vascular capacity (Table 3), and was maximally perfused, the heart would have to pump 70 l.min^{-1} to maintain blood pressure. Such a high cardiac output has never been reported in man, not even in champion endurance athletes (Ekblom and Hermansen, 1968). Hence, during intense exercise involving a large muscle mass, the muscle vascular beds cannot be maximally pefused: blood pressure control is critical and is achieved in part by some constriction of the arteries feeding the exercising limbs.

Table 2. Adaptive changes in trained versus untrained leg muscles following one-legged training (from Saltin et al., 1976; Klausen et al., 1981, 1982).

		Before	After	Reference
Peak	UT	2.6	2.7	Saltin et al.,1986
oxygen uptake	T	2.7	3.2	-
l.min^{-1}	T	2.8	3.3	Klausen et al., 1981, 82
Capillaries:				
per mm^2	T	4.23	5.16	Klausen et al., 1981, 82
per fibre	T	2.07	2.48	-
Mitochondrial enzymes (Vmax at 37°C; Umol.g^{-1}.min^{-1}):				
Succinate dehydrogenase	T	7.9	10.9	Klausen et al., 1981, 82
Cytochrome oxidase	T	9.7	17.5	-
Succinate dehydrogenase	UT	6.8	6.9	Saltin et al., 1986
	T	6.9	8.8	-

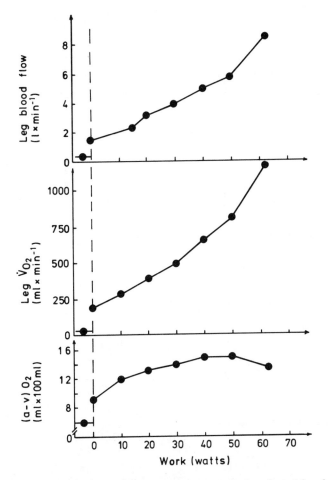

Figure 1. Mean values are presented for leg blood flow, arterio-
femoral venous oxygen difference and leg oxygen uptake.
Experiments were performed at rest, during no-load exercise (note:
the lower part of the leg was lifted with a rate of 60 per min) and
during increasing work intensities. The heaviest work rate
represented maximal work; time to exhaustion was in the range of 3-
6 min. A cuff was placed below the knee and inflated to
approximately 250 mmHg when measurements were performed. Number of
subjects for each data point varies between 2- above 20, with more
than 10 subjects for most points.

   In Table 4 is a summary of muscle O_2 transfer coefficients for
some of the links in the transport of O_2 to the muscle cells and
the capacity of the muscle mitochondria to utilise the oxygen
offered. From these data it is apparent that in sedentary and in
endurance-trained individuals, the capacity of the skeletal
muscles to consume oxygen duirng running or bicycling markedly
surpasses the amount offered by both respiratory and cardiovascular systems.

Table 3. Some variables characterising skeletal muscle of sedentary man. Data are from subjects studied in our laboratory during the last 12 years.

Muscle	Slow Twitch Fibres; %	Capillaries per mm^2	Citrate synthetase $\mu moles.g^{-1}.min^{-1}$
M.Soleus:	89	390	7.6
M.Gastrocnemius:	50	348	8.4
M.Quadriceps femoris,v.l.:	54	338	7.8
M.Trapezius:	48	348	6.8
M.Deltoideus:	52	308	7.9
M.Biceps brachii:	42	374	9.4

Table 4. Upper limits for O_2 transfer coefficients from the lungs to the heart for delivery to and consumption by the muscles in both sedentary and trained individuals.

Upper limit in the lungs to transfer oxygen sedentary and endurance athletes:	$90 - 100 \ ml.kg^{-1}.min^{-1}$
Upper limit by the heart to deliver oxygen sedentary:	$50 - 60 \ ml.kg^{-1}.min^{-1}$
Athletes:	$80 - 100 \ ml.kg^{-1}.min^{-1}$
Upper limit in the muscle to consume oxygen sedentary:	$150 - 200 \ ml.kg^{-1}.min^{-1}$
Athletes:	$200 - 300 \ ml.kg^{-1}.min^{-1}$

2. How large a fraction of the muscle mass is needed
   to elicit maximal oxygen uptake?

It would appear that man moving in the upright posture has adapted to using only a part of his muscle mass for locomotion. The result of this is that his cardiovascular dimensions are scaled to support only a share of the muscles in terms of their perfusion potential during more intense exercise.
   With this in mind, it would be interesting to estimate the mass of muscle, exercising intensely, which can be supplied with its maximal blood flow capacity. Using the present data, it appears that in sedentary man having a maximal cardiac output of 18-22 $l.min^{-1}$, 7-10kg of muscle, actively working, could tax the capacity of the heart. Another way of expressing this would be to

- 166 -

say that 1/4-1/3 of the total muscle mass of a sedentary person can consume 2.5-4.0 l.min^{-1} of oxygen, or the equivalent of the maximal oxygen uptake of a sedentary or somewhat trained person. In accordance with these estimates is the well-known fact that maximal oxygen uptake of a person is achieved in two-legged exercise, and little or no further increase occurs by adding arms to leg exercise (Åstrand and Saltin, 1961b; Hermansen, 1973; Gleser et al., 1974; Bergh et al., 1976; Table 5).

Table 5. Some data in the literature where comparisons have been made between the oxygen uptake achieved in short term exhaustive exercise engaging various combinations of the limbs and body in the exercise (b=bicycling; r=running; s=skiing; sp=use of ski poles). The estimated muscle mass involved in the exercise is very approximate and probably underestimated as muscles of the torso are also usually recruited during the exercise.

Exercise	Muscle Mass kg	Oxygen uptake peak l.min^{-1}	Reference
1-arm (b)	2- 3	1.55	Lewis et al., 1983
1-leg (b)	6- 8	2.34	-
2-legs(b)	12-15	3.12	-
2-arms(b)	5- 7	3.27	Åstrand & Saltin, 1961
2-legs(b)	12-15	4.66	-
2-legs(b)	12-15	4.47	Åstrand & Saltin, 1961
2-legs(r)	12-15	4.69	-
2-legs(b)	12-15	4.76	Åstrand & Saltin, 1961
2-legs + 2-arms(s)	17-22	4.48	-
2-legs(r)	12-15	4.71	Hermansen, 1973
2-legs(r) + 2-arms(sp)	17-22	4.82	-

Results from experiments in man where strenuous arm exercise was superimposed on already heavy leg exercise (Secher et al., 1977) also lend evidence to this view. The increase in cardiac output was not sufficient to meet the increased flow demands of the arms, and the additional flow could be accounted for by a concomitant reduction in leg blood flow. Thus, vasoconstriction in the contracting muscles of the leg occurred in spite of rising interstitial concentrations of metabolic vasodilator substances, for example increased lactate (osmolality) and K^+. That maximal muscle perfusion may be limited by the central circulation is already evident when two-legged exercise is performed. Thus, Klausen et al. (1982) found a decrease in leg blood flow when shifting from one- to two-legged exercise. It is well-known that the sympathetic nervous system plays a major role in regulating this blood flow distribution, and thereby blood pressure homeostasis. This becomes very evident at high rates of oxygen consumption, where, for example, the blood flow reductions to splanchnic (Rowell et al., 1965) and renal (Radigan and Robinson, 1949) vascular beds are directly proportional to the relative work intensity. That this is also the case in working skeletal muscle has recently been suggested by the finding that there is little, if any, sympathetic nervous outflow to the muscle vascular bed if the working muscle mass is kept small (Savard et al., 1985). This is further supported by the result of direct recordings of the sympathetic activity in man, which is not elevated when light arm exercise is performed (Victor, personal communication). In contrast, in intense exercise engaging a large muscle mass it is likely that a large fraction of the elevated plasma noradrenaline is a spillover from sympathetic nerve terminals located in arteries feeding contracting muscles (Savard et al., 1987b).

3. Functional significance of skeletal muscle
   capillaries and mitochondria

The conclusion of the above discussion is that the skeletal muscle capillaries and mitochondria are in excess of what is needed to achieve an individual's maximal oxygen consumption. Nevertheless, these do change with usage of the muscles and the pertinent question is what role these alterations in the muscle may have.

The increased number of capillaries elevates capillary blood volume, which in turns means that at the same muscle blood flow, mean transit time is lengthened (MTT = capillary blood volume/muscle blood flow). This is not the only positive effect of more capillaries: as the capillary surface area is enlarged, and if this increase in capillarisation is larger than any increase in muscle fibre size, the area for diffusion is also smaller. All these factors will contribute to improving the conditions of exchange between blood and muscle and will have some bearing on the extraction of oxygen (Saltin, 1985), but more importantly is the fact that they help to increase the uptake of substrates (especially FFA) from the blood stream (Kiens et al., 1987). When a muscle is 'overperfused', as is the case during exercise with only the knee-extensors of one leg, the role of the capillary bed size is easily demonstrated, also in terms of oxygen extraction (Fig.2). It is of interest to note that the critical MTT for a complete extraction of oxygen appears to be around 1 sec or just below.

The role of an enhanced mitochondrial enzyme activity, as is always observed with endurance training, is still not understood. However, with such a change marked alterations in the metabolic response to exercise are also found. Several physiologists have speculated about the causal relationship between the observed enzyme alterations and the metabolic response (Gollnick and Saltin, 1982), but the biochemists have so far failed to elucidate the mechanisms involved. Whatever the explanation is for the markedly altered metabolic response, it may be worthwhile here just to mention that RER and RQ measurements clearly indicate that more

lipids are utilised during and following endurance usage of
muscles; in addition, the reduced lactate production further points
to a 'sparing' of the limited muscle glycogen stores (Fig.3).
This is summarised in Table 6 where data on untrained and trained
individuals performing prolonged exercise at the same absolute and
relative work loads are compared. At the same absolute work level,
the trained individual can perform much longer, and although the
difference in maximal oxygen only amounts to 30%, the amount of
work performed is a factor of 2-3 times larger for the trained than
for the untrained individual. This is also true when comparisons
are made at the same relative work level. Work time is not much
different, but work output is. Of note is that the limited muscle
glycogen stores are utilised to a similar extent. Further, it is
the trained subjects' capacity to oxidise lipids which makes the
difference and is the cause of the very marked differences observed
in endurance performance.

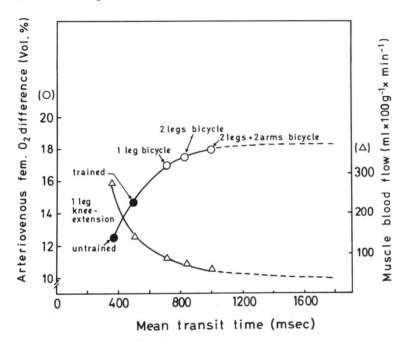

Figure 2. Estimated mean transit time (MTT) in relation to muscle
blood flow ($\triangle$,MBF) and femoral arteriovenous O_2 difference
($\bullet$, $\circ$, (a-v)O_2 fem). MTT data are based on a capillary density of
350 capillaries per mm^2 with a mean diameter of 6µ, and assuming
that all capillaries have a flow. Values of (a-v)O_2 were obtained
during maximal one-legged knee-extension (closed circles) and one-
and two-legged as well as arm and leg bicycle exercise (open
circles).

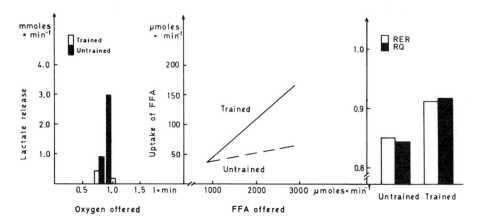

Figure 3. Effect of endurance training of skeletal muscle on
lactate release, uptake of FFA relative to delivery, and RQ
(respiratory quotient) determined over the exercising leg, and
RER (Respiratory exchange ratio). The data are from Henrikssen
(1977) and Kiens et al. (1987).

Table 6. Oxygen uptake, work output, respiratory exchange ratio
(RER) and substrate (lipids, carbohydrates) utilisation during
prolonged bicycling exercise in trained (T) and untrained (UT)
individuals working at the same absolute and relative work loads.

Subjects	Work Rate (watt)	Relative Exercise Intensity %	Oxygen Uptake ($1.min^{-1}$)	Work Time (min)	Total Amount of Work (kg)	RER	Lipids (g)	Carbohy-drates (g)
UT:	175	77	2.40	118	5.890	0.96	22	302
T:	175	59	2.43	400	19.700	0.81	335	400
T:	225	78	3.20	134	8.800	0.90	80	348

4. Maximal oxygen uptake - endurance fitness

It is apparently so that different links in the oxygen transport
system limit maximal oxygen uptake, peak oxygen uptake, and
endurance. In healthy individuals maximal oxygen uptake is set by
the pump capacity of the heart. On the other hand, peak oxygen
uptake, i.e. the oxygen uptake which can be attained when only a
minor fraction of the muscle mass is engaged in the exercise, is
limited by local factors within the muscle, and the more so the

smaller the muscle group. Endurance performance is a function of
the same conditions, namely capillary network and metabolic enzyme
levels in the muscle. Hence, both peak oxygen of an extremity or
muscle group and its metabolic potential should be related
closely, and to the same extent, to endurance (Kiens and Terrados,
1987). In whole body exercise (rowing - cross-country skiing -
swimming) or two-legged exercise (bicycling - running), endurance
may relate more to the local training status of the involved
muscles than to maximal oxygen uptake. This latter point is well
documented in rats where the endurance capacity was closely matched
with the mitochondrial enzyme levels in leg muscles, but not with
the maximal oxygen uptake (Davies et al., 1981). In man, similar
observations are most easily obtained during detraining where a
dissociation is found between the rate of fall in maximal oxygen
uptake and muscle enzyme levels: the former variable is maintained
fairly well over some weeks in spite of no training, whereas the
mitochondrial volume quickly returns to pre-training level. If
endurance tests are performed when this discrepancy between
maximal oxygen uptake and local muscle enzyme capacity is at its
largest, one can observe a marked reduction in performance. Under
more ordinary circumstances, it is not so easy to demonstrate that
maximal oxygen uptake and endurance fitness may not be directly
coupled, as the status of the muscle adaptation rather closely
varies with an individual's maximal oxygen uptake. In upper body
exercise of sedentary subjects, endurance performance is
considerably lower than when lower limbs perform at the same
relative work intensity (Pimental et al., 1984; Falkel et al.,
1986). This is most likely a reflection of an 'overperfusion' of
arm muscles during arm work relative to their mass when compared to
leg muscles, which may relate to the elevated blood pressure
observed during arm exercise (Stenberg et al., 1967; Clausen et
al., 1973). Thus, the measured peak $\dot{V}O_2$ of this muscle mass is
somewhat higher than it should be relative to its 'trained status',
i.e. the upper body is most commonly 'sedentary' relative to the
lower body musculature, and endurance time is correspondingly
shortened (Falkel et al., 1986).

One aspect of endurance fitness which puzzles many is that it
can be altered by a factor of 2-4 whereas maximal oxygen uptake
usually only varies by 20-50%. The explanation is, in part, given
in Fig.4. Endurance time is a function of the relative work
intensity and increases exponentially with decreasing relative
exercise rate (Tornvall, 1963). Hence, if maximal oxygen uptake is
increased by 20%, a work rate demanding 90% of maximal oxygen
uptake before training represents 'only' a relative work intensity
of 70% after the training, and endurance time can be expected to
increase by a factor of five or more (Fig.4). Similarly, the
amount of energy utilised increases in a similar fashion. The
ability to perform longer at the same relative exercise intensity
can also be improved with endurance training, but the magnitude of
this change is minor. These relationships are clearly demonstrated
in a study by Costill et al. (1973) on English long distance
runners. The speed at which the runners ran a 10-mile (16km) race
was related primarily to the maximal oxygen uptake, which varied
between 55 and 82ml.kg^{-1}.min^{-1}, whereas all ran at very similar
relative exercise intensities, i.e. between 82% and 92%, and no

systematic differences were found between those with high or low
maximal oxygen uptakes. It has therefore been suggested that
whereas speed or work intensity is set by the maximal oxygen uptake
and by the efficiency in the task performed (energy economy), the
time this speed is maintained for is more a function of the
efficiency in usage of the glycogen stores. Thus, the amount of
glycogen and the local training status of the limb muscles engaged
in the exercise, are decisive for the maintenance of a certain
relative work intensity, which, in turn, is well correlated to
measured levels of blood lactate at given running speeds. It is
possible to train various muscle groups of the body separately and
thereby enhance the peak oxygen uptake of the muscle as well as its
endurance capacity without improving the central cardiovascular
capacity and maximal oxygen uptake (Gaffney et al., 1981). This
extends to the training of one leg or each leg separately where
only a small effect on the maximal oxygen uptake has been
observed even though the peak oxygen uptake and endurance capacity
of the trained leg had improved (Saltin et al., 1976; Henriksson,
1977; Klausen et al., 1982; Kiens and Terrados, 1987).

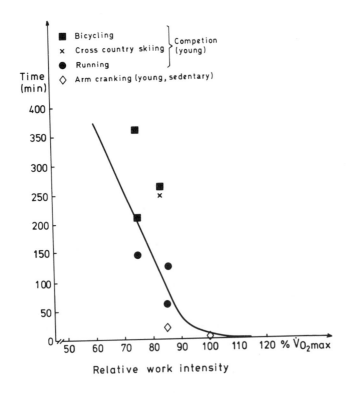

Figure 4. Time to endurance is given when exercising at various
relative work intensities (oxygen uptake during the initial phase
of the exercise in percent of the individual's maximal oxygen
uptake). The line represents data presented in articles by Åstrand
and Saltin (1961a) and Saltin (1973). Included are also some data

points from competition or training where measurements were performed of the relative work rate during the competition (training). The arm exercise data are those mentioned in the text.

5. Myocardial fatigue in prolonged exercise?

The drift in the central haemodynamic response to prolonged exercise has been well described (Ekelund and Holmgren, 1964; Saltin and Stenberg, 1964) and discussed most recently by Johnson (1987). The gradual reduction in stroke volume and elevation in heart rate which occur, resulting in a maintenance of the cardiac output, have been explained on the basis of a peripheral displacement of the blood volume during exercise, which is further exaggerated if the thermal load is high (Rowell, 1974). It has been postulated that the central circulation may not be able to meet with the combined demands for a flow to both the exercising muscles as well as to the skin, with the result that limb (muscle) blood flow is compromised. Recent studies indicate that this may not be the case (Savard et al., 1987a). It is of note that the drift in the heart rate and stroke volume relationship occurs also when the exercise is performed in the supine position (Ekelund and Holmgren, 1964; Saltin and Stenberg, 1964), and further that it can occur in the supine position when the thermal load is minimal (Nielsen et al., 1984). One suggestion has then been that an altered myocardial contractility may contribute to the central haemodynamic drift observed in prolonged exercise, and indeed, well-controlled in vitro experiments on the rat heart muscle have shown that the myocardium can fatigue (Maher et al., 1972, for further references, see: Tibbits, 1985). Indications of reduced ventricular contractility have also been reported in man during 24 hours of running (Niemelä et al., 1984). Ejection fraction was gradually reduced in spite of unchanged end-diastolic volumes, and rates of circumventricular shortening were retarded. Due to the limitations of the method (ultrasound), these measurements were performed at rest during brief intermissions of the running, and thus, it is not known whether the same patterns of alterations are present during exercise. In this connection it is of interest that Davies et al. (personal communication) observed in trained long distance runners a reduction of almost 3 $l.min^{-1}$ in cardiac output after 4 hours of exhaustive running at a set pace, at which time oxygen uptake had increased 200-300 $ml.min^{-1}$ ($\simeq 10\%$). Techniques are now available to study these problems during exercise in greater depth, which should give insights into the role of possible myocardial fatigue in exhaustion during prolonged exercise. At present, it would appear safest to conclude that fatigue in endurance exercise should be sought after in the skeletal muscles.

Acknowledgement

Data from studies performed in this laboratory have been supported by the Danish Heart Association and the Research Council of the Danish Sports Federation.

References

Andersen, P. and Saltin, B. (1985). Maximal perfusion of skeletal muscle in man. Journal of Physiology 366:233-249.

Åstrand, P.O., Cuddy, T.E., Saltin, B. and Stenberg, J. (1964). Cardiac output during submaximal and maximal work. Journal of Applied Physiology 19:268-274.

Åstrand, P.O. and Saltin, B. (1961a). Oxygen uptake during the first minutes of heavy muscular exercise. Journal of Applied Physiology 16:971-976.

Åstrand, P.O. and Saltin, B. (1961b). Maximal oxygen uptake and heart rate in various types of muscular activity. Journal of Applied Physiology 16:977-981.

Bergh, U., Kanstrup, I.-L. and Ekblom, B. (1976). Maximal oxygen uptake during exercise with various combinations of arm and leg work. Journal of Applied Physiology 41:191-196.

Clausen, J.P., Klausen, K., Rasmussen, B. and Trap-Jensen, J. (1973). Central and peripheral circulatory changes after training of the arms or legs. American Journal of Physiology 225:675-682.

Costill, D.L., Branam, G., Eddy, D. and Sparks, K. (1971). Determinants of marathon running success. Internationale Zeitschrift fur Angewandte Physiologie 29:249-254.

Costill, D.L., Thomason, H. and Roberts, E. (1973). Fractional utilization of the aerobic capacity during distance running. Medicine and Science in Sports 5:248-252.

Davies, K.J.A., Packer, L. and Brooks, G.A. (1981). Biochemical adaptations of mitochondria, muscle, and whole-animal respiration to endurance training. Archives of Biochemistry and Biophysics 209:539-554.

Dempsey, J.A. (1986). Is the lung built for exercise? Medicine and Science in Sports and Exercise 18:143-155.

Dempsey, J.A., Hanson, P.G. and Henriksson, K.S. (1984). Exercise-induced arterial hypoxemia in healthy persons at sea level. Journal of Physiology (London) 355:161-175.

Ekblom, B., Goldbarg, A.N. and Gullbring, B. (1972). Response to exercise after blood loss and reinfusion. Journal of Applied Physiology 33:175-180.

Ekblom, B. and Hermansen, L. (1968). Cardiac output in athletes. Journal of Applied Physiology 25:619-625

Ekblom, B., Wilson, G., and Åstrand, P.O. (1976). Central circulation during exercise after venesection and reinfusion of red blood cells. J. Appl. Physiol. 40(3):379-383.

Ekelund, L.G. and Holmgren A. (1964). Circulatory and respiratory adaptation during long-term, non-steady-state exercise in the sitting position. Acta Physiologica Scandinavica 62:240-255.

Falkel, J.E., Sawica, M.N., Levine, L., Pimental, N.A. and Pandolf, K.B. (1986). Upper-body exercise performance: comparison between women and men. Ergonomics 29:145-154.

Gaffney, F.A., Grimby, G., Danneskiold-Samsøe, B. and Halskov, O. (1981). Adaptation to peripheral muscle training. Scandinavica Journal of Rehabilitation Medicine 13:11-16.

Gleser, M.A., Hostman, D.H. and Mello, R.P. (1974). The effect on $\dot{V}O_2$max of adding arm work to maximal leg work. Medicine and Science in Sports 6:104-107.

Gollnick, P.D. and Saltin, B. (1982). Hypothesis: significance of skeletal muscle oxidative enzyme enhancement with endurance training. Clinical Physiology 2:1-12.

Henriksson, J. (1977). Human Skeletal muscle adaptation to physical activity. Thesis, Karolinska Institutet, Stockholm, Sweden.

Hermansen, L. (1973). Oxygen transport during exercise in human subjects. Acta Physiologica Scandinavica 22,suppl:399.

Holloszy, J.O. (1967) Biochemical adaptations in muscle. Effects of exercise on mitochondrial oxygen uptake and respiratory enzyme activity in skeletal muscle. Journal of Biological Chemistry 242:2278-2282.

Hoppeler, H., Howald, H., Conley, K., Lindstedt, S.L., Claassen, H., Vock, P. and Weibel, E.R. (1985). Endurance training in humans: aerobic capacity and structure of skeletal muscle. Journal of Applied Physiology 59:320-327.

Johnson, J.M. (1987). Central and peripheral adjustments to long term exercise in humans. In Human adaptation to prolonged activity. Eds.:Shephard, R. and Jacobs, I. Canadian Journal of Applied Sports Sciences. suppl. 1987.

Kaijser, L. (1970). Limiting factors for aerobic muscle performance. Acta Physiologica Scandinavica 346,suppl:1-96.

Kiens, B., Saltin, B., Christensen, N.J. and Essén-Gustavsson, B. (1987). Skeletal muscle substrate utilization with exercise. Effect of endurance training. American Journal of Physiology Submitted.

Kiens, B. and Terrados, N. (1987). Coupling between work performance and metabolic adaptation in an isolated muscle group in man. Pflügers Archiv Submitted.

Klausen, K., Andersen, L.B. and Pelle, J. (1981). Adaptive changes in work capacity, Skeletal muscle capillarization and enzyme levels during training and detraining. Acta Physiolica Scandinavica 113:9-16.

Klausen, K., Secher, N.H., Clausen, J.P., Hartling, D., and Trap-Jensen, J. (1982). Control and regional circulatory adaptations to one-leg training. Journal of Applied Physiology 52:976-983.

Lewis, S.F., Taylor, W.F., Graham, R.M., Pettinger, W.A., Schutte, J.E. and Blomqvist, C.G. (1983). Cardiovascular responses to exercise as functions of absolute and relative work load. Journal of Applied Physiology 54:1314-1323.

Maher, J.T., Goodman, A.L., Francesconi, R., Bowers, W.D., Hartley, L.H. and Angelakos, E.T. (1972). Responses of rat myocardium to exhaustive exercise. American Journal of Physiology 222:207-212.

Magaria, R., Cerretelli, P., Marchi, S. and Rossi, L. (1961). Maximum exercise in oxygen. Internationale Zeitschrift fur Angewandte Physiologie 18:465-467.

Mellander, S. (1981). Differentiation of fiber composition, circulation and metabolism in limb muscles of dog, cat and man. In Mechanism of vasodilatation. New York, Raven Press, pp 243-254.

Nielsen, B., Rowell, L.B. and Bonde-Petersen, F. (1984). Cardiovascular responses to heat stress and blood volume displacements during exercise in man. European Journal of Applied Physiology 52:370-374.

Niemelä, K.O. Palatsi, I.J., Ikäheimo, M.J., Takkunen, J.T. and Vuori, J.J. (1984). Evidence of impaired left ventricular performance after an uninterrupted competitive 24 hour run. Circulation 70:350-356.

Pimental, N.A., Sawka, M.N., Billings, D.S. and Trad, L.A. (1984). Physiological responses to prolonged upper-body exercise. Medicine and Science in Sports and Exercise 16:360-365.

Radigan, L.R. and Robinson, S. (1949). Effects of environmental heat stress and exercise on renal blood flow and filtration rate. Journal of Applied Physiology 2:185-191.

Rowell, L.B. (1974). Human cardiovascular adjustments to exercise and thermal stress. Physiological Reviews 54:75-159.

Rowell, L.B., Blackmon, J.R., Martin, P.M., Mazarella, J.A. and Bruce, R.A. (1965). Hepatic clearance of indocyanine green in man under thermal and exercise stresses. Journal of Applied Physiology 20:384-394.

Saltin, B. (1973). Oxygen transport by the circulatory system during exercise in man. In Limiting Factors of Physical Performance Ed.:Keul, J., Stuttgart, Georg Thieme Publ., pp. 235-252.

Saltin, B. (1985). Malleability of the system in overcoming limitations: functional elements. Journal of Experimental Biology 115:345-354.

Saltin, B. and Åstrand, P.O. (1967). Maximal oxygen uptake in athletes. Journal of Applied Physiology 23:353-358.

Saltin, B. and Gollnick, P.D. (1983). Skeletal muscle adaptability: significance for metabolism and performance. In Handbook of Physiology. Skeletal muscle Chap.19, pp. 555-631.

Saltin, B., Nazar, K., Costill, D.L., Stein, E., Jansson, E., Essén, B. and Gollnick, P.D. (1976). The nature of the training response. Peripheral and central adaptations to one-legged exercise. Acta Physiolica Scandinavica 96:289-305.

Saltin, B. and Stenberg, J. (1964). Circulatory response to prolonged severe exercise. Journal of Applied Physiology 19:833-838.

Savard, G., Nielsen, B., Laszczynska, J., Saltin, B. and Elmann-Larsen, B. (1987a). Muscle blood flow is not reduced in man during moderate exercise and heat stress. Journal of Applied Physiology In Press.

Savard, G., Kiens, B. and Saltin, B. (1987b). Limb blood flow in prolonged exercise; magnitude and implication for cardiovascular control during muscular work in man. In Human adaptation to prolonged exercise. Eds: Shephard, R. and Jacobs, I. Canadian Journal of Applied Sports Sciences suppl.1987.

Savard, G., Strange, S., Kiens, B., Christensen, N.J. and Saltin, B. (1985). Norepinephrine spillover from exercising skeletal muscle in man. In Procedings from the Canadian Association of Sports Sciences Meeting Oct. 1985.

Secher, N.H., Clausen, J.P. and Klausen, K. (1977). Central and regional circulatory effects of adding arm exercise to leg exercise. Acta Physiologica Scandinavica 100:288-297.

Stenberg, J., Åstrand, P.O., Ekblom, B., Royce, J. and Saltin, B. (1967). Hemodynamic response to work with different muscle groups, sitting and supine. <u>Journal of Applied Physiology</u> 22:61-70.

Terrados, N., Mizuno, M. and Andersen, H. (1985). Reduction in maximal oxygen uptake at low altitudes; role of training status and lung function. <u>Clinical Physiology</u> 5:75-79.

Tibbits, G.F. (1985). Regulation of myocardial contractility in exhaustive exercise. <u>Medicine and Science in Sports and Exercise</u> 17:529-537.

Tornvall, G. (1963). Assessment of physical capabilities; with special reference to the evaluation of maximal voluntary isometric muscle strength and maximal working capacity. <u>Acta Physiologica Scandinavica</u> 58:5-95.

Weibel, E.R. (1979). Oxygen demand and the size of respiratory structures in mammals. In <u>Evolution of Respiratory Processes</u> Eds: Wood, S.C. and Lenfant, C., New York, Dekker, pp. 289-346.

Discussion

Professor Åstrand, Stockholm
If you take a given weight of the heart muscle after training, is the metabolic potential and the force for that unit the same as before training?

Professor Saltin, Copenhagen, Denmark
In man there are no data. There are data on rat heart muscle on both sides. The problem in some of the studies of the rat is whether or not there is a matter of selection. Very few of the rats have survived the training programme in the studies where very significant improvements in performance of the myocardium had been demonstrated. In a way that may mean that not all have the adaptability, but those that have will survive.

Dr Nagle, Madison, Wisconsin
I would like you to clarify the point about the size of the muscle mass and the influence of the sympathetic nervous system.

Professor Saltin
The smaller the muscle mass, the less is the influence of the sympathetic nervous system. The sympathetic activity will be very pronounced with a large muscle mass involved in the exercise.

Dr Nagle
Another point is that you mentioned the factor that is setting the resistance is the pump function and then blood pressure is the defended function, so the cardiac output increases by a large amount with the pressure being defended throughout. You mentioned a cardiac output of 42 $l.min^{-1}$ in extremely well-trained athletes and that resistance then is probably dropping to maybe 2.5 or so peripheral resistance units. There seems to be no limit to that related to the pump functions of the heart.

Professor Saltin

Yes: I agree, and the critical thing is what is 'sensed'. The baroreceptors are the defence system to keep things in order. The question is whether there are more sensors than the baroreceptors or are they so sensitive so that they can beat by beat sense and adjust. If not we have to speculate on the existence of a system, maybe sensing the venous return or stretch receptors in the heart. There are studies of an expansion of plasma volume which will cause an increase in maximal cardiac output without a change in arterial pressure.

Professor Brooks, Berkeley, California

What do you think are the limits to $\dot{V}O_2$max? It seems from your presentation that end-diastolic volume is really the governing factor, given that myocardial contractility is about the same after training. So how much with training can we change end-diastolic volume and when in life can we do so?

Also what do you think about the possibility, coming from Dempsey's data which showed arterial desaturation at very high levels, that the limitations at high levels are in fact interactions between pulmonary function and cardiac output?

Professor Saltin

Gunnar Blomqvist and associates saw, as you indicated, that the end- diastolic volume is the limiting factor in dogs and you can come to a point where the pericardial sac will set a limit. They have in their studies of dogs opened the pericardium and found a further increase in end-diastolic volume and stroke volume. We have taken a different route in our experiments. When we have one leg trained and one untrained we see a lower heart rate when exercise is performed with the trained leg compared to the untrained one. Cardiac output is the same at the same submaximal work load for the trained and the untrained leg. The stroke volume is larger when exercising with the trained leg, as we would expect. How can that be? We have started some studies on venous return and filling pressure when exercising with legs of different training status. There was a larger end-diastolic volume exercising with the trained leg than with the untrained leg in the same person. What was astonishing was that the filling pressures were similar exercising with the untrained leg. Thus it looks like the heart, when exercise is performed with an untrained limb, is stiffer, i.e. it has a different compliance. We think there is something sensed in the skeletal muscle setting the stiffness of the ventricles and thereby setting the stroke volume and the cardiac output. Another way to say it is that you need to have trained muscle to elicit optimal stroke volume of the heart.

The point about the lung as a limiting factor, as nicely demonstrated by Dempsey's study, is that very very few athletes approach the limit where the transfer of oxygen in the lung is a limiting factor. Of course we may see more athletes approach this limit in the future. The picture is different for the thoroughbred horse. With the enormous pumping capacity of that animal's heart, most of these horses have reached the limit.

Dr Sutton, Canada

I wonder if you might like to consider a slightly different interpretation of some of your data related to prolonged exercise, where if I understand you correctly you are plugging for a central limitation based on evidence that the pump function may be failing. That interpretation might be that some of the problems in particularly prolonged exercise has to do with the capacitance system. Why I bring this up is that, as I understand the human data you presented, they suggested that pulse pressures fell and blood volume did not change very much; if it was central failure one might have expected changes in pulmonary pressure and perhaps even left atrial and right atrial filling pressures to have risen. I wonder if there was a possible fatigue of the compliance system where in fact a lot of blood is pooled there (this is in prolonged exercise), so the total blood volume is not substantially important, yet your filling pressures are high and are limiting. Is that a possibility and would you be able to interpret things in that light as well?

Professor Saltin

The point is well taken. This is an area where we can now make a significant contribution to understanding the limits. With all the non-invasive techniques now available which we did not have in the past, it is an area to look into: it is too early to come to a final conclusion. My point was that it may be not only a displacement of blood and the function of the capacitance vessels.

Professor Montoye, Madison, USA

In view of your discussion of the central cardiovascular factors which limit maximum endurance performance, would you give your explanation of the mechanism accounting for the decreased maximum heart rate as people age.

Professor Saltin

There are two major factors which contribute to the reduction in maximal oxygen uptake with age. One is lowered maximal heart rate, the other is reduced stroke volume. The latter variable is reduced due to increased after load (higher blood pressure), which in turn is a reflection of reduced elasticity of the aorta and larger arteries. The lowering of maximal heart rate has been shown to closely follow age-related reductions in the velocity by which the electrical activation of the heart can be propagated.

Dr Hardman, Loughborough, Leicestershire

One of the observations which you used to develop the argument that central cardiovascular factors are limiting during exercise with a muscle mass lower than your 'critical' muscle mass was that the $\dot{V}O_2$max of the untrained leg is not influenced by one-leg training. We have observed a significant increase in both the $\dot{V}O_2$max and the submaximum endurance (80% pre-training $\dot{V}O_2$max) of an untrained leg. Can you envisage circumstances under which this might occur?

Professor Saltin

An effect of one-legged training on the peak oxygen uptake of the 'other' leg is usually seen, but the magnitude is usually quite small. The one-legged exercise model, although we have used it in the past, I feel has limitations, especially in intense work. Stabilizing the body and keeping the body on the bicycle includes lots of arm work. In addition, the involvement of various limb muscles of the leg is most likely different in one-legged and two-legged exercise. Some transfer effects could be related to 'improved' technique exercising with the inactive leg.

Professor Poortmans, Brussels, Belgium

Would you agree that the athlete has enough oxygen available in most conditions, but that he is unable to utilize part of it because of enzyme activity limitations of the Krebs cycle and the respiratory chain?

Professor Saltin

No: On the contrary, if the endurance athlete in his/her discipline utilizes a large fraction of the muscle mass at a high relative work intensity, the potential for a blood flow supply to the muscles and its capacity for oxygen consumption is far from utilized.

Application of metabolic logic to the questions of causes of fatigue in marathon races

E.A. NEWSHOLME

The marathon is an endurance event that is gaining great popularity in many parts of the world. Why should this be so? The event has a kind of mystique about it that could have something to do with its legendary origins but more probably because it provides a challenge of just the right level for widespread attainment. No one can claim that running a marathon is easy but it is not impossibly difficult - and certainly less remote than the challenge, for example, of climbing Mount Everest. To gain personal satisfaction there is no need to run the marathon well; simply to run it at all is sufficient - and then comes the desire to improve.

The marathon is run over 26 miles 385 yards (42.2 km) and is completed by elite runners in a little over two hours at an average speed of 11-12 mph ($17.5-19.5 km.h^{-1}$) and a total energy expenditure of around 12000kJ. Many non-elite runners complete it in 150-170 minutes with a similar total energy expenditure and even at these slower times a number of processes come under considerable stress, which can limit performance and eventually result in exhaustion. For example, failure to lose sufficient heat results in elevation in body temperature, hyperthermia, loss of too much fluid in sweating can result in severe dehydration, and even simple physical damage, such as blisters, can halt the runner. However, the limitation for most runners is the supply of fuel to the muscle. In this chapter, an explanation of this limitation is provided and this should make running to exhaustion more interesting, should help to understand how simple dietary procedures can delay the onset of exhaustion and make it possible to answer such questions as, 'will the marathon ever be run in under two hours?' or 'will a woman ever run this distance faster than the fastest man?'

Before embarking on this explanation it is necessary to understand the nature of the fuels stored by the body, the amount stored, how they are mobilised when required, how they are used to generate ATP and how these processes are controlled. Additional and more detailed aspects of this subject will be found in Newsholme & Leech, 1983a).

1. Fuels

The body always has a demand for energy which is normally met from the food we eat. However eating is not a continuous process, so that the body has to store energy for use between meals, during more prolonged starvation or when a large amount of extra energy is needed as in endurance running. The two main energy stores in the human body are glycogen, a carbohydrate, which is stored in muscle and liver, and fat, which is stored in adipose tissue. Each store has its own particular function.

Glycogen is simply a polymer of glucose, that is, a chain of glucose molecules firmly welded together by removal of a molecule of water from each adjacent pair of glucose units. In this way, thousands of glucose units are combined into a single molecule. Although glucose can be polymerised into straight chains, glycogen is much-branched providing many ends where simultaneous breakdown can occur for rapid release of glucose units.

After a carbohydrate-containing meal glucose is produced by the process of digestion in the intestinal lumen and then absorbed into the bloodstream. The concentration of glucose in the bloodstream is maintained at about 5mM but, as the concentration rises after a meal, it is removed and stored as glycogen in liver and muscle. Since glucose is present in the bloodstream and in all cells, why cannot it be stored as glucose rather than the polymer? This would require a very high concentration of glucose (500mM or more) which, since glucose is a very reactive molecule, would interact with proteins and hence damage structures and interfere with function. (Indeed, concentrations as high as 8-9mM for long periods of time in diabetic patients may explain many of their long term clinical problems - see Newsholme & Leech, 1983b). The reactive group is removed in the formation of the polymer glycogen.

The second major storage fuel in humans is fat, which is composed of triglyceride molecules. Triglyceride is of quite a different chemical nature to glycogen, being a much smaller molecule and containing proportionally less oxygen; its composition is closer to the hydrocarbon fuels used in internal combustion engines. A triglyceride molecule consists of glycerol to which are attached, via ester links, three fatty acid units. Although several kinds of fatty acid occur in triglyceride, all have a similar structure, differing only in the number of carbon atoms (from 16 to 22) and in the number of double bonds present. Fatty acids with more than one double bond are known as polyunsaturated. The major store of triglyceride is in adipose tissue, which is composed of cells called adipocytes, each of which contains a large droplet of triglyceride, which occupies some 90% of the cell. Unlike most other tissues, adipose tissue does not form a discrete organ but is widely distributed throughout the body. It is found beneath the skin, subcutaneous adipose tissue, where it serves not only as a fuel store but also as insulation against heat loss; it surrounds the major organs such as the heart and kidneys where it provides some mechanical protection. In the male, it is also present at the front of the abdominal cavity where it is known as omental fat and this store can be very large. In the female, who possesses significantly more adipose tissue than the male, it is also present in the breasts, the upper thighs and

the buttocks and is responsible for her more rounded appearance.
One mechanical principle adhered to by the body is that the
largest amount of adipose tissue occurs near to the centre of
gravity where it interferes less with locomotion.

2. Making the fuels available

Neither glycogen nor triglyceride can traverse the membrane of the
cell in which they are stored. So they must be broken down to
smaller units before transport, glycogen to glucose and triglyceride
to glycerol plus fatty acids.

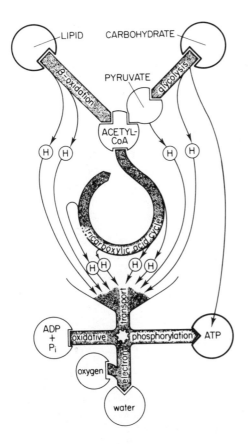

Figure 1. An outline of the major metabolic pathways involved in
the oxidation of fat and carbohydrate. (Taken from Newsholme and
Leech, 1983b).

    The conversion of glycogen to glucose involves hydrolysis,
that is, splitting by addition of water. In cells this does not
occur directly but first involves attack by a phosphate ion which
splits off a terminal glucose unit as glucose 1-phosphate. The

reaction is catalysed by the enzyme phosphorylase and has the advantage that this glucose 1-phosphate can enter the sequence of energy-yielding reactions described below without further phosphorylation. If it is required for export, which will be the case, for example, when liver is providing fuel for muscle during exercise, the phosphate group must be removed to produce glucose which can then leave the liver cell for the bloodstream and maintain the blood glucose concentration.

The hydrolysis of triglyceride to glycerol and fatty acids is a simpler process, catalysed by the enzyme triglyceride lipase. The fatty acids cross the cell membrane of the adipocyte into the blood in which they are carried to the muscle or other tissue. The transport of fatty acids poses a problem since they are not at all soluble in the blood plasma. The problem is overcome by combining the fatty acid molecule with albumin, a soluble protein present in the plasma. The binding is fairly tight but, as the blood passes through a working muscle, the fatty acid-albumin complex dissociates into albumin and fatty acids and the latter diffuse into the muscle fibre. This occurs because the concentration of fatty acids within the muscle is very low due to their removal by the process of oxidation (Fig.1).

Table 1. Fuel stores* in average man

Tissue fuel store	Approximate total fuel reserve		Estimated period for which fuel store would provide energy		
	g	kJ	Days of starvation+	Days of walking-	Minutes of marathon running=
Adipose tissue triacylglycerol	9000	337000	34	10.8	4018
Liver glycogen	90	1500	0.15	0.05	18
Muscle glycogen	350	6000	0.6	0.20	71
Blood and extracellular glucose	20	320	0.03	0.01	4
Body protein	8800	150000	15	4.8	1800

*Normal man possesses 12% of the body weight as triacylglycerol and normal woman about 26%. Davidson et al., (1979) state that normal man (65kg) possesses 9kg of triacylglycerol and this value is used in this table. Higher amounts of stored triacylglycerol have been given by Cahill (1970) and Wahren (1979) but much lower amounts will be present in the well-trained endurance athlete. Periods for which the fuel will last are calculated as below.

+Assuming that energy expenditure during starvation is 10 050 kJ.day^{-1} (i.e. normal energy expenditure of 13 400 kJ.day^{-1} is reduced by 25% on starvation).

-Assuming that energy expenditure during walking (6.4km.h^{-1}) for 65kg man is 31 248 kJ.day^{-1} (Durnin and Passmore, 1967).

=Assuming energy expenditure of 84kJ.min^{-1}.

The data illustrate the time for which the fuel stores would provide energy, provided this was the only fuel utilised by the body. (This table is taken from Newsholme and Leech (1983b)).

3. How much fuel is stored

The amounts of stored glycogen and triglyceride are far from equal as can be seen from Table 1. Some 98% of energy reserves are held in the form of triglyceride, enough to tide the average man over several weeks of starvation. Why should this be? The simple answer is that fat is a far more efficient fuel for storage. In a storage fuel, the ratio of its energy content to its mass is of paramount importance. The energy content of each of the two fuels can be compared by burning them in a calorimeter in which all the available energy is released as heat that is then measured. In the calorimeter, the fuels undergo the same overall chemical reaction (and therefore produce the same amount of energy) as they would if oxidised in a cell. Burning 1g of pure glycogen releases 16 kJ, whereas burning 1g of a typical triglyceride releases 35kJ.
 Clearly this establishes triglyceride as the more efficient storage fuel but the difference becomes even more pronounced when it is realised that, in the cell, triglyceride is stored in a pure state but glycogen is not. Glycogen, with its branched structure and multitude of hydroxyl groups, is inevitably associated with a large number of trapped water molecules. More than half of the mass of the stored glycogen is composed of water and when this is taken into account, triglyceride emerges as the better storage fuel by a factor of at least five. The importance of storing triglyceride is emphasised by a simple calculation; if a 70kg man stored glycogen instead of fat, for the same energy reserve, his weight would become about 105kg.
 Why, then, is glycogen stored at all? There are at least two reasons. Firstly, the brain requires a constant supply of glucose, since it cannot oxidise fatty acids, and liver glycogen provides a readily available reserve for this vital tissue. Secondly, tissues may need to generate ATP under conditions when the amount of oxygen present is inadequate for complete fuel oxidation; glucose, but not fat, can produce ATP in the absence of oxygen.

4. Making the ATP

Muscle work depends on an adequate rate of ATP generation within it, since this is the chemical that actually powers contraction. Unfortunately, the processes involved are rather complex.
 It is worth asking why metabolism should be so complex, for there are good reasons. The first point to make is that it is not difficult for glycogen or triglyceride to give up some of its chemical energy and rearrange its atoms to form appropriate amounts of carbon dioxide and water. All that is needed is to add a little heat, for both burn readily releasing their chemical energy as heat. But what is needed in the cell is a process in which a large proportion of the chemical energy in these compounds is used to generate ATP from ADP and phosphate. This takes a bit more doing

and, not surprisingly, the process is very gradual and involves
many small steps. In fact, the processes are not so much complex
as full of detail. For present purposes most of these details can
be omitted since they fill many excellent textbooks.

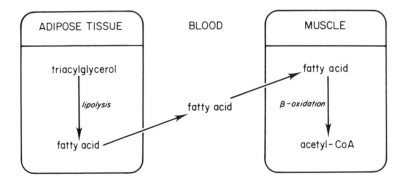

Figure 2. The source and metabolism of fatty acids by muscle.
(Taken from Newsholme and Leech, 1983b).

Both glucose and fatty acids are converted to carbon dioxide and
water by a long series of steps, each involving a small chemical
change and catalysed by a different enzyme. Some of these enzymes
are floating about free in the sarcoplasm of the muscle fibre
while others are bound to membranes (for example, in mitochondria)
in a more organised way. Each enzyme catalyses a relatively simple
chemical reaction in which just a few atoms are rearranged. A
sequence of enzyme-catalysed reactions which operate in a
coordinated fashion to bring about an overall chemical change is
known as a metabolic pathway. Several such pathways are involved
in the complete oxidation of fuels.

At this scale, individual reactions are not shown but the major
routes are apparent (Fig.2) A sequence of reactions known as
glycolysis converts each molecule of glucose 6-phosphate (derived
from glucose or glycogen) to two molecules of pyruvate. En route
there is a net synthesis of both ATP and $NADH_2$. The latter can
enter the electron transfer chain and thus generate more ATP. The
pyruvate undergoes a further transformation into acetyl coenzyme A
(acetyl CoA) which enters the Krebs cycle. This seemingly complex
sequence of reactions, explained in more detail below, actually
carries out no more than the complete oxidation of acetate to carbon
dioxide, one of the products of fuel oxidation. A little ATP is
formed by direct coupling but most of the very large amount of
chemical energy made available is trapped in the synthesis of $NADH_2$.

The same 'map' can be used to follow the fate of fatty acids.
They undergo a series of oxidations, once more producing $NADH_2$
(together with some $FADH_2$ which can also provide energy for
oxidative phosphorylation) in which two-carbon fragments are
split off in the form of acetyl CoA. These, too, enter the Krebs

cycle for further and complete oxidation.

Finally, all the $NADH_2$ and $FADH_2$ molecules produced in these reactions are fed into the electron transfer pathway. There they are oxidised by molecular oxygen with the concomitant synthesis of large amounts of ATP.

With this overview in mind it is possible to consider these pathways in a little more detail.

4.1 Glycolysis
It takes 12 enzyme-catalysed reactions to convert glucose to pyruvate but the initial reactions vary according to whether glucose from the blood or glycogen within the muscle is the fuel. The first reaction for glucose is its phosphorylation, catalysed by the enzyme hexokinase. This reaction actually consumes ATP and this can be seen as an investment which helps to prepare the glucose molecule for subsequent reactions. It is repaid with interest at a later stage. All subsequent intermediates in glycolysis are phosphorylated and, after an internal enzyme-catalysed rearrangement of atoms to form fructose 6-phosphate has occurred, a second phosphorylation, again using ATP, takes place to form fructose 1,6-bisphosphate. This reaction is catalysed by the enzyme phosphofructokinase. Further reactions split this 6-carbon sugar into two 3-carbon compounds, oxidise them and recover the phosphate groups as ATP. All these reactions occur in the cytosol of the cell.

4.2 Preparation for the Krebs cycle
The end-product of glycolysis is pyruvate. As long as oxygen is available to the muscle (which it must be for marathon running) this pyruvate is converted into acetyl CoA. This is achieved by a short pathway in which the three enzymes are clustered together into what is known as the pyruvate dehydrogenase complex. These enzymes split off carbon dioxide, carry out an oxidation to form more $NADH_2$ and attach the resulting acetate to a largish molecule called coenzyme A to provide the compound known as acetyl CoA the synthesis of which occurs in the mitochondria as do the further reactions in the Krebs cycle.

4.3 Krebs cycle
The acetyl CoA now enters a sequence of reactions which were elucidated by Sir Hans Krebs in the late 1930s and which are designated the Krebs cycle. The reactions themselves are rather complex but basically what is happening is that the two-carbon compound acetate is attached to a four-carbon 'carrier' molecule (oxaloacetate) and then gradually oxidised away, producing carbon dioxide, $NADH_2$ and $FADH_2$, until the oxaloacetate is regenerated and can accept the next molecule of acetyle CoA.

4.4 β-oxidation
The first step in fatty acid oxidation is activation by attachment to coenzyme A to form fatty acyl CoA. Once this is done, a set of enzymes acting sequentially oxidises the carbon atom third from the end to which the coenzyme A is attached. This is the so-called β-carbon. As a result the terminal pair of carbon atoms are split off, with the coenzyme A still attached, as acetyl CoA and in this form enter the Krebs cycle. The latter can be seen, therefore, as

common for both the oxidation of glucose and fatty acids and as
such is sometimes known as the final common pathway for oxidation.

4.5 Electron transfer and oxidative phosphorylation
At this point it is worth noting that very little ATP has been
produced and that molecular oxygen has played no part. This
section changes all that. Deep in the heart of each mitochondrion,
small structures attached to the inner membrane are the real
powerhouse of the cell, for this is where the ATP is generated in
aerobic muscles. In a long series of oxidoreduction (or electron
transfer) reactions, electrons from $NADH_2$ are passed via flavo-
proteins, quinones and cytochromes eventually to oxygen which is
reduced to water, the latter is the other major product of fuel
oxidation.

4.6 The yield of ATP
One advantage of understanding the details of the metabolic
pathways involved in fuel oxidation is that it allows the
calculation of the number of molecules of ATP that can be generated
from the oxidation of each of these fuels. Since glycogen is a
very large molecule, and of indefinite size, it is more useful to
calculate the yield from glucose and this is done together with
that for a molecule of the fatty acid, palmitic acid (Table 2).
Direct comparison of the two is misleading, since they differ in
size. In fact, almost equal proportions of the chemical energy in
each can be made available in the form of ATP, the rest being
released as heat. Since fatty acids contain inherently more
chemical energy than carbohydrates, on a weight for weight basis,
they do of course produce more ATP. Table 2 also contains
information on the number of ATP molecules produced from anaerobic
metabolism which is of value when marathon running is compared to
sprinting.

Table 2. Yield of ATP from various fuels under aerobic and
anaerobic conditions. It is assumed that fuels are utilised by
pathways described in the text.

Fuel	Conditions	ATP yield (mol) per mol of fuel utilised
Glucose	aerobic, complete oxidation	38
Glucose	anaerobic, conversion to lactate	2
Glycogen	aerobic, complete oxidation	39
Glycogen	anaerobic, conversion to lactate	3
Palmitate	aerobic, complete oxidation	129

The following discussion will emphasise that in the marathon
run fuel stores, especially carbohydrate, are limiting so that the
most efficient use of this fuel must be made. This is achieved by
complete oxidation of glucose to carbon dioxide and water. This
requires, therefore, that the muscle has a good supply of oxygen

and this together with glucose and fatty acids, are provided by the bloodstream; in addition, a store of fuel, glycogen, within the muscle and the ability to oxidise these fuels, that is, the presence of mitochondria, are also required.

5. Running on carbohydrate

The data presented in Table 1 show that both carbohydrate and fat are present as fuel reserves in man and Fig.2 shows that either can be used to generate ATP. But are they alternatives and, in an actual race, is one used before the other? There are two complementary ways of answering such questions. One is to calculate whether a fuel could supply energy at a given rate and the other is to measure, in some way, what fuel is actually being used during exercise. Both approaches have been used.

The body possesses three reserves of carbohydrate which could be used to generate ATP during exercise:- glycogen in liver, glycogen in muscle and glucose in blood. The latter is so small that it could provide the elite marathon runner with energy for only one minute (Table 1) but it provides the means by which glucose, which is mobilised from liver glycogen, is transported to the muscles.

Extensive studies on exercising man have been carried out by Felig and Wahren (1975) on the firemen of Stockholm who had volunteered to run on a treadmill while undergoing physiological and biochemical tests. These investigators measured the concentration of glucose in blood entering and blood leaving the leg muscles during exercise and were able to calculate that approximately 0.2g glucose per minute was being taken from the blood by the muscles. This was close to the rate of glucose release from the liver and undoubtedly arose from the breakdown of liver glycogen. In Felig and Wahren's study, this provided about 30% of the energy utilised. Although this experimental information is important, it is restricted to normal individuals; such studies have not been done on elite marathon runners who, from a physiological and biochemical point-of-view, are far from normal. It is of interest to know how much glucose would be needed to power all the energy requirements of an elite athlete during a marathon race. To estimate this we can work backwards from something that is much more readily measurable, the rate of oxygen consumption by an elite runner in the laboratory under conditions that simulate the marathon. This is approximately $4l \, min^{-1}$ which corresponds to a consumption of 5.4g glucose per minute, or at least 700g during a race. Measurements of enzyme activities in human muscle confirm that glucose could just be metabolised at this rate in human muscle but, since the store of glycogen in the liver is equivalent to only about 100g of glucose, this clearly cannot provide the major source of fuel. Furthermore, such a high rate of utilisation if maintained for any significant period of time could endanger the blood glucose concentration. In elite marathon runners it must be of the utmost importance that the rate of glucose utilisation by muscle is matched closely to the rate of glucose release from the liver.

The remaining store of carbohydrate in man is muscle glycogen. The amount of this will depend upon recent dietary history but a typical 70kg male may have glycogen equivalent to 350g of glucose in his muscles. On this basis, muscle glycogen could provide approximately one-half of the energy needed for a marathon. To find out whether this glycogen is actually used during exercise involves measuring the glycogen content of the muscles. It is not possible to obtain muscle from elite marathon runners during a race but Scandinavian physiologists have used the needle biopsy technique to sample muscle of volunteers during sustained exercise on a bicycle ergometer (see Hermansen et al., 1967). The effort involved was such that exhaustion occurred after about 100 minutes and the studies showed that muscle glycogen is used during exercise of this kind and at a fairly steady rate over the whole exercise period. Thus it seems unlikely that the rate of utilisation of blood glucose will achieve a rate of 5g per minute, at least for any length of time, since muscle glycogen will also be used and as will be seen below, fatty acids will also be oxidised. A particularly interesting fact to emerge from these studies was that exhaustion coincided with the glycogen stores reaching very low levels. Furthermore, the time to exhaustion was directly proportional to the amount of glycogen in the muscles at the beginning of the exercise. A simple explanation would be that muscle glycogen is being used as the fuel and when this runs out exhaustion occurs, just as a car stops when it runs out of petrol. However, our calculation has already shown that the carbohydrate stores of the body are not adequate to provide all the energy required to complete a marathon. This paradox could be explained if an additional fuel was used simultaneously with carbohydrate; this fuel is fatty acid.

6. Running on fat

Compared with carbohydrate the amount of fat stored in the average person is enormous; about 10% of the mass of an average male, and more of an average female, is fat, although in some elite marathon and ultramarathon runners it may be lower than 5%. Because of its high energy content this could supply at least the basic energy requirements for many weeks without further intake of food. If fat was the sole fuel used, a calculation similar to that carried out for carbohydrate shows that about 300g would be used during a race, so that the total stores would provide energy to satisfy the demands of even the elite runner for more than three days and three nights of running. So is fat used during the run, and if so, why does exhaustion occur so soon? In brief, the answer is that fat is used but, if it was the sole fuel, it could not provide energy at the high rate demanded by the marathon runner. The evidence for the latter is as follows. Firstly, if the carbohydrate stores of the body are depleted prior to a run, for example, by eating a low carbohydrate diet for several days, exhaustion occurs earlier in a run. This is an experiment a runner can readily perform for himself; obtain from the physician or dietician a diet that provides less than 25g of carbohydrate each day, but enough fat and protein to produce satiety. Follow the diet for three days and note running performance. Secondly, in a study on ultra long-distance runners involved in a 24 hour race, Davies and Thompson

(1979) found that after 10 to 12 hour of running the power output
declined to a level where the oxygen consumption was about half of
that achieved maximally; at this stage very little carbohydrate is
left in the muscle or liver so most of the energy must be derived
from fat oxidation, implying that this could provide energy at
only half of the maximal aerobic capacity. Thirdly, studies on a
patient with a deficiency of the enzyme phosphofructokinase in
muscle, who was therefore unable to carry out glycolysis and hence
glucose oxidation and so was totally dependent upon fatty acid
oxidation, showed that, during endurance running his maximum
oxygen consumption was only 60% of that expected (P. Cerretelli,
personal communication). The general conclusion is, therefore,
that fatty acids are used during aerobic exercise but that the
rate at which they can be used is limited to about 50% of the
maximum rate of ATP production required. If a greater rate of
power output is required, the difference must be made up by
oxidation of carbohydrate, mainly muscle glycogen.

7. Switching fuel utilisation

If the reasoning so far is correct, the marathon runner would
achieve his best performance employing the following strategy. Use
fatty acids from the very beginning of the race at the maximum
rate consistent with safe transport and make up the deficit in
energy production by oxidation of carbohydrate (mainly muscle
glycogen) at a rate determined by requirements. However, although
fatty acids will be mobilised from adipose tissue, their
concentration will not exceed 2mM and this is lower than that of
glucose (Table 3). So, will not muscle prefer to use glucose in
preference to fatty acids, especially as the runner will probably
have been on a high-carbohydrate diet before the race? The answer
is 'no' because of a very sophisticated control system which ensures
that when glucose and fatty acids are both available to the muscle,
the latter are used in preference but any deficit in energy
production is made up by glucose oxidation. This control mechanism
is now described.
    If the concentration of ATP in the muscle fibre falls below a
'pre-set' level, as it will when muscle contraction commences, this
sets in train a series of events which increase the catalytic
activity of key enzymes in glycolysis. These are the enzymes that
have previously limited the flow rate. Conversely, a rise in ATP
concentration will reduce the flow-rate. Such negative feedback
serves to maintain the concentration of ATP within narrow limits
($\pm$ 25%) despite very large changes in its rate of utilisation.
This control mechanism is of extreme importance in the control of
glycolysis during sprinting. In the present context, the
important point is that fatty acid oxidation increases the
effectiveness of ATP as a feedback inhibitor of glycolysis and
hence glucose and glycogen utilisation are decreased. Two
important features of this control are worthy of note. Firstly,
since the rate of fatty acid oxidation is determined by the fatty
acid concentration in the blood and this in turn is determined
by the rate of fatty acid release from adipose tissue, it follows
that this latter process can actually exert some control over the

rate of carbohydrate utilisation in the body. Secondly, although fatty acid oxidation reduces the rates of glycolysis and pyruvate oxidation, these processes still operate more rapidly than at rest. Indeed the mechanism is such that, if the demand for energy by the muscle increases, despite the oxidation of fatty acids, carbohydrate utilisation will increase to meet this demand. This increased rate will be maintained until the energy demand is decreased or until the body runs out of carbohydrate.

Table 3. Concentrations of fuels in blood during endurance exercise in humans, horses and dogs.

Animal	Time of exercise (minutes)	Concentration of fuel in the blood (mM)	
		glucose	fatty acid
Human	0	4.5	0.66
	40	4.6	0.78
	180	3.5	1.57
	240	3.1	1.83
Horse	0	4.4	0.29
	360	2.0	1.4
Dog	0	6.1	0.6
	60	5.5	1.1
	120	5.5	1.8
	180	5.0	1.9
	240	5.0	2.1

The values are means of at least six individuals. The humans were exercised on a cycle ergometer (Felig and Wahren, 1975). The horses were ridden over 50 miles (80km) of hilly country at an average speed of about 8mph or 12.8km^{-1} (Hall et al., 1981). The dogs were run on a treadmill and the workload increased over the four hours (Paul and Holmes, 1975).

8. Causes of fatigue

Fatigue can be objectively defined as an inability to maintain power output. Fatigue also involves factors which can only be described subjectively - pain and discomfort. These are warning signs that the rate of energy expenditure is exceeding, or soon likely to exceed, the rate at which ATP can be generated. The judicious runner must react, but not overreact, to these signs. The runner should know from experience the likely meaning of the pain in his legs and the desire to stop running. Undoubtedly damage can result if these signs are ignored for too long but, in the end, even the muscles of the elite athlete will refuse to

maintain a required power output to avoid serious damage. The
intriguing question, for which the answer is by no means obvious,
is just what causes fatigue. A number of possibilities have been
suggested and, indeed, they may all contribute. Dehydration is a
possible cause; loss of water will decrease the blood volume and
could reduce the rate of supply of blood-borne fuels such as
glucose and fatty acids and of oxygen to the muscle. Muscles
produce heat when they contract and this can increase body
temperature sufficiently to cause a massive diversion of blood to
the skin, for cooling, and so deprive the muscles of fuel and
oxygen. Dehydration and hyperthermia are two real dangers of
marathon running. However, the author considers a metabolic cause
of fatigue may be very common.

Marathon runners have named one particular manifestation of
fatigue that they experience as 'the wall'. Typically the 'wall'
is hit between 20 and 24 miles (32-38km) and further progress seems
impossible. With the information already presented it is possible
to speculate on a metabolic explanation of the 'wall'. Up to this
point the runner has been operating at about 80% of his maximum
aerobic power output, oxidising both fatty acids and glucose.
However, as the glycogen stores in the muscle become depleted the
rate of glycolysis and hence that of glucose oxidation will decrease
progressively. If the high power output is maintained, the ATP
concentration must fall, since it is now being used at a rate
greater than it can be generated from fatty acids. However, the
decrease in ATP concentration in muscle even at extreme exhaustion
is not very large and it would still be expected that this would
provide sufficient substrate for the myosin ATPase in the
cross-bridge. It is more likely that a control system exists within
the muscle that detects a decrease in this concentration which then
either directly inhibits this ATPase or interferes with the calcium
ion control system so that the cross-bridge cycle activity cannot
be maintained. This would prevent a massive decrease in the ATP
concentration that could be lethal to the cell.

In addition, this decrease in ATP concentration in the muscle
results in the sensation of extreme discomfort and pain. The
mechanism is not known but it is possible that nerve endings
between the muscle fibres detect a chemical change resulting from
the lowering of the ATP concentration and an electrical signal is
transmitted to the brain. This signal is then 'interpreted' as
discomfort of pain depending on its strength. There is no doubt
that the consequence of a marked decrease in the glycogen content
of muscle is that power output decreases so that the runner slows.
In endurance races, almost all participants slow down as the race
proceeds and the winner is usually the athlete who slows down
least. The slowing down will allow fatty acid oxidation to provide
a greater proportion of the energy demand.

A hypothetical example will make this clear. A non-elite
marathon runner can run a mile no faster than 6 minutes 20 seconds;
this can be taken as a rough indication of his maximum aerobic
power capacity. His best time for the marathon is 3 hours 28
minutes, so that on average, he runs each mile in 8 minutes. This
means that he runs at 80% of his maximum capacity output for the
whole marathon. Let us assume that, for most of the race, fatty
acid and glucose oxidation contribute equally to the power output

(that is 40% of the maximum each). However, at 22 miles (35km) the liver and muscle glycogen stores approach depletion - unless there is any other means of obtaining glucose or unless fatty acid concentrations in the blood can increase, the power output must fall. If the entire contribution from glucose oxidation was lost, the power output would fall from 80% to 40% of maximal and his speed should fall from 8 minutes per mile to 16 minutes per mile or less than 4 miles per hour ($6.4km.h^{-1}$). This is obviously fatigue - and could explain why many non-elite runners begin to walk in the later stages of the race despite an earnest desire to keep running.

There is, however, one means by which extra glucose could be produced under these conditions of fatigue. Some of the protein of the muscle may be broken down in the later stages of the race to provide amino acids which can be converted to glucose in the liver. The process of conversion of amino acids to glucose is known as gluconeogenesis, which simply means new glucose synthesis or glucose synthesised from non-carbohydrate sources. This will result in an extra supply of glucose and may allow the runner to overcome 'the wall'. However this is achieved only at the expense of damage to the muscle and the earlier this occurs in the race the more damage will be caused.

In summary, it appears that the marathon run is beyond the normal physyiological limit of the body's fuel supply. The distance is too long and the pace is too fast. Provided that fatty acid could supply all the energy requirements, the running could be maintained for very very long periods of time. This is presumably how migrating birds are able to fly very long distances; unfortunately how they overcome the limitations in supply of fatty acids is not known. Man is designed metabolically for very long distance walking, not running.

How does the successful marathon runner overcome these difficulties? The answer must be in a variety of ways. Experience will allow him to consume energy at the optimum rate; if he finishes the race with any glycogen left in his muscles he could have run faster; if he runs out of muscle glycogen before the end of the race both he and his performance will suffer. There is also evidence that training increases the ability of muscle fibres to remove fatty acids from the blood and so maintain a higher power output when carbohydrate is not available. The ability of elite long-distance runners to compete effectively could be due to their possession of a lower threshold to pain from the sensory nerve endings within their muscles so that they can ignore the warning signals and risk the consequences.

Although there is no doubt that fatigue can occur due to changes within the active muscle, there is evidence that factors within the CNS may also be partially responsible: this is known as central fatigue (Bigland - Ritchie 1981). One specific amine, 5-hydroxytryptamine (5HT), is known to be involved in the CNS in the regulation of sleep (see Wurtman, 1983). It seems possible therefore that sleep and fatigue caused by endurance exercise could be brought about in part by an increase in the brain concentration of 5HT. The question arises as to the mechanism by which endurance exercise could influence the concentration of 5HT in the brain. The following hypothesis can be put forward. Since none of the enzymes involved in the synthesis of 5HT in the brain approaches saturation with substrate (see Newsholme and Leech, 1983b), an increase in the concentration of tryptophan in the brain could lead to an increase in the rate of formation and hence possibly in the concentration of 5HT and, in addition, the rate of transport of tryptophan across the blood brain barrier controls in the brain concentration of tryptophan. Of considerable importance is the fact that the carrier responsible for the transport of tryptophan and tyrosine across the blood brain barrier also transports the branched-chain amino acids - leucine, isoleucine and valine - into the brain. It is therefore of considerable interest and possible importance that it is only these latter three amino acids that are utilised exclusively by muscle. This provides the basis of a metabolic link between muscle and brain via the plasma amino acid levels. These amino acids in the plasma will compete against each other for binding to this carrier in the brain and hence will compete for transport into the brain. If the rate of uptake of branched-chain amino acids by muscle is increased during sustained exercise so that their plasma concentrations will be decreased, this will lead to an increase in the plasma ratio of plasma concentrations of aromatic amino acids to branched chain amino acids. This should favour the entry of aromatic amino acids into the brain and the increased brain concentration of tryptophan should cause an increase in the concentration of 5HT; this might then result in a change in the rate of neuronal activity and this will be manifested as central fatigue. This hypothesis has been tested in the rat and some evidence in support has been obtained (Acworth et al., 1986). It is also possible that changes in the concentration of 5HT in some specific areas of the brain could be responsible for the improvement of mood that is experienced by many people after exercise.

9. Manipulating metabolism

Knowledge of the oxidative processes producing energy for the marathon runner and of the metabolic limitations enable a number of suggestions to be put forward to improve performance, or at least not to impair it!

(i) To ensure that the glycogen stores are as high as possible prior to the race, the regime of 'glycogen stripping' has been recommened. However, for a runner training more than about 50 miles (80km) per week, this may be replaced by the 'glycogen loading' regime. This simply means that a large quantity of carbohydrate should be eaten in the two to four days before the race, depending upon the individual. The precise time will need to be ascertained by trial and error - loose bowels and excessive urination usually mean the peak glycogen level has passed. In what form should this extra carbohydrate be taken? The normal response of the body to food is to replete glycogen stores first and then to convert any additional carbohydrate to fat for storage in the adipose tissue. The marathon runner needs to encourage the former but discourage the latter. This can be done simply by eating normal amounts of food but increasing the proportion of carbohydrate; the best pattern is three or four meals spaced out over the day with a couple of snacks in between. The nature of the carbohydrate is also important. It should be complex carbohydrate, not simple sugars, so that bread, potatoes, cereals, rice, pearl barley, spaghetti and pasta are beneficial. The intake of food containing the simple sugars, chocolate bars, sweetened drinks, honey, jam, should not be excessive and only accompany the complex carbohydrate. The rate of digestion of complex carbohydrates is slow and hence the absorption of sugar into the body takes place over a long time and this encourages the storage of glycogen instead of fat. The rate of digestion depends not only on the state of the carbohydrate but also on the presence of fat and protein. These will slow down passage through the small intestine and favour the slow, gradual absorption of glucose. Hence meat, cheese, fish, egg should be eaten at each meal but less than usual, since carbohydrate must replace much of the protein.

As indicated earlier, glycogen is stored in association with water so that during the 'loading' phase it may be necessary to increase the intake of liquid to avoid dehydration. A simple means of testing this is to observe the colour of the urine - it should be clear not amber.

The large quantity of glycogen plus water in the muscles can give a feeling of heaviness to the legs in the first few miles of the marathon but if the explanation is known it should dispel anxiety. Furthermore the feeling will soon disappear as the excess glycogen is used and the trapped water released, and the benefits will be felt after 15 miles (24km).

(ii) If the amount of carbohydrate stored by the body limits the marathon runner, does it not make metabolic sense to eat easily-digested carbohydrate (e.g. glucose) just prior to the race? The answer is 'no'. The reason emphasises the integrated nature of metabolic processes in the body. The mobilisation of fatty acids during endurance running is largely due to changes in the blood levels of two important hormones, adrenaline and insulin. The former stimulates fatty acid mobilisation, the latter inhibits it.. Adrenaline is released by the adrenal medulla in response to the excitement and stress prior to the start of the race and is further increased during the race. The insulin level, however, decreases as the race proceeds. These changes probably account for the smooth increase in the rate of mobilisation of fatty acids during the run. Eating, especially carbohydrate, causes the release of insulin, in large amounts, which will inhibit fatty acid mobilisation just when it is needed to conserve valuable glycogen stores.

Some runners find it beneficial to eat little or nothing after the evening meal on the day preceding the race, although an intake of fluid should be maintained. Provided that as much rest as possible is taken, this period of starvation will use little glycogen but should encourage fatty acid release from adipose tissue depots. However, such a period of starvation must be from individual choice; many runners find they run better after a good carbohydrate breakfast but this should be taken several hours before the race.

(iii) If it is not recommended to eat carbohydrate before the race, is it advisable to take carbohydrate-containing drinks during the race? The answer is a qualified 'yes'. After about 5 miles

(8km) of running, easily-digested carbohydrate (e.g. glucose) can be taken because, at this stage, it does not result in insulin secretion. However, the amount ingested should be limited.

(iv) The mobilisation of fatty acid is gradual throughout an endurance run and does not approach the maximum (approximately 2mM) until an hour or so of running. It is, however, possible to mimic the effect of adrenaline on adipose tissue with caffeine and stimulate fatty acid mobilisation. On the basis of laboratory experiments, it has been suggested that a strong cup of black coffee taken about one to two hours before the race will increase the blood fatty acid concentration so that it is available for oxidation as soon as the race begins (Costill et al., 1977). This will ensure that maximal or near-maximal rates of fatty acid oxidation occur early in the race so that less glycogen will be used at this stage.

(v) The control mechanism that operates between fatty acids and glucose will eventually establish a pattern of fuel utilisation during the race in which fatty acid, glucose and glycogen oxidation all contribute to ATP formation. As already explained, it is important to encourage as much fatty acid oxidation as possible and, although this cannot be measured in every individual, by experience from long training runs athletes will get to know the pace they can maintain for long periods. Once this is established in a race it is disadvantageous to vary it unless absolutely necessary (e.g. running uphill) since this will disturb the fuel oxidation pattern and encourage a greater rate of oxidation of the limited carbohydrate stores.

(vi) What the runner does at the end of the race is as important for his well-being as his preparation. The race is followed by rest, relaxation and usually, elation at having completed the distance. This can cause problems because the body is short of carbohydrate and probably short of fluid. The removal of the demand for large amounts of energy by the muscles and the relaxation may decrease the emphasis placed on the control of the blood sugar level by the body so that it can easily fail to protect from the phenomenon of hypoglycaemia, which is characterised by dizziness, sweating, weakness and nausea. In addition, low blood volume can reduce the flow of blood to the brain as the cardiovascular system readjusts to rest and this will exacerbate any degree of hypoglycaemia. Consequently, the important post-marathon requirements are liquid and carbohydrate. However, as with the pre-run condition, simple carbohydrates can be dangerous; they will now result in insulin secretion, which will lower the blood fatty acid level and force all tissues to use glucose so that severe hypoglycaemia can result. Ideally, the carbohydrate should be complex but in a liquid form (to prevent dehydration). Since the body can now rapidly lose heat, the ideal post-marathon activity is drinking hot thick vegetable soup slowly while wrapped in a warm tracksuit or blanket.

References

Acworth, I., Nicholass, J., Morgan, B. and Newsholme, E.A. (1986). Effect of sustained exercise on concentrations of plasma aromatic and branched chain amino acids and brain amines. Biochemistry and Biophysics Research Communications 137:149-153.

Bigland-Ritchie, B, (1981). EMG and fatigue of human voluntary and stimulated contractions. Ciba Foundation Symposium 82:89-101.

Cahill, G.F. (1970). Starvation in man. New England Journal of Medicine 282:668-675.

Costill, D.L., Coyle, E. and Dalsky, G. (1977). Effects of elevated plasma FFA and insulin on muscle glycogen usage during exercise. Journal of Applied Physiology 43:695-699.

Davidson, S., Passmore, R and Bronk, J.F. (1979). Human Nutrition and Dietetics. Edinburgh, Churchill Livingstone.

Davies, C.T.M. and Thompson, M.W. (1979). Aerobic performance of female marathon and male ultramarathon athletes. European Journal of Applied Physiology 41:233-245.

Durnin, J.G.G.A. and Passmore, R. (1967). Energy, Work and Leisure, London, Heinemann.

Felig, P. and Wahren, J. (1975). Fuel homeostasis in exercise. New England Journal of Medicine 293:1078-1084.

Hall, G.M., Lucke, J.N. and Masheter, K. (1981). Metabolic and hormonal changes during prolonged exercise in the horse. In Biochemistry of Exercise, IVA (edited by J. Poortmans and G. Nisset, pp.88-92. Baltimore, University Park Press.

Hermansen, L., Hultman, E. and Saltin, B. (1967). Muscle glycogen during prolonged severe exercise. Acta Physiologica Scandinavica 71:129-139.

Newsholme, E.A. and Leech, A.R. (1983a). The Runner: Energy and Endurance, 21 Pitts Road, Headington, Oxford, Fitness Books.

Newsholme, E.A. and Leech, A.R. (1983b). Biochemistry for the Medical Sciences. Chichester, England, John Wiley and Sons Ltd.

Paul, P. and Holmes, U.L. (1976). Free fatty acids and glucose metabolism during increased energy expenditure and before training. Medicine and Science in Sports 7:176-184.

Wahren, J. (1979). Glucose turnover during exercise in healthy man and in patients with diabetes mellitus. Diabetes 28:82-88.

Wurtman, R.J. (1983). Behavioural effects of nutrients. Lancet 1:1145-1147.

Discussion

Dr Jansson, Stockholm

In situations with carbohydrate (glycogen) depleted muscles we know that we can't keep up a high exercise intensity and thus the quantitative importance of glycogen as fuel has been put forward. However, do you think that glycogen has a qualitative importance as e.g. supplying the Krebs cycle with intermediates or producing 'glycolytic ATP'?

Dr Newsholme

Yes, I think it has qualitative importance - perhaps in maintaining the concentration of a key regulatory metabolite - perhaps one of the intermediates of glycolysis or the high ATP/ADP concentration ratio. The depletion of glycogen would then result in lowering of the concentration of this important putative regulator. The most important question is how is contractile activity controlled and what factors regulate this process - is it, for example, a key glycolytic intermediate?

Dr Jansson

I would like to comment regarding the glycogen depleted muscle. In recent studies we have shown that, at the point of fatigue during endurance exercise (65% of maximal oxygen uptake), which coincides with muscle glycogen depletion, there is a definite increase in muscle IMP and hypoxanthine contents, indicating a change in the muscle energy state at fatigue during endurance exercise.

Dr Newsholme

This is very interesting and potentially important - could the IMP play a role in decreasing the contractile activity of the muscle e.g. by restricting Ca^{2+} release from the sarcoplasmic reticulum or by inhibiting the actomyosin ATPase? These suggestions could be tested.

Dr Jansson

Can fatigue be seen as a question of supplying the Krebs cycle with intermediates or producing ATP direct into the cytoplasm?

Dr Newsholme

In other words what is the biochemical nature of the fatigue that results when the glycogen levels in the muscles are decreased? We are at the same stage as when we discussed the cause of fatigue in anaerobic activity in that we don't really know, primarily because there haven't been any attempts to study fatigue at a biochemical level to indicate the process that is limiting in that particular system. My question to you in return would be do we know how important is, for example, the excitation-contraction coupling or the ability to release Ca? Could glycogen metabolism somehow be related to the excitation-contraction coupling because it produces glycolytic ATP? Cardiologists also believe that to maintain normal contractile activity in the heart, glycolytic ATP or glycolysis is needed. So there is some degree of common ground between the cardiologist interested in what happens in terms of an acute heart attack and our interest in terms of what happens with fatigue at the end of sustained exercise when the glycogen stores are depleted.

Equally it could be that ATP might be required for maintaining troponin in a particular characteristic position to take up Ca ions. The relationship between troponin C, troponin I and tropomyosin could be important and that has not been adequately studied. Alternatively it might be that it is the actomyosin ATPase, the cross-bridge ATPase, which is able to sense glycolytic ATP, a small change in the ATP/ADP ratio, or indeed some

intermediate of glycolysis. All of these would be potential
possibilities by which there could be a glycolytic input into the
regulation of the contractile process. Each one of these -
excitation-contraction coupling, the troponin system, the ATPase
system - is a major problem for investigation in the future. I
think that is where our future problem lies in understanding the
molecular basis of fatigue.

Professor Williams, Loughborough
We have been studying fatigue during endurance running by having
our subjects run half-marathons and marathons on the laboratory
treadmill where we can actually monitor some of the changes going
on. We have found in nearly 100 experiments on people running to
exhaustion that when they get near the point of exhaustion rarely
do the RER values fall below 0.85. The idea that comes from cycle
ergometry that you see a gradual fall in the RER values, suggesting
there is an increased fat metabolism and that you need to reduce
the exercise intensity to get below the threshold at which fat
metabolism can cover the energy needs of the muscles, this idea does
not appear in our experiments. One interpretation is that runners
may slow to a walk, not to permit fat metabolism to cover the
energy demands, but rather to change their gait and this allows
them to use muscle groups which had not hitherto been glycogen
depleted. So the first observation is that the onset of fatigue is
not preceded by a fall in the RER values, suggesting that the
glycogen is very low. Work by David Costill in the early 1970s,
which included muscle biopsy sampling, has shown that at the point
of fatigue there is still glycogen in the muscle. Secondly, it
might be that the difference is between the elite runner and the
recreational runner and this allows another interpretation. The
recreational runner may slow down from 60-70% $\dot{V}O_2$max to 40% $\dot{V}O_2$max
to allow heat loss, redistribution of blood volume and so on to an
O_2 cost equivalent to walking. The elite endurance runner drops
from 80% to 50% $\dot{V}O_2$max, from say 5 minute to 6.5 minute miling,
permitting a redistribution of cardiac output but with a change in
gait. The point is that fatigue doesn't coincide with apparent
decrease in glycogen during the running. Besides when you feed
subjects with carnitine to try to improve the translocation of the
acyl fatty acids into the mitochondria, that doesn't improve
things either. A final point is that when subjects are pre-fed or
loaded with carbohydrate they can complete the marathon compared
with a control condition where they stop at about 17 miles
(27km). They do so with a depressed fatty acid and an elevated
carbohydrate metabolism.

Dr Newsholme
In terms of what is the limit in fatty acid oxidation, if indeed
there is a limit, I'm not sure if we know the answer to that. My
feeling is that it is the actual rate of diffusion of the fatty
acids into the muscle itself. The fact that fatty acids are bound
to albumin means that the concentration of free fatty acids, which
governs diffusion, is quite low. My feeling is that it is a
physical limitation, which is diffusion and this gets back to
things like capillary density and muscle fibre size and therefore
any biochemical intervention will not be effective. The only means

of improvement will be by training to affect capillary density: so
I don't find it surprising that biochemical manipulations will not
affect the rate of fatty acid oxidation. In terms of the fact
that the RER values do not appear to fall and that there may be
some glycogen remaining, we have to return to a point made earlier
by Eric Hultman. This is the question of what is limiting the
rate at which glycogen and therefore carbohydrate is metabolised.
Is the system able to sense that very soon there is going to be a
major depletion of glycogen and this will produce some small
change in the rate of glycolysis? As the concentration of glycogen
decreases below or around the Km value, there will be a small
decrease in the rates of ATP and intermediate formation and these
changes could be sensed to produce the fatigue mechanism prior to
total depletion of glycogen. This would be much more difficult to
detect; it is much easier to say as glycogen is depleted there is a
dramatic change which should be detectable in the RER values.

In terms of a change in gait, it doesn't surprise me that this
occurs as muscles are fatiguing. This would allow movement to be
achieved using different non-fatigued muscles. I don't think this
is an either/or mechanism but both may operate hand in hand. Your
work is suggesting that the cause of fatigue will be much more
difficult to determine.

Dr Nagle, Madison, Wisconsin
You suggest that the limitation of fatty acid uptake is at the
muscle cell. Could you follow up the lines of evidence for that?

Dr Newsholme
The lines of evidence for that are extremely limited because no
studies to my knowledge have been done in attempting to assess that
limitation. The way to do this would be to take measurements of
the fatty acid concentrations both in the bloodstream and in the
muscle itself and to measure the levels of the intermediates,
particularly fatty acyclenzyme a, fatty acylcarnitine, under such
conditions and to my knowledge this has not been done.

Professor Brooks, Berkely, California
Some years ago Havel and colleagues did that: they indicated that
there is a significant uptake of fatty acids from the blood. They
only suply about half of the fat combusted so there is an
intramuscular pool which is very active.

My comments refer to amino acids. I would like to challenge the
notion that amino acids are not fuels for exercise. We have made
measurements on the rat during prolonged exercise: leucine alone
supplies 1% of the total CO_2 excreted and the same thing can be
concluded for humans. You might say that 1% is not very much but
it is 1% for one of twenty odd amino acids. So we should consider
the ketoanalotic as well as branched chain amino acid metabolism,
as well as other amino acids. For instance, Lemon has demonstrated
that exercise results in increased urea excretion which would
explain about 5% of the total kilocalories used and then when
subjects are glycogen depleted there is an additional 5%, now
accounting for 5 to 10% of the total kilocalories. Admittedly this
is a small proportion but on many occasions endurance competitions
are decided by margins of a fraction of 1%.

Dr Newsholme

You may well be right in the assumption that amino acids can make a
greater contribution than 1%. My intent in making that comment was
to answer the question of branched chain amino acids being
important as an energy source in muscle. Although they can be
oxidised by muscle in the human, that does not appear to be the
case in the rat. What is interesting in the rat is that branched
chain amino acids are taken up, are transaminated and the keto
acids are released. However, recent data of Wagenmakers in
Liverpool suggest that their contribution to total energy for
motion even in man is very limited. This suggests another function
for amino acids.

Professor Brooks

Walker has shown that oxidation does take place in the human, using
labelled keto analogues.

Dr Newsholme

That certainly is a suggestion of a difference of opinion. There
is therefore a controversy as to how much is actually oxidised in
the two situations.

    Coming back to the other point, the amino acid metabolism <u>in
the liver</u>, which would be providing nitrogen for urea and
gluconeogenesis, could provide an additional important contribution.
There is a great deal of controversy as to how much this might be
but it certainly could be 5 to 10% and this could be important in
competition.

Dr Sutton, Hamilton, Canada

I wonder if you would like to take us through more of the
neurotransmitter hypothesis of fatigue. You emphasised the
serotonergic aspects of fatigue but in terms of most of the
biological functions one hears about, the dopaminergic transmitters
seem to be fairly important. Is it conceivable that you could
construct a hypothesis related to the use of precursor amino acids
in muscle that could have the same sort of impact on brain
neurotransmitter function, or levels or turnover in brain at the
point of fatigue? That may in fact be a more attractive hypothesis
if one is to assume a neurotransmitter route.

Dr Newsholme

You are arguing that it might be rather noradrenergic or
dopaminergic. We do find changes in noradrenaline in the whole
brain and we are currently looking at this in various areas of the
brain. So far we have found no changes at all in dopamine which
seems to stay relatively constant. The increases we have seen have
been particularly in 5-HT and in some instances in noradrenaline
but not dopamine. As to which neurotransmitters are important in
the whole area of neural changes, it depends on the investigation
and the current hypothesis. Certainly there is some evidence that
5-HT might be involved in changes: feeding high levels of
tryptophan has been found to be helpful in improving mood and this
has been used successfully in treating mildly depressed patients.
There have also been successful attempts in the U.S.A. to use

exercise in the treatment of mildly depressed patients. It is a
reasonable suggestion that 5-HT could be involved in this.

Mr McLaren, Liverpool Polytechnic
Well trained endurance athletes are able to utilise FFA at an earlier
timepoint than less trained individuals - this has a potential
glycogen sparing effect. What is/are the control mechanism(s)
involved? Is it a change in insulin sensitivity by adipose tissue?

Dr Newsholme
Yes: this would be the simplest answer at this stage of our
knowledge. The adipose tissue might also be more sensitive to
increases in the level of the catecholamines.

Dr Wootton, University of Southampton
Brigette Essen has demonstrated the substantial contribution of
intramuscular lipid stores to energy metabolism during prolonged
exercise. Do these observations alter our understanding of how
delivery and uptake of blood-borne FFA by the muscle is rate-
limiting lipid oxidation?

Dr Newsholme
I suggest not, since I would argue that the capacity for β-oxidation
of fatty acids will not be much greater than the maximum rate of
diffusion of fatty acids into the muscle - thus the muscle could
use either exogenous or endogenous fatty acids at maximal rates but
not both. However, the evidence for this is very limited.

Professor Poortmans, Brussels, Belgium
One of your potential factors causing fatigue is the limitation of
the entry of free fatty acids into muscle. Knowing that you still
have sufficient amounts of intramuscular triglycerides which could
be used, how relevant would your previous hypothesis be?

Dr Newsholme
If the limitation in the rate of oxidation of fatty acids is the
entry of fatty acids into muscle, then the capacity to use them,
the beta oxidation capacity is, in my opinion, unlikely to exceed
significantly this delivery rate when adipose tissue lipolysis and
blood flow are maximal. So even though intramuscular triglycerides
are available, I consider they will not, in this situation, be
additive to free fatty acids supplied from the bloodstream and
cannot be used at a higher rate than that of exogenous fatty
acid. Because of the huge store of triglycerides in adipose
tissue, it seems likely that this would be the usual source of fatty
acid and the intramuscular pathway would be used only when the
external supply was inadequate.

Professor Poortmans
Would you be in favour of the idea of people taking supplementary
carnitine daily when one knows that the rate limiting step is that
of carnitine acyl-CoA transferase activity?

Dr Newsholme
Even if the limiting step in fatty acid oxidation is carnitine

palmitoyl transferase, this should not imply that the activity of the enzyme is limited by or regulated by the concentration of carnitine in the muscle. It is possible that, in marathon runners at the peak of their training, sufficient muscle damage and loss of carnitine might occur to warrant dietary supplementation. Of course, for athletes other than marathon or ultramarathon runners, carnitine supplementation would be contra-indicated since fatty acid oxidation should be kept to a minimum.

Biomechanical aspects of endurance

E.C. FREDERICK

The role of biomechanical factors in endurance is mainly mediated
through changes in the mechanical requirements of work and
efficiency. This paper discusses the mechanical constraints;
gravity, mass, friction, centripetal force, aerodynamics, and
hydrodynamics and their effects on endurance performance.
Efficiency and the economy of movement are also discussed to
underscore the broad role of biomechanics in improving endurance.
Improving the economy of movement reduces the metabolic power
consumed in performing a particular task, and so makes more energy
available for enhancing performance by increasing the vigor of
movements or sustaining a given workload for a longer period.
Intrinsic and extrinsic factors known to affect the economy of
movement are reviewed. Suggestions are made for future research in
this area by taking a synthetic and experimental approach to the
further elaboration of mathematical models, especially link-
segmental models, which might predict fruitful approaches to
enhancing economy and efficiency. Special attention should be paid
to a better understanding of segmental energy transfers, center of
mass excursion and elastic strain energy storage as potential
mechanisms for enhancing metabolic economy.

1. The role of mechanical constraints

Endurance, the capacity to sustain a relatively high intensity of
physical work, is strongly affected by a number of biomechanical
factors. The challenge of endurance performance is to generate as
little mechanical power as needed to maintain performance with a
minimal expenditure of metabolic power. Biomechanics affects this
relationship between mechanical and metabolic power in many ways.
The breadth of this biomechanical influence can most easily be seen
by looking at the mechanical constraints on endurance performance.

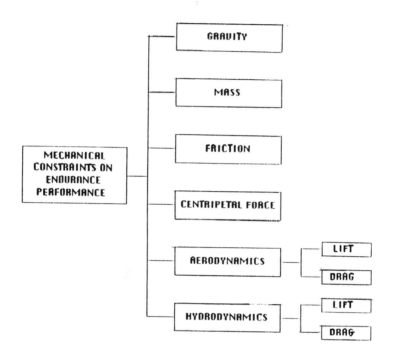

Figure 1. The major mechanical contraints on endurance performance
are listed. Although the listing is not complete most of the
mechanical factors that limit performance are included. It should
also be noted that the items on the list are not independent and
may be highly interrelated.

Fig.1 outlines several of the major mechanical constraints on
performance in endurance sports. This is not a complete listing or
a correct taxonomy, but it does enumerate the major factors. It
should also be pointed out that there is much overlap and
interdependence among the various factors. For example, many of
the equations that describe certain of these factors, such as
frictional, centripetal, aerodynamic, and hydrodynamic forces, may
have a gravitational acceleration term and/or a mass term. Seldom
does one of these constraints have an opportunity to work
independently of the other factors.

   In a sense these mechanical constraints are what we have to work
with. If endurance is to be improved by biomechanical means it
will be done by affecting one or more of these constraints. For
example, the bicyclist who assumes a tucked position, drafts a
competitor and wears a drag reducing helmet and body suit is trying
to reduce aerodynamic constraints. He may also be reducing rolling
friction by using high pressure tires with a smooth and narrow
tread. He reduces gravity and mass constraints by using
lightweight components. He tries to minimize the toppling effect
of centripetal forces by leaning into turns. All of these examples
address mechanical constraints in a way that reduces physical power

requirements which in turn reduces the metabolic power required to pedal at a given speed. Bicycling becomes more energetically economical and endurance is enhanced when these factors are taken into account.

Frederick (1983) has reviewed extrinsic mechanical aids to performance which work by affecting one or more of these constraints. His review cites a number of documented aids to performance including: selecting appropriate environmental conditions (e.g. lower gravity and air density); wearing aerodynamically designed clothing and light and resilient footwear; using aerodynamic javelins and golf balls; archery shooting with optimally designed bows and arrows; rowing in smooth and correctly shaped racing shells; and running on surfaces of properly tuned compliance and with correctly banked turns. Not all of these examples deal with endurance sports, but those that do carry with them the potential to improve performance by between 1% and 15%.

It is apparent, from the above, that biomechanics plays a diverse role in endurance performance. There are many ways in which equipment and movement can be altered to affect mechanical and metabolic power. When we discuss the relationship between these two factors we are dealing with the concept of efficiency. Efficiency and economy of movement will become the focus of the remainder of this paper as we try to explore the possibilities for improving endurance by biomechanical means.

2. Economy of movement

2.1 Effiency versus economy
Most sports biomechanists think of efficiency as the ratio of power out to power in. In other words, efficiency is an expression of the proportion of metabolic power required to produce a given amount of physical power output. If we look at the power produced, for example, on a cycle ergometer relative to the metabolic power expended we see that humans are about 15% efficient at low power outputs. To generate 45 watts of power on a cycle ergometer we need to expend about 300 watts of metabolic power (Stegemann, 1981:p.71). The problem with such calculations is that they do not completely measure the mechanical power produced. When we pedal a cycle ergometer, work is being done to move the mass of the limbs and trunk and to perform a variety of non-productive counter movements as well as isometric 'work'. If one simply sits on an ergometer and pedals with no load, oxygen uptake goes up because work is being performed, but, in fact, no measurable work is being done. Much of this internal 'work' is excluded from most calculations of efficiency. In addition, as Lafortune and Cavanagh (1983) have pointed out, significant work is also being done on the cycle itself in distorting the frame and bending components, and that is not included in the work measured by a conventional ergometer. These examples underscore the difficulties in assessing mechanical power and efficiency.

It turns out to be very difficult to precisely measure or to calculate the mechanical power output of a moving human body, and so exact measurements of efficiency are not possible for sports movements. However, the concept is an interesting one and helpful in elucidating the influence of biomechanics on endurance.

Let's start with the assumption that we are dealing with endurance sports where metabolic power is limiting. A given athlete trains physiological systems to the point where a certain level of metabolic power consumption can be sustained for a set amount of time and the limit then becomes the amount of mechanical power that can be expended given the metabolic power available. A runner, for example, might be able to sustain 90% of his $\dot{V}O_2$max for 30 minutes. That works out to about 1500 W for a champion class runner. The total mechanical power requirement of running at a speed of $5.5m.s^{-1}$ is roughly 800 W. In this example, the runner is then constrained only by the amount of physical work he can perform with the available energy during the allotted time. The more efficiently he moves the faster he can run and the better his performance. He might effect such an improvement in efficiency by changing the pattern of movement to reduce mechanical power output that is not contributing to forward movement, e.g. reducing unnecessary excursions of the center of mass of the body. Or, he might modify a number of extrinsic factors that are increasing his extraneous workload, e.g. reduce air resistance with a wind suit, or, wear lighter shoes. If he can reduce the power requirement to say 750 W by manipulating these factors then he would be able to run about 6% faster with the same expenditure of metabolic power. This is a gross oversimplification of a complex topic but it underscores the influence of mechanical constraints on endurance.

This paper deals with the question of how biomechanics influences endurance performance by focusing on mechanical factors affecting the economy of movement. It becomes clear from the previous discussion of mechanical constraints that a number of factors that influence endurance are closely linked to the moderation of extraneous mechanical work and to the efficiency of movement. But, as mentioned, work and power output are difficult to determine for complex movements such as those used in sports. For this reason physiologists and biomechanists usually retreat to the relative comfort of the term 'economy of movement'. Economy of movement is defined as the relative metabolic power or energy required to perform a given task. The task might be, for example, to swim at a velocity of $2m.s^{-1}$, to run at $4m.s^{-1}$, or to dribble a soccer ball 100m in 20 seconds. Metabolic power requirements are usually measured via oxygen uptake. The notion here is that the less energy it takes to perform the task the more economical the movement.

By inference we might be tempted to also say that the movement is more efficient as well but that may not be the case. In fact in most cases of improved economy, i.e. a reduction in the metabolic power requirement to perform a task, the agent of change is most likely to be a reduction in the mechanical power requirement. In this case, efficiency may remain unchanged or even decrease. With that note of caution in mind we can proceed to examine the biomechanical factors that may influence endurance through the agency of improved economy of movement.

2.2 Factors that affect economy of movement
Economy of movement is an important factor in all endurance sports but its role has been particularly well explored in distance

running. A number of authors have shown a strong correlation
between success in distance running and the economy of running
(Costill & Fox, 1969; Costill & Winrow, 1970; Gregor and
Kirkendall, 1978). So it is desirable to modify running style, and
presumably the patterns of movement used in other endurance sports,
in a way that improves economy of movement. The contributions of
biomechanics to this issue are primarily in determining the kinetic
and kinematic patterns that are consistent with greater economy.
Some answers lie in a synthesis of current findings relating
various factors to the economy of movement.

A number of factors have been shown to influence the economy of
movement. They can be divided into two principal categories:
factors that extrinsically influence the economy of movement and
factors that affect economy intrinsically. Table 1 and 2 summarize
a number of factors that have been shown to have a relationship to
the economy of movement.

Extrinsic factors include environmental effects and the effects
of surfaces and equipment. Intrinsic factors include biological
rhythms and kinanthropometric, psychological and biomechanical
factors. It should be pointed out that these tables include
factors that have been shown by direct experimental evidence to
affect economy as well as factors that have been shown to be
statistically correlated with economy. Because factors with a
statistical relationship may not have a direct effect on economy,
those factors are indicated with an asterisk.

Table 1. Extrinsic factors known to influence the economy of
movement. These statistically significant factors can be
positively or negatively associated with economical movement.

Extrinsic Factor	Source
Environmental Factors	
Ambient temperature	Sato et al., 1983
Wind	Pugh, 1971
Surface-Related Factors	
Grade	Pugh, 1971
Surface compliance	Passmore & Durnin, 1955; Ralston, 1981
Surface resilience	Strydom et al., 1966
Equipment-Related Factors	
Orthotics	Hayes et al., 1983
Shoe sole hardness	Frederick et al., 1983
Shoe weight	Frederick, 1985a
Weight on head or trunk	Soule & Goldman, 1969

Table 2. Intrinsic factors known to influence the economy of
movement. These statistically significant factors can be
positively or negatively associated with economical movement.

Intrinsic Factor	Source
Kinanthropometric Factors	
Body weight	Cureton et al., 1978
*Leg length	van der Walt & Wyndham, 1973
Psychological factors	
Relaxation	Benson et al., 1978
Hypnotic suggestion	Morgan & Brown, 1983
Biological Rhythms	
Circadian rhythms	Reilly & Brooks, 1982
Circannual rhythms	Zahorska-Markiewicz & Markiewicz, 1984
Kinetic and Kinematic Factors	
*Center of mass excursion	Williams, 1980
Mechanical energy transfers	Shorten et al., 1981; Pierrynowski et al., 1980
*Net positive work rate	Williams, 1980
*Impact force	Williams, 1980
*Foot strike	Williams, 1980
*Foot contact time	Williams, 1980
*Extraneous arm motion	Williams, 1980
*Angle of trunk inclination	Williams, 1980
*Angle of shank inclination	Williams, 1980
Lower knee flexion velocity in support	Frederick et al., 1983
*Plantar flexion at toe off	Williams, 1980
Stride length	Cavanagh & Williams, 1982

Under kinanthropometric constraints such as body weight and leg
length, one should also include the distribution of body weight.
As an example, consider the predicted effect of foot size on the
economy of running. Extreme departures from the normal foot size
at a given height can bring advantages or disadvantages to the
endurance athlete. Fig. 2 shows the relationship between foot size
and the calculated energy required to transport the feet during
running (data from Frederick, 1985a). These calculations show the
consequences of having large versus small feet. At the extremes
this effect is large enough to have a significant influence on
endurance. One can imagine a host of other anatomically-mediated
biomechanical effects, but this is a poorly explored area of
investigation.

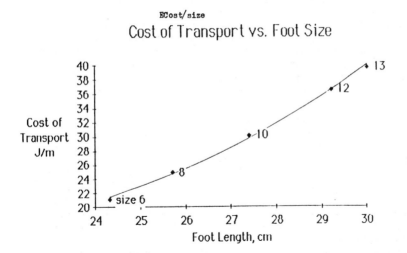

Cost of Transport vs. Foot Size

Figure 2. The estimated metabolic cost of carrying the weight of
the feet during running for various foot sizes. The metabolic
costs are calculated from the data presented in Frederick (1985a).
Foot masses are computed from the data in Chandler et al. (1975)
assuming geometric scaling of foot mass with length.

Many of the factors listed in Tables 1 and 2 are immutable, such
as foot size, or simply a consequence of the circumstances of the
movement or the environmemt in which the movement is performed.
Others, however, are changeable and beg to be explored as potential
keys to the biomechanics of economical movement. This is
especially true of those factors connected with the kinetics and
kinematics of movement.

2.3 Further approaches to improving economy with biomechanics
A few central themes have the potential to unite these variables
into a single mechanism or group of mechanisms that have broader
implications for improved economy of movement. One such theme is
the transfer of energy between and within body segments. Both
Williams (1980) and Shorten et al. (1981) have shown a strong
statistical association between segmental energy transfer and
economical movement, and their mathematical models support that
notion. As further support, Norman, Caldwell and Komi (1985) have
shown that a major biomechanical factor related to success in cross-
country skiing is the capacity to effect greater transfers of
mechanical energy. Pierrynowski, Winter and Norman (1980) have
elaborated on the role of energy transfers in walking efficiency.
   It should be pointed out, however, that there are problems with
between segment energy transfer calculations because the
constraints are selected on an arbitrary basis and independently of
the pattern of muscle activation. Within segment transfers do not
suffer these problems and so may yield more useful insights. In
either case, it should be noted that several of the biomechanical
variables that are correlated with economical movement may in fact
be cross-correlated with the segmental transfer of energy. Such
factors as the angle of the shank, knee flexion velocity and net

positive work rate (Williams, 1980) may be part of a multi-segmental strategy to enhance segmental energy transfers.

These observations should be followed up on in two ways. First, a synthesis of improved mathematical models that incorporate electromyographic data and more precise anatomical measurements of the line of pull of muscles might help us predict what kinematic adjustments in movement might cause greater transfers of energy. Second we need to test these ideas experimentally. A starting point might be the determination of which kinematic patterns the models predict will enhance energy transfer and then to determine if in fact energy transfer improves economy. It has been suggested that this might be done by using biofeedback techniques to modify subjects' kinematics and to then test this hypothesis (Frederick, 1985b). Sanderson and Cavanagh (1986) have recently demonstrated the feasibility of feedback training for modifying the biomechanics of cycling. The use of feedback training shows great promise for future investigations of this subject.

Another possible mechanism for economical movement is the excursion of the body's center of mass, although this approach has limitations. Point-mass models treat the body as if it were a single point mass located at its center of mass. These models have illuminated some of the factors underlying the work and energy relationship but they suffer from the fundamental problem that kinetic energy is not a vector quantity. So, tracking the body's center of mass is not sufficient for estimation of the total kinetic energy of the body. Shorten (1983) has shown that his method underestimates the total kinetic energy of the body even if the kinetic energy of the limbs relative to the center of mass is factored in. Because of this inherent limitation we do not have the support of good mechanical models to pursue this possibility experimentally.

Despite this limitation in mathematical modelling there may still be a specific effect due to the excursion of the body's center of mass. Although a direct association has never been proven, good sense tells us that a number of the intrinsic variables which correlate with economy probably are cross-correlated with center of mass excursion. Such variables as leg length, stride length, and angle of the shank, knee flexion, plantar flexion at toe-off and angle of inclination of the trunk may be linked with the center of mass excursion. It would be interesting to directly test the role of these effects on economy by experimentally manipulating kinematics.

A third possibility is that the storage and return of strain energy in tendon and muscle is the major determinant of running economy. We might test the importance of this factor by training subjects to run with styles that our models (e.g. Pierrynowski et al., 1980; Shorten, 1983; Williams, 1980) predict should enhance or diminish elastic storage. Indeed it may be that most of the kinetic and kinematic factors associated with an economical running style are subsets of a strategy to maximize the elastic storage of energy. Such factors as foot strike index, contact time, knee flexion, stride length, leg length and so on may contribute to the storage of strain energy.

Even these three larger themes of energy transfer, center of mass excursion and strain energy storage may be interconnected. Indeed, one sees very quickly how mechanically interdependent these factors are. We need a rational approach to dealing with a synthesis of these ideas and the link-segmental seem the best hope for leading us through this maze of seemingly linked ideas.

Strategies for optimization have been proposed by Hatze (1983) and Hay (1973). This might be another interesting approach to improving economy of movement even though their methods are not specifically suited to this problem. Despite this limitation it would seem that optimization of the repetitive movements used in endurance sports should lead to more energetic economy and enhanced endurance.

3. Conclusion

Biomechanical factors play a broad and varied role in the development of endurance. Mechanical constraints on endurance performance include gravity, mass, friction, centripetal force, and both aerodynamic and hydrodynamic lift and drag. The influence of biomechanical effects on endurance is mainly mediated through changes in the mechanical power requirements resulting from these constraints. Such changes in mechanical power are usually expressed as improvements in the efficiency, or more commonly, the energetic economy of movement. A review of the intrinsic and extrinsic factors known to affect the economy of movement points toward several potential areas for future improvement in endurance performance via the manipulation of biomechanical factors, especially kinetic and kinematic factors. This is one of the areas of research on endurance that should lead to significant advances in the next decade. Further elaborations of mathematical models and the development of feedback techniques for experimentally testing theories about what makes movements economical should give us new insights into the role of biomechanics in endurance.

References

Benson, H., Dryer, T. and Hartley, L.H. (1978). Decreased oxygen consumption during exercise with elicitation of the relaxation response. Journal of Human Stress June:38-42.
Cavanagh, P.R. and Williams, K.R. (1982). The effect of stride length variation on the oxygen uptake during distance running. Medicine and Science in Sports and Exercise 17:30-35.
Chandler, R.F., Clauser, C.E., McConville, J.T., Reynolds, H.M. and Young, J.W. (1975). Investigations of the inertial properties of the human body, US Department of Commerce Report. DOT HS-801 430.
Costill, D.L. and Fox, E.L. (1969). Energetics of marathon running. Medicine and Science in Sports and Exercise 1:81-86.
Costill, D.L. and Winrow, E. (1970). Maximal oxygen uptake among marathon runners. Archives of Physical Medicine and Rehabilitation 51:317-320.

Cureton, K.J. Sparling, P.B., Evans, B.W., Johnson, S.M., Kong, U.D. and Purvis, J.W. (1978). Effect of experimental alterations in excess weight on aerobic capacity and distance running performance. Medicine and Science in Sports and Exercise 10:194-199.

Frederick, E.C. (1983). Extrinsic biomechanical aids. In Ergogenic Aids in Sport, (edited by M. Williams). pp.323-339. Champaign: Human Kinetics Publishers.

Frederick, E.C. (1985a). The energy cost of load carriage on the feet during running. In Biomechanics IX -B, (edited by D.A. Winter, R.W. Norman, R.P. Wells, K.C. Hayes and A.E. Patla) pp.295-300. Champaign: Human Kinetics Publishers.

Frederick, E.C. (1985b). Synthesis, experimentation and the biomechanics of economical movement. Medicine and Science in Sports and Exercise 17:44-47.

Frederick, E.C., Clarke, T.E., Larsen, J.L. and Cooper, L.B. (1983) The effects of shoe cushioning on the oxygen demands of running. In Biomechanical Aspects of Sport Shoes and Playing Surfaces, (edited by B.M. Nigg and B.A. Kerr), pp.107-114. Calgary: The University of Calgary, Alberta.

Gregor, R.J. and Kirkendall, D. (1978). Performance efficiency of world class female marathon runners. In Biomechanics VI -B (edited by E. Asmussen and K. Jorgensen), pp.40-45 Baltimore: University Park Press.

Hatze, H. (1983). Computerized optimization of sports motions: an overview of possibilities, methods and recent developments. Journal of Sports Sciences 1:3-12.

Hay, J.G. (1973). Some thoughts on the ultimate in high jumping technique. Sixth Congress of the International Track and Field Association, Madrid 1973.

Hayes, J., Smith, L and Santopietro, F. (1983). The effects of orthotics on the aerobic demands of running. Medicine and Science in Sports and Exercise 15:169.

Lafortune, M.A. and Cavanagh, P.R. (1983). Effectiveness and efficiency in bicycle riding. In Biomechanics VIII -B (edited by H. Matsui and K. Kobayashi), pp.928-936. Baltimore: University Park Press.

Morgan, W.P. and Brown, D.R. (1983). Hypnosis. In Ergogenic aids in Sports (edited by M. Williams), pp 223-252. Champaign: Human Kinetics.

Norman, R., Caldwell, G. and Komi, P. (1985). Differences in body segment energy utilization between world-class and recreational cross-country skiers. International Journal of Sports Biomechanics 1:253-262.

Passmore, R and Durnin, J.V.G.A. (1955). Human energy expenditure. Physiological Reviews 35:801-836.

Pierrynowski, M.R., Winter, D.R. and Norman, R.W. (1980). Transfers of mechanical energy within the total body and mechanical efficiency during treadmill walking. Ergonomics 23:147-156.

Pugh, L.G.C.E. (1971). The influence of wind resistance in running and walking and the mechanical efficiency of work against gravity. Journal of Physiology 213:255-276.

Ralston, H.J. (1981). Energy expenditure. In Human Walking (edited by V.T. Inman, H.J. Ralston and F. Todd). pp.62-77. Baltimore: Williams and Wilkins.

Reilly, T and Brooks, G.A. (1982). Investigation of circadian rhythms in metabolic responses to exercise. Ergonomics 25:1093-1107.

Sanderson, D. and Cavanagh, P.R. (1986). An investigation of the use of augmented feedback to modify the application of forces to the pedals during cycling. Medicine and Science in Sports and Exercise 18(2):S63.

Sato, M., Yasutaka, S., Inuoue, K., Fukuba, Y., Fujiie, K. and Yoshioka, H. (1983). The effect of air temperature on maximal oxygen uptake. Journal Anthropological Society Nippon 91:377-388.

Shorten, M.R., (1983). Mechanical energy models and the efficiency of human movement. International Journal of Modelling and Simulation 3:15-19.

Shorten, M.R., Wootton, S.A. and Williams, C. (1981). Mechanical energy changes and the oxygen cost of running. Engineering Medicine 10:213-217.

Soule, R.G. and Goldman, R.F. (1969). Energy cost of loads carried on the head, hands or feet. Journal of Applied Physiology 27:687-690.

Stegemann, J. (1981). Exercise Physiology: Physiologic Bases of Work and Sport. Chicago: Yearbook Medical Publishers.

Strydom, N.B., Bredell, G.A.G., Benade, A.J.S., Morrison, J.F., Vigoen, H.J. and van Graan, C.H. (1966). The metabolic cost of marching at 3mph over firm and sandy surfaces. European Journal of Applied Physiology 23:166-170.

Williams, K.R. (1980). A biomechanical and physiological evaluation of running efficiency. Unpublished doctoral dissertation. Pennsylvania State University.

van der Walt, W.H. and Wyndham, C.H. (1973). An equation for prediction of energy expenditure of walking and running. Journal of Applied Physiology 34:559-563.

Zahorska-Markiewicz, B and Markiewicz, A. (1984). Circannual rhythm of exercise metabolic rate in humans. European Journal of Applied Physiology 52:328-330

Discussion

Dr Legg, Farnborough, Hants
Are there any connections between the changes in momentum and the mass of the shoe?

Dr Frederick, Pensylvania, USA
Certainly the transfer of energy between segments might be affected by the mass of the shoe and the mass of the shoe itself might affect the timing of the events that are involved. Those two things are linked to one another. The changes in momentum that occur within the limb during the movement may also be affected by the mass of the shoes. So there are possibilities there and our model did not include terms for change in momentum or energy transfer: it was a very basic model simply to demonstrate the possibilities modelling can present. If we were to calculate all

the work that was done, it is likely that the actual work would be
higher than that shown.

Professor Raven, Fort Worth, Texas
When you put a different shoe on your subject, are you sure you
have maintained the pattern of movement of the centre of gravity?
Is the economy changing because you have altered the path of the
centre of gravity during the movement?

Dr Frederick
That possibility exists but in most cases we control for it. We
can sew pouches on the sides of the shoe. In some cases, we add
weight so that the distribution of weight and the balance of the
shoes are the same. We don't monitor the path of the centre of
gravity in three-dimensional space: but we do make some reasonable
assumptions. Since we control the geometry of the surface and the
geometry of the shoe very carefully, we know we are not doing
anything drastic to shift the movement pattern; and since we
control the distribution of mass over the body, we think we are
doing as well as we can to control for that but we don't have
measurements to show how successful our controls have been.

Professor Raven
Peter Cavanagh has made the suggestion that we can change the
spring characteristics of soles, their visco-elastic properties and
cushioning, and these might affect take-off. Is this something we
might have to control for in performance?

Dr Frederick
There is a problem with the shoe in that its mass is very small so
the amount of energy that the shoe can actually contribute to
locomotion is quite small: it is a very small percentage of the
total energy. What shoes are good at doing is tricking the body
into changing its movement pattern and then altering the kinetics
in that way. Because we are sensing animals, we sense the pressure
under the foot and sense the angles of the foot and so on, we make
adjustments in response to that. Our objective is to take an
indirect approach to improving performance through shoe design and
say that since we can have very little energy returned from the
surface itself, let us take another strategy and try and trick the
body into moving economically. A perfect example was in our five-
shoe study where we showed that when we picked the proper
combination of resilience and compliance we minimised energy
expenditure by reducing the knee flexion velocity response of the
body. The key, I think, is to understand the mechanical
consequences of what you are doing when you tinker with shoe
design.

Professor Åstrand, Stockholm
I would like to hear your comments about why children walk and run
relatively uneconomically. C.T.M. Davies has shown that if you
load them with extra weights the energy cost per total weight will
decrease, particularly at the higher speeds. There is some
speculation that the ability to utilise the elasticity of activated
muscles is weight dependent.

Dr Frederick
There is a very interesting phenomenon here that has to do with
mass. First, the metabolic power is proportional to mass to the
2/3 power: so there is a possibility there to explain some of the
difference. If oxygen uptake is expressed as $ml.kg^{-1}.min^{-1}$, then
it is expected that smaller bodies will have higher relative $\dot{V}O_2$
values: but there is another possibility I want to speculate more
on the neurological problem. Running or moving efficiently is a
very subtle thing. The sorts of ideas we expressed earlier on
gross changes in the centre of mass and so on don't seem to be as
important as subtle changes in the movement pattern of the leg and
the timing of the movement in the leg. I think it may simply be a
matter of learning. That is reinforced by Davies' findings: when
you superimpose that extra weight on the subject, you are reducing
the learning factor and the energy costs of transport become a
relatively more significant part of the whole picture. I might
also add that children show significantly higher forces on landing
relative to body weight than do adults. They tend to hit the
ground much more firmly, which again is related to the idea of
learning and refining the subtleties of movement. This might
result in a higher cost of cushioning further raising oxygen
uptake.

Professor Brooks, Berkeley, California
You showed that by manipulating one extrinsic factor, the shoe
size, you could change the economy. The range of change was about
2.5%. If you devoted the time to changing the mechanics of
movement, say by altering the arm carriage or the stride length,
but sticking to one pair of shoes, how productive could that be?

Dr Frederick
In some other experiments we manipulated the knee flexion velocity
and the range of knee flexion. We showed there is a great
sensitivity of energy expenditure to the angle of the knee at
maximal knee flexion and a great sensitivity to the velocity of
knee flexion as well. The point is well taken that we have much
more room for improvement in manipulating the pattern of movement
and we have a much more powerful effector of economy of movement if
we manipulate the kinematic and kinetic factors rather than the
equipment. This comes back to the earlier statement that the shoe
is really just a tool for modifying movement. We don't see it as
having very many direct effects: the effects are indirect and they
work through the agency of kinematic adjustments.

Dr Radford, University of Glasgow
It has been observed among some elite sprinters that once their
acceleration phase is over (after 60m in 100m race) very light
shoes or bare feet cause a problem in the control of the stride
cycle. Do you have any suggestions as to why this would be?

Dr Frederick
First off, shoe weight is mainly a factor for endurance events. We
have no data on the effects of load carriage on the feet in
sprinting, but I would speculate that there might be some possibly

important effects of weight on the changes in momentum of the
foot. Perhaps this leads to a loss of our sense of where the foot
is, or a lessening of the ability of the foot to match its
velocity at foot contact with the speed over the ground, or it may
make it harder to bring the foot forward as it tries to catch up
with the rest of the body. These are just guesses, however; I have
no real explanation for your observation.

Dr Radford
A second question concerns injury. Endurance athletes will select a
running shoe, and certainly a training shoe, with an eye to injury
prevention as much as anything else. Do you have any information
on the incidence of injury with the different shoes in the studies
you have reported?

Dr Frederick
Shoes seldom cause injury or prevent injury, in my opinion.
Training errors are more powerful effectors of injury by at least
an order of magnitude. Given that shoes are a contributing
factor, however, unfortunately it is impossible to generalise a
recommendation of a given shoe for injury prevention. Each of us
is an experiment of one and we have to determine our own needs for
cushioning, rearfoot control (stability), flexibility and so on.

Dr Spurway, University of Glasgow
My neighbour, Dr. Prior, and I both feel that barefoot running must
require more skill-development than adaptation to different shoes
would need; before, typical Western athletes could do it with
equal efficiency. Before dismissing bare feet as mechanically
comparable only to rather poor shoes, should you not study some of
the few runners in our society who regularly run without shoes?
You might start by turning to some account the fact that Ms. Zola
Budd has been excluded from competing in Edinburgh this week.

Dr Frederick
Of course our objective was not to study barefoot running, and I am
certainly not prepared to make any sweeping conclusions about
barefoot running based on what little data we have. Having said
that I would like to mention that all of the subjects in this study
were habituated to treadmill running in the two weeks prior to the
experiments. I agree with you that there should be a training
effect which may reduce the kinematic and metabolic effects we have
demonstrated, but I would guess that the effects would never return
to the 'normal' level. Unfortunately, I am only able to speculate
since we do not have any data characterising this training effect.

Dr Jacobs, Toronto, Canada
The maximal knee flexion velocity during running, which you
referred to, was well over $500^{\circ}\ s^{-1}$. How was that velocity
determined and was it over the entire range of flexion or just a
selected range?
   These values are a good example of how sceptical we should be
about the application of strength measurements, such as those I
presented earlier, to forces produced during actual sporting
activities, when angular velocities of contraction are well in

excess of the reliable measurement range of commercially available isokinetic apparatus.

Dr Frederick
The maximum knee flexion velocities in our study were measured using high speed cine at 200 fps. The hip, knee and ankle were digitized to come up with a knee angle in each frame of total contact and angular velocities were computed from the change observed in this angle. Generally knee flexion velocity rose very quickly during the first 50ms of contact and peaked at about 500 to $600^{\circ}.s^{-1}$ some time in the first 50ms. We should remember that these velocities occur during a collision with the ground at about $1m.s^{-1}$ (vertical velocity). The kinematics and kinetics would be quite different to what would be going on with an isokinetic apparatus. Still I agree with your words of caution. Certainly instantaneous flexion velocities of $500^{\circ} s^{-1}$ and beyond are possible and isokinetic equipment should be able to measure such velocities however transient.

Cartilage and joint limitations on exercise

D.S. MUCKLE

Endurance in sport may be restricted by an overloading of the
hyaline cartilage and joints leading to a marked limitation in
performance. In this article special reference is given to the
chronic injuries which occur in sporting events such as long
distance running. Those factors which may influence the onset of
osteoarthritis are discussed, primarily with regard to the knee
after meniscectomy when excessive compartmental overload and shear
forces develop. The part played by the synovium in refractory
joint problems is mentioned and the biochemical compounds
(e.g. prostaglandins, proteases) which have an important pathological
role in chronic effusions are highlighted. Chronic injuries to the
ligaments are outlined, being most frequent in the ankle, shoulder
and knee. One of the most difficult problems with exercise
overload is damage within the muscles or musculotendinous junctions
as seen in the chronic groin, hamstring and Achilles tendon
injuries. The therapeutic measures for each condition are briefly
detailed.

1. General principles

During recent years exercise physiologists have identified many
factors that influence endurance in, for example, distance running.
These include $\dot{V}O_2$max, muscle fibre type and their recruitment
order, substrate availability, metabolic potential and the use of
aerobic and anaerobic energy pathways. Although the cardiopulmonary
limitations on sporting performance are easily recognised, the
musculo-skeletal limitations are often forgotten. Thus athletes
will accept a recurrent injury (for example a pulled hamstring) as
a nuisance in their quest for higher goals without realising that
the musculotendinous junctions are acting as a barrier to further
achievement. Or, as a second example, the infrapatellar synovial
folds can become chronically inflamed due to the repetitive minor
trauma of a marathon, leading to knee pain, synovial hypertrophy
and fibrosis. In fact, in any sporting event players can surpass
their skeletal capacity for exercise. This is not surprising when
one considers the forces involved. It has been shown for example
that the knee reaction during repetitive drop-jumping is 24.4 times
body weight (Smith, 1975) with a quadriceps force of 16.5 times body
weight. Forces predicted in the ankle region during running are
10.0 times body weight in the calf and 13.3 times body weight in

the ankle (Burdett, 1982).

It is true that correct training methods may prevent such problems arising but in all sports associated with prolonged and vigorous exertion there will be an ultimate musculoskeletal block. This fact especially emerges if an overload is allowed to develop, as for example in weight lifting when a stress fracture of the lumbar spine may be produced. This is because raising and holding heavy weights requires a high level of back-muscle activity and results in a compressive force on the spine. Young athletes lifting with maximum effort may produce a force of 8000-9000N.

In the erect posture, the apophyseal joints resist most of the shear forces acting on the spine as well as about 16% of the compressive force (Adams and Hutton 1985). Repeated stresses and overloading however may produce an abnormally high resistance in the lumbar region especially if there is some degree of disc degeneration. The resistance to shear compression is as a result borne by extra-articular impingement of the facet tips on the adjacent laminae or pedicles and thus a stress lesion of the pars interarticularis may be induced.

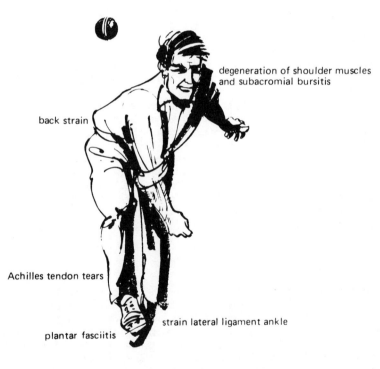

degeneration of shoulder muscles and subacromial bursitis

back strain

Achilles tendon tears

plantar fasciitis

strain lateral ligament ankle

Figure 1. Overload syndromes may be specific in certain sports (the cluster effect).

How can one stay within the limits of cartilage and joint function during exercise? Without becoming too involved in Newtonian physics it is pertinent to recall that force is a product of mass times acceleration and that an equal and opposite force is generated for each precipitating force. Being overweight, incorrectly prepared with poor muscle power and co-ordination, or avoiding correct warm-up procedures will increase the risk of undue forces being applied; counter forces from the hard road surfaces, wooden boarded courts and so on can magnify the problem. In physiological terms any force initiated should not exceed the capability of the supporting structures. When this happens the overload ensues; it may be either acute, chronic or or acute on chronic (Fig.1).

Before dealing with the specific problems it is worth recalling that a number of tissues are involved. All may be affected by injury. These tissues include:- hyaline cartilage, synovium, menisci, ligaments, muscle and musculotendinous structures.

2. Acute injuries

It is obvious that a sudden incident, for example, a direct kick on the ankle at soccer, will result in an acute limitation of joint function. So will a tearing episode in the Achilles tendon during downhill skiing or cross-country running. The products of the soft tissue reaction (prostaglandins, bradykinin and others) and the damage to the neuroreceptors will lead to an immediate reduction in function due to pain, swelling and reflex muscle spasm. In addition the supporting structures (e.g. ligaments) or the propulsive elements (e.g. tendons) will cease to act when injured. The appropriate therapy, either conservative or surgical, will rapidly restore function and sport can often be resumed within several weeks. An important adjunct to immobilisation of the damaged tissues is the use of prostaglandin inhibiting drugs. Prostaglandins are not stored in the cells but newly synthesised and released in response to stimuli that are numerous and diverse. Non-steroidal anti-inflammatory agents, by blocking the conversion of arachidonic acid from the cell wall to prostaglandins, can enhance recovery after soft tissue trauma (Muckle 1974). Strangely, these agents are not so effective in chronic injuries, and usually act only as an analgesic under these circumstances.

3. Chronic injuries

Most people involved with sport recognise the problematical chronic injuries and these are the main basis of this article. They may begin insidiously or be a direct sequel of an acute injury which has recurred either during training or the endurance event itself. Many chronic injuries are accepted by the athlete providing they are no more than a nuisance value and causing minimal discomfort and swelling during some part of the exercise programme. Thus in a review of tennis elbow it was found that 45% of players who played daily, (often in a professional capacity) developed pain; while 33% of those who played 3-4 times per week had elbow pain compared to only 7% of persons playing 2-3 times per month (Legwold, 1984). Thus repetitive forces converging at the epicondyles of the humerus cause micro-tears in the collagen. The newly formed granulation tissue, which has been called angiofibroblastic hyperplasia, is of poor quality, slow to heal and usually painful. However, such an overload could be prevented by very simple measures. These include using a racket with the largest comfortable grip, having a light racket i.e. 12.5 oz (350g), and by ensuring the racket is strung to 52-55lb (24-25kg) with gut or 16 gauge nylon. Also it has been observed that with a good tennis technique there is less likelihood of developing a tennis elbow simply because better players protect their forearm muscles from overload. They use their forearm muscles for racket control rather than power.

4. Hyaline cartilage

The effect of injury on the hyaline cartilage (Donohue et al. 1983) is one of the most important facets of sports medicine since the relationship between excessive activity and osteoarthritis has remained enigmatic for many years. Several studies have failed to show a direct relationship between endurance exercise (such as road-running) and hyaline cartilage wear. Some reports on professional sportsmen such as soccer players have not revealed an increased incidence of osteoarthritis in reviews carried out several years after retirement (Adams, 1979). However, other studies (Muckle, 1980) which have specifically incriminated the injury aspect have shown that many sportspeople including soccer players do have a high incidence as a consequence of meniscectomy or ligamentous damage. Rugby players and American Football players have a similarly related increased risk. Thus for an adequate appraisal of hyaline cartilage injury, one must take into account the two differing groups of sportspeople, namely those with limited acute trauma i.e. the repetitive sports such as running, rowing and tennis and those where the chance of an intra-articular injury is great i.e. the contact sports. However, whether the cause of the hyaline cartilage damage is from severe direct trauma or due to minor but repetitive incidents (such as road running on uneven hard surfaces in poor quality shoes) the same lesions occur; namely flaps, fissures and erosions (Fig.2). Some joints such as the great toe (Fig.3), patellofemoral and lumbar spine are more vulnerable than others to overloading. In the earliest phase the affected joint feels sore, stiff and may swell. Warning changes are found in the synovium which becomes frond like, friable, oedematous and reddened. The problems now multiply from two sources. Firstly, the mild effusion leads to minor joint instability with increased stress and shear forces, eventually producing a reflexly reduced muscle bulk (e.g. quadriceps atrophy). Secondly as mentioned previously, the synovium secretes prostaglandins and related compounds which have a detrimental effect on hyaline cartilage by releasing proteases which may further initiate cartilage breakdown (Chrisman et al. 1981). However, with superficial injuries confined to the substance of the cartilage the response observed in experimental animals has been shown to lack both inflammatory and repair components as occurs in vascular tissues. However, in a deep penetrating injury when the defect crossed the subchondral plate to violate the underlying bone, a vascular response is elicited and the haematoma thus formed quickly becomes converted into a dense

fibrous plug with evidence of fibrocartilage repair (Mankin, 1982).
In training for marathon running many of the lower limb joints
may be vulnerable but it has been shown that the knee is most
frequently affected, being involved in almost 25% of all running
injuries (Krissoff and Ferris, 1979). It was once believed that the
normal slight varus angulation of 9° in the knee commonly
produced problems in the lateral compartment but dynamic loading
patterns have indicated that even with a slight valgus deformity
most of the loading is in the medial compartment (Harrington, 1983).
This may help to explain the fissuring often seen in the hyaline
cartilage on the medial tibial plateau and the vertical or oblique
tears which are most common in the medial meniscus. In addition,
other factors may cause knee pain in runners and it is wise to
check the overall alignment of the leg by noting lower limb
length, the degree of hip rotation, the presence of genu varum or
valgum, genu recurvatum, patella alta, tibiovara, tibial torsion,
heel alignment, heel-forefoot alignment, gastrocnemius/soleus
tightness and foot-type. A small anatomical deviation in the lower
limb may cause compensatory motion in the knee joints leading to
knee pain or one of the related overuse syndromes such as patellar
tendinitis, iliotibial band friction syndrome and so on which will
be described later.

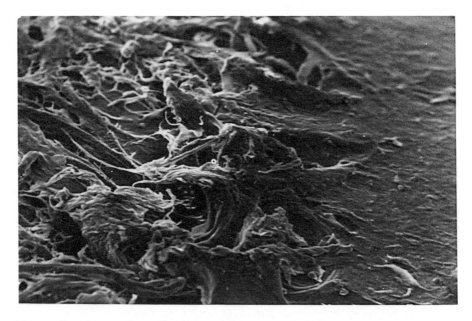

Figure 2a. A scanning electron microscopy study showing surface
damage to the femoral condyles, the hyaline cartilage is disrupted
due to shear forces and impact damage. (x200).

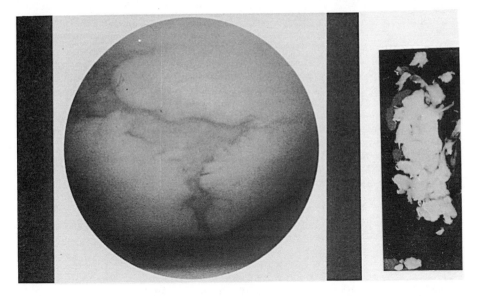

Figure 2b. The gross appearance as seen at athroscopy, with areas of hyaline cartilage loss (the debris removed from the joint by lavage is seen by the side of the arthroscopic picture).

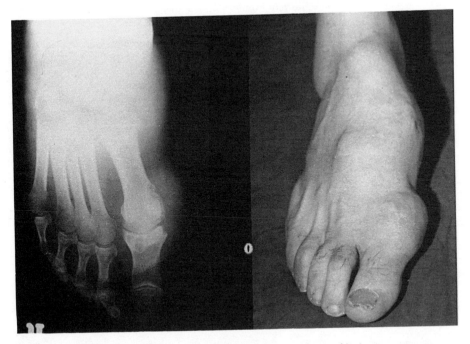

Figure 3. Secondary hallux rigidud seen in a long distance runner: the Xray shows a hazy area around the MT/PP joint due to deposition of gout crystals.

5. Synovium

The synovium which lines the capsule has both secretory and absorptive capacity. Absorption capacity may be reduced by disease, fibrosis or the presence of a diffuse pigmentation as for example occurs after a marked haemarthrosis. In addition particles of hyaline cartilage can become ground down thus releasing prostaglandins and other substances to produce an acute or acute-on-chronic synovial inflammation (Fig.4). Once inflamed the synovium becomes vulnerable in its own right by compression between articulating surfaces. This entrapment is most obvious in the knee where long delicate fronds of synovium are compressed between the femoral condyles and tibial plateaus. These lesions often mimic a meniscal problem with joint line pain and pseudolocking. The infrapatellar fat pad with the alar folds are particularly vulnerable especially when there is marked compressive forces between the patellar complex and the femur, as for example occurs in long-distance cycling. Indeed cyclists often show osteoarthritic defects in the posterior aspect of the patella. Their onset of anterior knee pain is often diagnosed as chondromalacia but it differs from the ubiquitous type of chondromalacia which is normally found in young girls and is often self-limiting. However, in the racing cyclist fissures and flaps often progress to small erosive areas on either the medial or lateral facets.

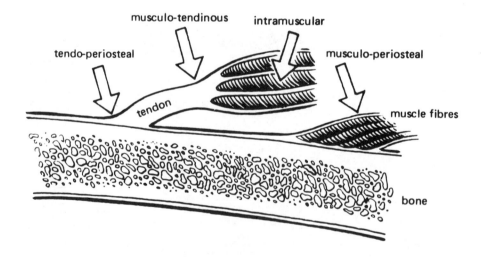

Figure 4. The musculotendinous junctions where the 'pulled muscle' syndromes commonly occur.

6. Menisci

The menisci undergo degenerative changes with age. The onset of symptoms is less dramatic than the classical vertical or oblique tear which often presents as a locked knee. With a degenerative meniscus the patient, often middle-aged, experiences a dull ache on the affected joint line commonly with a feeling of knee instability but without true locking unless a detachment or tear develops. This additional mishap may occur on the indoor tennis or squash court or during downhill running or during the squats in circuit training. Degenerative changes on the ipsilateral femoral condyle (Fig.2) or tibial plateau are not inevitable and there may be little correlation between local osteoarthritis and degenerative menisci. However, should both conditions occur in the same knee compartment then the removal of a degenerative meniscus means that more weight bearing is taken on the osteoarthritic area and further fissuring, fragmentation and hyaline loss develops. Arthroscopy will determine the extent and location of meniscal pathology and the state of the hyaline cartilage, ligaments and synovium. It will also indicate whether any other generalised joint pathology is present, such as gout or chondrocalcinosis. If the meniscus is very badly frayed or has a horizontal cleavage lesion there may be no option other than a total meniscectomy but the prognosis for vigorous sport afterwards must be guarded (Muckle, 1986; Muckle and Vijaya, 1986).

7. Ligaments

Although ligaments are often thought as static stabilisers of joints they have a dynamic aspect related to their proprioceptive function. Thus there is often an intimate relationship between many tendinous structures, the capsule and ligaments, shown by a close intermingling of their collagen fibres, as for example occurs in the posterior part of the knee with the oblique ligament which is really a prolongation of the semimembranosus tendon. Thus tendon power, passive ligament stretching and reflex muscle control are closely linked and finely balanced by complex proprioceptive pathways.

Prolonged exercise can cause chronic pain in the ligamentous structures especially around the ankle, shoulder and elbow. In the ankle a partial tear can heal with minimal scar tissue but with an annoying tendency for reflex instability - when the ankle suddenly gives way during a rapid turn while exercising. The cause is not often clear but may be due to failure of the proprioceptive impulses from the capsular structures. Wobble-board and muscle strengthening exercises, ultrasound and sometimes short-term plaster of paris immobilisation (2-3 weeks) can be used. Steroid injections rarely help instability episodes unless there is marked local tenderness, and surgery is only employed as a final resort. The scarred areas can be excised or the ligaments augmented with local tendinous material such as a split portion of the peroneus brevis.

The shoulder capsule with its musculoligamentous cuff may be heir to a variety of impingement syndromes i.e. the acromioclavicular and coracoid are the best known and are frequently found in tennis, golf and squash. Local steroid injections are often beneficial and can be repeated on one, two or three occasions. Around the elbow the medial and lateral collateral ligaments may become inflamed with prolonged throwing e.g. javelin or discus. Chronic sprains of the collateral ligaments in the thumb and fingers may be seen in volleyball and basketball. They are treated as already described. Strangely the knee ligaments are so strong that they rarely suffer from chronic discomfort unless there has been a previous disruption (e.g. medial ligament in skiing) or there is impingement against a large osteophyte. It is worth noting that with increasing age there is a reduction in tensile strength, stiffness and energy absorption, amounting to 50% from 25 to 50 years of age (Noyes and Good, 1976). Since axial force transmission can reach several times body weight - for example in the patello-femoral joint and quadriceps expansion it reaches four fold during walking (Bishop, 1977) - there becomes an increased likelihood of ligament or tendon disruption in middle-aged athletes. Also if the load is applied slowly the weak point in the joint is the bone-ligament anchorage; however in activity emphasising speed the ligaments become the vulnerable structure due to an acute overload.

8. Muscle and musculotendinous structures

Lesions of the musculoperiosteal junction (Fig.4) may cause problems in the thigh and can with repeated small bleeds lead to myositis ossificans. The musculotendinous junction or tendoperiosteal junction often falters in the groin, hamstrings and elbow (where the local epicondylitis may be referred to as tennis or golfer's elbow). However, the pathology as seen at surgery is frequently slight but the degree of incapacity for sport is usually great. Three local steroid injections can be used at 2-4 weekly intervals, with ultrasonics and deep friction massage. However, should these measures fail then surgery offers success in over 80% of cases. After a tenotomy the repair tissue, principally composed of collagen, will take approximately 3-6 months to mature and athletes should expect some local tenderness during this interval. Graduated physiotherapy is most important because too prompt a return to vigorous activity may provoke further bleeding and excessive scar formation while too tardy a return may produce a weak scar which retears.

Tendons may be subjected to chronic thickening (as found in the Achilles tendon region) or to rupture (as, for example, the biceps brachii). Achilles tendon injuries account for 18% of all running injuries. With repeated road-running, the gastrocnemius and soleus muscles are overused and become hypertrophied. As a result runners lose flexibility in the musculotendinous unit. Pain usually develops at this junction and can be located anywhere along the length of the Achilles tendon including the tendo-calcaneus insertion. Chronic Achilles tendinitis often presents as a tender indurated area at the lower part of the tendon. Prevention requires stretching exercises for the gastrocnemius (with the knee extended) and soleus (with the knee flexed). These exercises should be performed before and after each run. Treating Achilles tendinitis is often a problem. From the runners point of view he

or she may have to rest the inflamed area for several weeks or
switch to alternate day activity, avoiding hills and running on
smooth soft surfaces whenever possible. A quarter to half an inch
(0.6 - 1.3cm) heel may be required for the shoe. Ice therapy and
oral anti-inflammatory drugs often are given. However, steroid
injections around the Achilles tendon are contraindicated because
they may predispose to tendon rupture (Fig.5). An orthotic device
may be required if there is some evidence of malalignment of the
extremities, for example genu varum, tibio-vara, calcaneovalgus or
pronated flat foot. In addition there are two bursae just above
the insertion of the Achilles tendon, a precalcaneal bursa between
the skin and the Achilles tendon and a retrocalcaneal bursa between
the tendon and the bone. Such bursae may become chronically
inflamed and be confused with Achilles tendinitis. They can be
treated by raising the shoe, ultrasonics and occasionally a localised
steroid injection into the bursa.

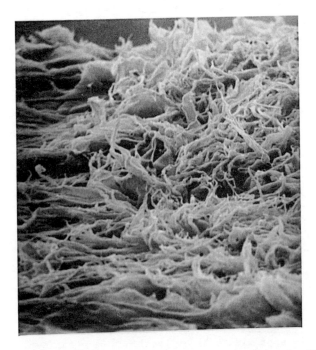

Figure 5. Collagen fibres showing rupture in the Achilles tendon.
(S.E.M. x200).

In addition posterior tibial tendinitis is a very common overuse
syndrome in runners. It is often confused with Achilles pain.
However, pain and swelling occur behind the medial malleolus and
along the postero-medial border of the tibia to the origin of the
posterior tibial muscles. An aching pain is common after long
runs on uneven surfaces. Frequent running in one direction on
banks, sloping tracks or roads may be a precipitating cause. In
addition excessive pronation of the foot may be found. Physical

examination reveals a crepitant tenosynovitis in the flexor area
extending along the anterior and medial tibial borders. There may
be pain on supination or inversion of the foot. Once again
attention must be directed to the running surface and well fitting
comfortable running shoes, with ice therapy, anti-inflammatory
agents and ultrasonics. In refractory cases with stenosing
tenosynovitis the flexor tendons may be decompressed.

If there is a tarsal tunnel syndrome with pain radiating across
the inner aspect of the foot from stenosis and irritation of the
posterior tibial nerve then a decompression operation is performed
as in the carpal tunnel syndrome of the wrist. Discomfort over the
lateral aspect of the ankle may be due to dislocation of the
peroneal tendons behind the lateral malleolus. This may occur in
any sport, especially rugby or soccer, when the ankle is vulnerable
to tackles from the side and behind.

Patellar tendinitis, often known as 'jumper's knee', is
confirmed by point tenderness over the patellar tendon usually at
the inferior pole. In teenagers the condition is often
misdiagnosed as Osgood-Schlatter's syndrome which is an apophysitis
affecting the tibial tubercle. With acute patellar tendinitis
ultrasonics, ice therapy and isometric exercises may be required
and counter support can be given by a brace. Occasionally surgery
is required to excise the scar tissue. Popliteus tendinitis is a
common cause of lateral knee discomfort especially in people who
frequently engage in running downhill. The discomfort is found
over the lateral joint line just anterior to the fibular collateral
ligament. By rotating the femur internally on weight-bearing, pain
is often reproduced along the popliteus muscle. Treatment is as
for patellar tendinitis but a brace or orthotic device in the shoe
may be required to correct the excessive transverse rotation of
the tibia. Another syndrome found with downhill running and causing
lateral knee discomfort is the iliotibial band friction syndrome.
In this condition the physical findings are tenderness over the
iliotibial band in the distal third just above Gerdy's tubercle
on the upper tibia where the friction point occurs. Local steroid
injections may be beneficial.

Pes anserinus bursitis, medial and lateral gastrocnemius
tendinitis and semimembranosus bursitis are all extra-articular
causes of knee pain which are indicated by a local point tenderness.
They are treated as described for patellar tendinitis.

Hip and thigh pain are relatively infrequent in distance
runners, and hamstring strains are much more common in sprinters.
Adequate stretching exercises must be encouraged before an event.
Hamstring strength should approximate to at least 60% of quadriceps
strength.

Treatment of the acute hamstring strain includes ultrasound,
ice, anti-inflammatories and rest. However, a partial tear in the
musculotendinous structures or in the muscle may be replaced by
low quality granulation tissue. Too long a period of immobilisation
after injury often turns this granulation tissue into a contracted
scar with poor structural organisation of the regenerating muscle.
Thus a relatively short period of immobilisation of approximately
10 days combined with gentle active exercises can induce a quicker
resorption of early granulation tissue and a better structural
organisation of the injured muscle (Lehto et al., 1985). Chronic

hamstring problems may occur at either their pelvic origins or their knee insertion. Often there is some degree of thickening around the tendon and on occasions adhesion of the local nerves (such as the lateral popliteal nerve to the biceps femoris muscle) causing referred pain. In addition in approximatley 20% of cases of torn pulled hamstrings there is either an associated disc or stress fracture in the lower lumbar spine.

Trochanteric bursitis and gluteal tendinitis should be considered in the differential diagnosis of chronic hamstring discomfort.

Chronic adductor tendinitis which usually occurs with the insertion of the adductor longus into the pelvis may be associated with either osteitis pubis (when there are erosive changes in the pubic bone) or lower abdominal discomfort from counter pulling of the rectus abdominis muscle. Often pain may be referred down the obturator nerve to the inner aspect of the thigh. A local steroid injection and ultrasonics may be beneficial and muscle stretching (both passive and active) can be carried out. Occasionally tenotomy of the chronically inflamed tendon may be required. As in all cases of pulled muscles in the lower limb attention must be directed to any muscle imbalance, poor style and technique, adequate running shoes and faulty running surface. Any discrepancy in leg length will require a corresponding shoe raise, if greater than 0.9 to 1.2cm (3/8 to 1/2"). Indeed some observers believe even a small amount of leg length discrepancy can lead to undue forces in the hip, groin and back over long-distance events, and such discrepancy, however small, requires rectifying.

The third most frequent injury found in long-distance events is shin-splints. This syndrome includes diverse problems such as anterior and posterior tibial tendinitis, tibial periostitis, tibial stress fractures and the acute and chronic tibial compartmental syndromes. Usually there is point tenderness at the medial mid-tibial border. Careful history and examination may be supplemented with a radioisotope scan to exclude a stress fracture. Acute swelling within the leg compartments leads to pain and induration with some degree of anaesthesia or numbness in the distribution of the affected nerve; for example anterior tibial nerve involvement produces pain down the anterior aspect of the leg towards the dorsum of the foot. The pressure within the tibial compartment can be measured with acute swelling but with chronic compartmental syndromes monitoring is more difficult. To decompress the muscles, fasciotomy can be performed in the affected compartment through a small incision and the results are usually good. If there is point tenderness at the tendoperiosteal junction a small operation can be performed to incise the fascial insertion into the tibia. This is most commonly performed on the medial aspect of the tibia.

Plantar fasciitis is a common cause of disabling foot pain in sport. Excessive strain on the plantar fascia may be associated with a tight gastrocnemius/soleus complex or limited ankle dorsiflexion. It may also be found in Reiter's syndrome and other conditions. Heel spurs often develop and they are a response to chronic inflammation and don't, as such, require excision. A heel pad often relieves pressure over the most tender area but a heel raise may have to be applied as well. However, if this condition becomes refractory, ultrasonics, steroid injections and if necessary incision of the fascia produce quick relief of symptoms. During the 3-4 months after surgery care must be taken about running on hard surfaces.

9. Conclusion

There is little doubt that as new records are chased and fresh heights of endeavour are scaled, the situations which induce overload in sport will increase. However, this is one aspect of sport which is so often preventable if there is close co-operation between player, doctor and coach, and a commonsense attitude is adopted.

References

Adams, I.D. (1979). Osteoarthrosis and sport. Journal Royal Society of Medicine 72:185-188.
Adams, M.A., and Hutton, W.C. (1985). The effect of posture on the lumbar spine. Journal of Bone and Joint Surgery 67B:625-634.
Bishop, R.E.D. (1977). On the mechanics of the human knee. English Medicine 6:46-52.
Burdett, R.G. (1982). Forces predicted at the ankle joint during running. Medicine and Science in Sports and Exercise 14:308-317.
Chrisman, O.D., Landenbauer-Bellis, I.M. and Punjambi, M. (1981). The relationship of mechanic trauma and the early biochemical reaction of osteoarthritic cartilage. Clinical Orthopaedics and Related Research. 161:275-284.
Donohue, J.M., Buss, D., Ogema Jr, T.R. and Thompson, R.C. (1983). The effects of indirect blunt trauma on adult canine articular cartilage. Journal of Bone and Joint Surgery 65A:948-957.
Harrington, I.J. (1983). Static and dynamic loading patterns in knee joints with deformities. Journal of Bone and Joint Surgery. 65A:247-259.
Krissoff, W.B., and Ferris, W.D. (1979). Runner's injuries The Physician and Sportsmedicine 7:55-64.
Legwold, G. (1984). Tennis elbow. The Physician and Sportsmedicine 12:168-182.
Lehto, M., Dunace, V.C. and Restall, D. (1985). Collagen and fibronectin in a healing skeletal muscle injury. Journal of Bone and Joint Surgery 67B:820-828.
Mankin, H.J. (1982). The response of articular cartilage to mechanical injury. Journal of Bone and Joint Surgery 64A:460-466.
Muckle, D.S. (1974). Comparative study of ibuprofen and aspirin in soft tissue injuries. Rheumatology and Rehabilitation 13:141-147.
Muckle, D.S. (1980). Osteoarthrosis of the knee following meniscectomy. M.D. Thesis. Univ. Newcastle.
Muckle, D.S. (1982). Injuries in Sport. Bristol, Wright.
Muckle, D.S. (1986). Preservation of the meniscus. Rheumatology in Practice 4:14-15.

Muckle, D.S. and Vijaya, T.R. (1986). Peripheral repair as an
alternative to meniscectomy. Journal of Bone and Joint
Surgery 68B:159
Noyes, F.R. and Good, E.D. (1976). The strength of the anterior
cruciate ligament in humans and rhesus monkeys:age related and
species related changes. Journal of Bone and Joint Surgery
58A:1074-1082.
Smith, A.J. (1975). Estimate of muscle and joint forces at the
knee and ankle joint during jumping activity. Journal of Human
Movement Studies 1:78-86.

Discussion

Dr Legg, Farnborough, Hants
You have mainly concentrated on injuries related to sport. I
wonder to what extent the sorts of injury you have described occur
in normal life or are associated with industrial types of
occupations.

Mr Muckle
Half of my patients in the soft-tissue injuries clinic in Cleveland
come from industry. We do meet, amongst people in the oil-rig
industry who have to clamber around, patellar tendinitis and locked
knees, for example. In some of the slingers we see tennis elbow
and tenosynovitis of the wrist. Thus there is no great difference
in these injuries between what we see in the general public and
what we meet in athletes. Although the demands on athletes are
usually regarded as much greater than on industrial workers, some
of the slingers and other workers in the oil-rig business lift
enormous weights each day. The injuries are comparable with those
of athletes and in our soft-tissues unit there is no distinction
made between them in their treatment.

Professor Stockwell, Edinburgh
You mentioned that repetitive direct injuries are a cause of
osteoarthritis. In view of the current hypothesis about fatigue
and wear in repetitive and normal stress, is there any evidence or
indication that athletes with no history of injury have an
increased frequency of osteoarthritis?

Mr Muckle
There is no absolute evidence as far as I know. It has not been
shown that osteoarthritis is an inevitable consequence of 20 years
of marathon running, for example. Similarly stress fractures of
the femoral neck in athletes are not necessarily followed 10 or 20
years later by osteoarthritis in the hips. One can extrapolate
that this might be the case but the effects are not all
detrimental. There are positive beneficial effects of exercise on
the joints and these should be considered.

Dr Frederick, Pennsylvania, USA
Two papers in the May 1986 issue of the Journal of the American
Medical Association examined the epidemiology of osteoarthritis in

sportsmen. It was reported that the incidence of osteoarthritis was lower in runners than in swimmers. This calls into question some of our ideas about repetitive impact causing injuries. The opposite hypothesis was offered that the pressure changes that occur during repetitive impact movements tend to move the joint pool around and bathe the cartilage to promote more healthy soft tissue. These and earlier studies done in Finland seem to suggest that activity is good for the joint and even a modest amount of impact doesn't seem to have an effect on osteoarthritis. The subjects were people who had been taking part in the activities for roughly 20 years.

Mr Muckle
It is interesting that in physiological terms exercise does help joints. However, if you have patients with disruption within the joint, meniscal disruption or whatever, and they do exercise, osteoarthritic changes can be made considerably worse. It is strange because these people with an osteoarthritic knee can often swim but not do many other sports.

Professor Raven, Forth Worth, Texas
One of the common injuries in running is stress fractures. I wonder if you had a recommended treatment modality.

Mr Muckle
Stress fractures can produce local symptoms before the radiological change. We do use bone isotopes to ascertain stress fractures within, for example, the tibia. It interests me that stress fractures can also have an indirect effect. We have data suggesting that stress fractures cause hamstring injuries. We do have a fair number of patients with recurrent hamstring problems that end up with stress fractures of L5-S1. This is not a common site of stress fracture but is noted in soccer players with recurrent hamstring problems and shows up in bone scans. Whether there is a reflex which causes the muscle spasm and then the tear, we don't know. With stress fractures that are radiologically non-apparent, we tend to treat them with rest. If they are radiologically apparent, rest is also the recommended treatment.

Dr Wootton, Southampton
There has been a lot of discussion recently on the interaction between essential fatty acid metabolism, free radical damage and inflammation of joints. Could you comment on this in the light of your experience?

Mr Muckle
Fatty acid precursors lead to prostaglandin production in the cell wall by trauma. Such changes can, and should, be blocked by anti-inflammatory agents, thus shortening recovery time after a joint injury.

Mr McLatchie, Hartlepool, Cleveland
Could you comment on the relationship (if any) between joint flexibility and the development of osteoarthritis? Does, for instance, the mobility of the shoulder joint protect it from

osteoarthritis even when it is heavily loaded over many years, as
in international weight lifters.

Mr Muckle
There is some evidence that families suffering from familial joint
hypermobility have an increased incidence of osteoarthritis; and
that footballers who were showing joint hypermobility had an
increased incidence of ligament injuries and thus secondary
osteoarthritis - in a 12 year review of knee osteoarthritis by the
speaker.

PART IV   WOMAN AND SPORT

This decade will undoubtedly be remembered as the one in which the
female athlete emerged to assume a prominent position in the
sporting field. Women's participation in so-called exclusive
'men's sports' such as rowing, soccer, long distance swimming and
marathon running has increased more significantly than ever before.
The games of 1900 were the first Olympiad to include women's
events: tennis and golf. This inclusion was not without
opposition. Pierre de Coubertin, a prominent member of the
International Olympic Committee argued that women's sports may be
against the 'laws of nature' and as late as 1920 he tried to expel
all women from the Olympic Games. However, the participation of
women in Olympic Games has progressively increased and in 1984
only seven Olympic sports remained in the masculine domain.

The increased participation of women in sport both in number of
events and quality of performance has led to a greater scientific
interest in investigating this area.

This section on women and sport addresses four main issues.
Dr Else Nygaard presents the opening paper outlining the
physiological differences between men and women. This
comprehensive review of her own data together with that of other
researchers in the field of blood pressure, metabolism, hormone
regulation, energy stores and skeletal muscle highlights the naive
assumption on the part of many investigators to assume that the
adaptations to exercise should be the same for males and females.
It also clearly illustrates that studies combining males and
females in the same subject group are not necessarily homogeneous.

Having been introduced to the sex differences Dr Jerrilyn Prior
then focuses attention on the specific area of menstrual cycle
irregularities. She criticises methodological aspects of some of
the early literature, but at the same time presents a positive
prospective for future research. Clear guidelines are given, not
only for the investigation of menstrual irregularities but for the
investigation of 'normal' menstrual activity. A model is developed
throughout the paper of viewing the menstrual cycle irregularities
as an adaptation to exercise. Although the adaptation is
apparently reversible, it can be associated with low oestrogen
levels and subsequent osteoporosis.

It is this latter point that is explored further by Dr Anne
Loucks. The presentation is based on a review of controversial and
at times confusing literature which is often shelved with ad hoc

recommendations. After a logical and clear introduction to the topic Dr Loucks centres the discussion on the causal relationship between athletic amenorrhoea, skeletal demineralisation and the risk of osteoporotic fractures. Particular credence should be given to the fact that reversal of the demineralisation is only partly successful even when treatment is commenced early. The paper therefore correctly finishes with recommendations for preventative therapy.

It is appropriate that the final paper should draw on an expanding area of research, that of psychology and the athlete. Inter-relating these two topics and applying it to the female was the remit of Dr Nanette Mutrie. The paper suggests wide ranging application not only to females participating in competitive sport but to the benifits of exercise to both males and females who suffer from depression. Dr Mutrie illustrates the benefits of exercise to this population from her own experimental work. The paper promotes some of the beneficial effects of exercise on a sex which in the past has suffered a cultural bias that discourages female participation in sport.

Dr Myro Nimmo

Exercise-related adaptive changes of the menstrual cycle

J.C. PRIOR

Conditioning exercise alters the menstrual cycle and reproductive hormones in dynamic and adaptive ways. Many of the changes are subtle and occur within cycles of normal length. The adaptation model as proposed by Hans Selye (1939) allows a frame-work in which the interacting, complex hormone-mediated events of the reproductive cycle can be viewed.

This paper discusses the validity of early studies showing amenorrhea in collegiate runners in light of more recent studies in which accurate assessment is made of exercise intensity, menstrual cycle characteristics, body weight and life circumstance.

Characteristic menstrual cycle changes in response to increasing conditioning exercise are:

(1) Decreased premenstrual symptoms - especially fluid, breast tenderness and subsequently, mood-related symptoms,

(2) Luteal phase shortening, and/or insufficiency

(3) Anovulation,

(4) Progression to oligoamenorrhea or rarely amenorrhea

A return to 'normal' may occur at any point depending on the rapidity of decreased training load and factors of individual susceptibility (gynaecological age, training prior to puberty, weight loss, environmental or emotional stressors and heredity).

It is postulated that the pattern of reproductive change associated with conditioning exercise is the same as that related to weight loss, severe physical illness or major psychological stress. The adaptive changes are probably modulated through the pulse-frequency characteristics of gonadotrophin-releasing hormone which are influenced by central opioids and catecholamines.

1. Introduction

Dissecting things that differ has been a major task of science.
Characterization of LH receptors, delineation of intracellular
hormone-initiated actions and manipulation of the genetic coding of
E. Coli to make key hormones are exciting and important scientific
developments.

To understand the exercise-related changes of the menstrual
cycle, however, requires an approach other than that of classic
scientific dissection. It requires integration of differing
conceptual frameworks, methodologies and analysis. At present,
the tools for these studies are still being developed and perfected.

The conceptual framework for understanding the integrated
response of the reproductive system to exercise comes from the
pioneering work of the McGill University anatomist, Hans Selye
(1939). He developed the concept of 'adaptation.' Rats were
subjected to varying external conditions (stressors) while
reproduction was monitored. Signs of estrus were observed daily
over several months. Exercise on a motor-driven treadmill, food
deprivation, diet composition change or morphine were imposed on
litter-mate rats.

Hans Selye's work, in part, offered the methodology as well as
the concepts. Longitudinal studies were used and some
quantification was made of both the stress imposed and the
response. The changes, however, were not evaluated statistically.
Time series analysis and multiple stepwise analysis of variance of
paired data are statistical tests which may be applied to this
type of experiment.

Two more recent observations have also helped understanding of
adaptive reproductive system changes. First, data from an
epidemiologic study by Frisch and McArthur (1973) demonstrated that
some aspect of the individual's height and weight was related to
the timing of menarche. Second, observations related to
reproductive and hormonal changes of anorexia nervosa indicated
that these changes were weight-related, probably of hypothalamic
origin and were similar to those occurring with starvation (Warren
and Van de Wiele, 1973; Vigersky et al., 1976). Challenged by
these ideas, I postulated an endocrine 'conditioning' process with
exercise (Prior, 1982b).

Hans Selye's concept of adaptation, the awareness that nutrition
is closely linked with reproduction and the observation that
starvation changes hypothalamic function, have helped to lay the
groundwork for a new integrative approach. It is now possible to
look at exercise-associated reproductive system change as a dynamic
process. Eventually it may be understood how the hypothalamus
processes and integrates the external and internal environmental
stimuli to preserve the individual, while temporarily suppressing
reproduction.

In the exercise studies, the experimental and control rats were
carefully matched; every factor was identical except for exercise
load and the time of its introduction. By one month both groups
were running 3.5km per day but one group had exercise imposed
suddenly, the other, gradually. The group which gradually adapted
to running maintained a normal estrus cycle throughout the
remainder of the exercise program. The group in which exercise was

immediately increased, incurred reproductive alteration and this
was still present three months later. Fig. 1 illustrates the
contrast between the abrupt versus gradual imposition of exercise
in rats. Selye's concept of adaptation involves several key ideas.

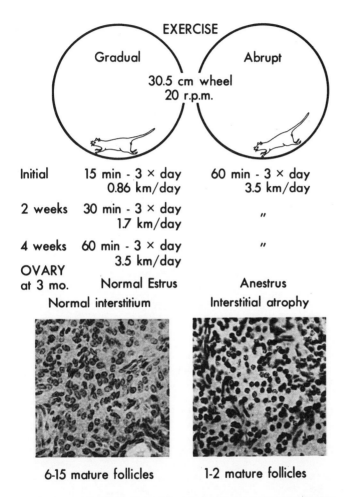

EXERCISE

Gradual — Abrupt

30.5 cm wheel
20 r.p.m.

Initial	15 min - 3 × day 0.86 km/day	60 min - 3 × day 3.5 km/day
2 weeks	30 min - 3 × day 1.7 km/day	"
4 weeks	60 min - 3 × day 3.5 km/day	"
OVARY at 3 mo.	Normal Estrus Normal interstitium	Anestrus Interstitial atrophy

6-15 mature follicles   1-2 mature follicles

Adapted from Han Selye Endocrinol 1939;25:615

Figure 1. This illustrates the concept of 'general adaptation'
developed by Hans Selye. Exercise was introduced abruptly or
gradually in rats. The photomicrographs show normal versus
atrophic interstitium in rat ovaries. Data are redrawn from
Selye, J. Endocrinology 1939; 25:615-624.

(1) The time course of change affects response. Gradually-imposed stressors caused no perceptible change but sudden imposition of the same stress caused major disruption.

(2) Reproductive system change was reversible even if stress was continued.

(3) Differing stressors caused the same reproductive system response.

2. Tools for documenting adaptive changes of the menstrual cycle

Good, population-based studies of the normal menstrual cycle are almost non-existent. Several epidemiologic questions about the normal menstrual cycle remain unanswered:

(1) What is the incidence of short luteal phase cycles in a population of a given age (or gynaecological age) range when activity is minimal, weight for height are normal and unchanged and the 'home' environment is stable?

(2) What is the incidence of anovulation in the normal population defined as above?

(3) What is the incidence of oligoamenorrhea (cycle length greater than 35 days) in the normal population as defined above?

(4) What is the incidence of amenorrhea (cycle interval greater than 180 days) in the normal population?

(5) What are the prevalences of short luteal phase, anovulatory, oligoamenorrheic and amenorrheic cycles in the above population?

(6) What is the menstrual cycle variation in a given woman when activity, nutrition and habitation remain constant?

The answers to these questions will determine whether changes in menstrual cycle characteristics are due to exercise, or to normal variations for a given individual of that age and life circumstance. It is therefore important to first define the population norm.

The largest population study using a reliable tool, although no data are available concerning the subject selection, is by Vollman (1977) using basal temperature analysis. Of 621 women studied, age range 11 to 58 years (mean 29.5), the incidence of short luteal phase and anovulatory cycles was 14.6% and 7.2% respectively. There was a much higher incidence of both short luteal phase (27.5%) and anovulatory (20.6%) cycles during the first 10 years post-menarche (gynaecological ages 1 - 10).

A Swedish study using questionnaire data documented that 3.3% of the population sample had no menses for three months during the previous year (Pettersson et al., 1973). These affected women were under 35 years of age, weighed less, experienced more psychological stress, and reported a greater incidence of previous menstrual irregularity than controls. They were also more likely to be unmarried and in demanding intellectual occupations.

Several studies document a high incidence of menstrual cycle change in young women who are not 'at home'. Metcalf et al., (1983) found a 24.6% incidence of anovulation and a 14.8% incidence of short luteal phase cycles in women 5 to 8 years post-menarche who were in boarding homes or dormitories. A Japanese study used basal temperature monitoring of all young female nursing students at a military college. Sixty-five per cent of the students were anovulatory during the school year. During holidays 27% of this group resumed ovulatory menses (Nagata et al., 1986). Some of the women in the anovulatory category may have had very short luteal phases (<5 days), since temperature records were analyzed by visual rather than quantitative methods.

Any menstrual cycle change ascribed to exercise must be carefully controlled. An ideal methodology is a prospective longitudinal study in which each woman is her own control together with control group similarly followed over time. A population cannot be expected to be 'normal' (ovulatory with regular, normal length cycles) when young women under stressful conditions are studied.

The next problem for the scientist is documentation of cycle length and quantity of menstrual flow. Questionnaire data is notoriously inaccurate. Some women will mark the onset of flow on a calender or record menstrual intervals. Others simply cannot remember. This has necessitated the development in our laboratory of a 'Daily Symptom Diary' (DSD) which is ordered around the menstrual cycle. Recording starts on day 1 (the first day of bleeding) and asks for information on flow characteristics and the number of menstrual pads or tampons used each day. From this it is possible to obtain clear data about menstrual dates and changes in menses.

The third analytical problem is that a normal length cycle of 21-35 days (Abraham, 1978), does not mean a cycle is hormonally normal. The use of the term 'eumenorrheic' to describe 'regular' cycles without phase documentation is erroneous no matter how sophisticated the work may be (Drinkwater et al., 1984; Loucks and Horvath, 1984).

Ovulation can be documented with reasonable certainty by careful gynecological history. If a woman describes 'regular' cycles of normal interval accompanied by cyclic premenstrual symptoms called 'molimina', ovulation can be diagnosed with a high degree of confidence. This was confirmed prospectively using progesterone values and basal temperature (Magyar et al., 1979).

We have confirmed that absence of molimina is highly predictive of anovulation. If a woman answers negatively to the question, 'Can you tell, by the way you feel, that your period is coming?' she is usually anovulatory as documented by a mid-luteal progesterone level of <5 ng/dL (Personal communication, J.C. Prior and Y. Vigna, 1985). A presumptive diagnosis of anovulation can be made when the woman does not spontaneously describe breast, fluid, appetite or mood changes in the week preceding onset of menstrual flow.

The DSD refines the historical diagnosis of molimina by giving premenstrual symptoms a grading scale, requiring a daily evaluation of each symptom. Symptom cyclicity can be quantitated (Sampson, and Prescott, 1981) using mean square sine wave analysis. Furthermore the data can be analyzed using non-parametric tests to indicate whether an individual changes over time. The DSD becomes a way of monitoring and evaluating cycle-related subjective feelings.

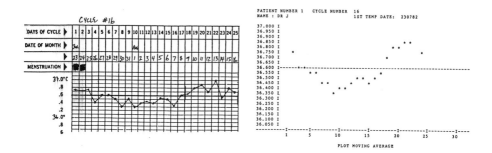

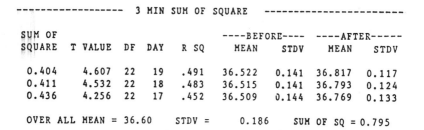

```
------------------     3 MIN SUM OF SQUARE    ------------------------
```

SUM OF SQUARE	T VALUE	DF	DAY	R SQ	----BEFORE---- MEAN	STDV	----AFTER----- MEAN	STDV
0.404	4.607	22	19	.491	36.522	0.141	36.817	0.117
0.411	4.532	22	18	.483	36.515	0.141	36.793	0.124
0.436	4.256	22	17	.452	36.509	0.144	36.769	0.133

OVER ALL MEAN = 36.60   STDV =   0.186   SUM OF SQ = 0.795

Figure 2. Temperature data analyzed by the mean temperature method of Vollman can quantitatively determine luteal length as shown in the upper left. Luteal length, estimated by a computer-generated 3-point moving average method of the same cycle, is presented on the upper right. Analysis of the data shows that the greatest difference between means before and after the intercept is on day 19. The t value of this difference is significant.

The next development needed is the documentation of ovulation and determination of phase lengths. Early and dynamic menstrual cycle changes associated with exercise often occur within cycles of normal length. Shangold et al.'s (1979) early observation of a short luteal phase in one woman runner used daily sampling of cervical mucus, a method which is not practical for studies involving significant numbers. Daily hormone sampling method employed by Bonen et al. (1981) is inconvenient for subjects and is expensive. Bullen's group (1985) used overnight urine sampling, a method which is tedious for subjects and practical only in a controlled environment. The final method and the one used in our laboratory is the serial recording of oral basal temperatures (Prior et al., 1982a, 1982b, 1985).

Basal body temperature (BBT) data are reliable when obtained from carefully taught subjects who record morning temperatures. Researchers graph the data and analyze it using the mean temperature method of Vollman (1977). Data entry and analysis by computer (Prior, Schulzer, Lau et al., personal communication, 1986) permits the calculation of a running mean to smooth the curve. Least sum of square testing assigns the intercept at a point of greatest difference between follicular and luteal phase mean temperatures. These mean temperatures are then tested for significance. Fig. 2 shows a Vollman-type graph of one cycle contrasted with the computer-generated smoothed curve of the same data. The statistical results are listed below. Validation and correlation of basal temperature data with frequent hormone sampling is in progress (Personal communication, Prior, Bonen, Schulzer, 1986).

Nutrition is another important factor which must be evaluated prospectively. Although some factor of caloric intake versus energy expenditure (Warren, 1983) or of weight for height (Frisch and MacArthur, 1973) profoundly influence reproduction, the true determinant(s) is yet unknown. A 3- or preferably 7-day dietary diary will often provide important information. It may uncover an eating disorder, or indicate that the individual has a very low metabolic rate which may in turn indicate hypothalamic modulation related to conditioning exercise.

Measured body weight and height and some assessment of morphometrics (subcutaneous fat measurements, body density determination, and/or skeletal and muscle characteristics) is necessary. A simple measure such as body mass index (weight in kg/height in meters squared) can be used.

The final tool needed is quantification of exercise. Although exercise distance and time are useful, these measurements do not take into account the indvidual conditioning. They also do not accommodate changes in performance as that individual increases training.

Methods are available for quantifying 'work load' or for estimating, after a sophisticated measurement of maximal aerobic capacity ($\dot{V}O_2max$), the percentage at which an individual is working. Because $\dot{V}O_2max$ changes over time in a given individual during a training study, serial measurements are required. A simpler method which can be used to compare an individual with herself over time or with others, involves calculation of a 'training impulse' (Banister and Hamilton, 1985).

The training impulse is calculated by the following formula:

$$TRIMP = (t_e)(k) \frac{(HR_e - HR_o)}{(HR_m - HR_o)}$$

TRIMP = training impulse
t_e = mean exercise in minutes
HR_m = maximal heart rate
HR_o = basal heart rate
HR_e = heart rate after exertion
k = constant

The maximal heart rate would ideally be measured during a maximal exercise test or by telemetry during a 200m sprint, but can be calculated roughly by the following formula:

220 - age (in years)

The TRIMP formula is based on known heart-rate responses to exercise load and the relationship between oxygen utilization and the exercise heart rate.

In summary methods of improving our understanding of the adaptive changes occurring with exercise include:

(1) Prospective, longitudinal studies in which each individual is her own control.

(2) Daily symptom diary records of cycle length, flow length and characteristics, moliminal symptoms and dysmenorrhea.

(3) BBT documentation of menstrual cycle phase characteristics (ideally supplemented with baseline and hormone sampling over time).

(4) Assessment of body morphometrics and dietary intake.

(5) Quantification of exercise load relative to the changing conditioning of the individual over time (i.e. TRIMPS).

(6) Analysis of data using time-series statistical modelling methods.

3. Exercise and reproduction - prospective, controlled data

Having clarified the measurement variables, examination of reproduction and conditioning exercise studies is now possible. Only prospective studies are reviewed although controlled hormonal data from other studies are cited when they shed light on possible mechanisms. The largest, most carefully-controlled training study was recently published by Bullen et al., (1985). These authors studied university students (mean age 22 +/- 0.6 years) who were documented by BBT and urinary hormone values as having a normal

ovulatory cycle at study onset. Training began in a camp setting
after one control cycle while sedentary. Twenty-eight women were
randomly assigned to weight-maintenance (n=12) and weight-loss
(n=16) groups. The women began by running 4 miles/day in two
sessions, 5 days/week. They gradually increased to 10 miles/day
during the fifth week. Running heart rates were monitored
telemetrically and were 70 - 80% of periodically-determined
maximal aerobic capacity.

The results of this study illustrate the difficulty of analyzing
these prospective menstrual cycle data. Quantitative basal
temperature data on phase lengths, correlations with weight change
and predictive modelling were not attempted. The weight-loss
group had a higher incidence of delayed menses and anovulation than
the weight-maintenance group. This documents the synergy between
the reproductive effects of nutrition and exercise. A pattern of
change from shortening of the luteal phase to anovulation with or
without oligoamenorrhea was also shown.

The final and important observation from this study is that all
changes (43% of the women were anovulatory and 38% had luteal phase
alterations) were reversible. This was documented by continued
basal temperature and symptom diary monitoring over 6 months.

The first longitudinal study of women during exercise training
showed delay in pubertal progression in young ballet dancers (Warren
1980). There was a rapid return to or initiation of menses and
change in the secondary sex characteristics when a dancer was
injured and less active.

Boyden and colleagues prospectively followed 29 women in a
training study (1982a, 1982b, 1983, 1984). Subjects, initially
running 13.5 miles/week, gradually added 30 and 50 miles/week to
their training. Although the study notes that baseline estradiol
levels decrease singificantly, and the area under LH and FSH
response curves to gonadotropin releasing hormone (GnRH) decrease,
menstrual cycle data are vague. 'Menstrual cycle change' (decreased
flow) occurred in 18/19 women. There were no consistent
intermenstrual interval changes (1983), but 13/14 women developed
oligoamenorrhea (1982b). The value of careful prospective
documentation is obvious. No data exists concerning ovulation,
phase intervals or reversibility of changes.

Ronkainen et al. (1985) from Finland have recently shown that
circumannual light cycle changes may be synergistic with exercise
training in altering menstrual cycle hormone concentrations. The
additive factor of body weight decrease with exercise like that
documented in teenage gymnasts (Warren, 1983), was also shown in
the Finnish study.

Two prospective longitudinal studies followed competitive
teenage swimmers in exercise programs of different intensities.
The first study showed initially low estradiol levels returning to
normal despite increased training (Carli et al., 1983). The second
study documented increases in beta endorphins and catechol
estrogens with decreases in FSH, LH and prolactin (Russell et al.,
1984). Nutritional change and menstrual cycle characteristics
were not documented in either study.

Several longitudinal studies of individuals have documented
reversibility of the menstrual cycle with decreased training
(Shangold et al., 1979; Prior et al., 1982a; Frisch et al., 1984).

Reversible infertility due to luteal phase insufficiency has been temporally related to exercise training (Prior et al., 1982a). The relationship of training with luteal phase alterations and anovulation has been recently reviewed (Prior, 1985).

From individual data and larger series analysis (Prior et al., 1982c, 1983), a model of menstrual cycle change in ovulatory gynecologicaly-mature woman starting a conditioning program has been developed (Fig. 3). Women in their 30s show less obvious change in cyclicity and bleeding patterns than the 22 year old women Bullen et al. reported (1985). The initial change from sedentary to moderate activity is marked by decreases in the premenstrual symptoms of breast tenderness and fluid retention. These changes are significant by 3 months of training (Prior et al., 1986). As both intensity and distance of running increase to 1 hour/week at 60% of maximal aerobic capacity, luteal phase shortening may occur.

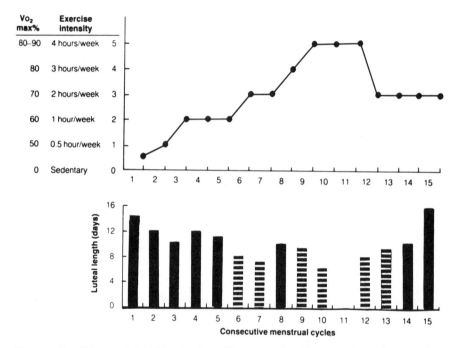

Figure 3. This model illustrates the reproductive system changes in a sedentary woman following the onset and gradual increase in conditioning exercise. The intensity of training is consistent with a marathon race in cycle 12.

After six training cycles, whether as a runner intensifying her training for a marathon or as a sedentary person gradually increasing exercise, significant decreases in premenstrual feelings of depression are reported (Personal communication, Prior et al., 1986). These premenstrual symptom changes occur without luteal phase shortening or anovulation.

The model in Fig. 3 shows a training pattern for a marathon in cycle 12. Anovulation may occur at the peak of training, especially if there is weight loss. Following a decrease in training after the marathon, a short luteal phase (cycle 13) may persist, but usually returns to normal in 6 - 8 weeks. This decreased exercise intensity is at a level which was associated with luteal phase shortening in cycle 6. There is also return of premenstrual symptoms. If weight gain occurs, these symptoms may become quite severe.

4. The 'adaptation model' and menstrual cycle change with exercise

At present there is only speculation about the mechanisms which cause dynamic menstrual cycle change. Many of the changes resemble those which occur in anorexia nervosa (Warren and Van de Wiele, 1973; Vigersky et al., 1976), with critical illness (Woolf et al., 1985) or with major psychological stress. The one attempt to show changed hypothalamic function in amenorrheic runners was technically inadequate (Dixon et al., 1984). Prospective training studies of hypothalamic and gonadal function in men and women are still being evaluated (Prior et al., unpublished).

Reduced frequency of GnRH secretion is postulated to be the underlying mechanism of anovulation (Reame et al., 1985). Major suppression of LH pulsatility was documented in cyclic (but not necessarily ovulatory) runners (Cumming et al., 1985). Treatment of oligoamenorrheic cycles with pulsatile GnRH resulted in ovulation and pregnancy in a woman who maintained her training schedule (50 miles/week) and did not change weight (14% body fat) (Haynes et al., 1985).

Changes in central opioid and/or dopamine levels may modulate the pulse frequency characteristics of GnRH with conditioning training. Exercise-related β endorphin levels clearly increase with training, although met-enkephalin levels return to control values with increased conditioning (Howlett et al., 1984). Documentation of altered LH secretory pattern in athletes following endorphin blockade with naloxone has yielded negative results (Dixon et al., 1984; Prior, unpublished data), except for the initial observation (McArthur et al., 1980).

In summary, conditioning exercise is a model which can be used to understand the reproductive systems' capacity to adapt. The tools are accumulating using which, we can complete the conceptual, epidemiological and hormonal profiles necessary to describe, predict and understand adaptation and exercise. No longer is it adequate to assume a cycle of normal length is hormonally normal.

These studies may lead to increased understanding of the hypothalamus. They may yield information about risk factors for osteoporosis, endometrial and breast cancer. It will be an exciting scientific discovery if dissection uncovers no differences between the reproductive responses to weight loss, psychological stress, physical illness and conditioning exercise.

Acknowledgements

I am proud to thank Joyce Elliot Smith for her unending support.
The perspicacity and perception of Yvette Vigna, the diligence of
Milinda Schulz and the patience of Neptune made this work possible.

References

Abraham, G.E. (1978). The normal menstrual cycle. In Endocrine
    Causes of Menstrual Disorders (edited by J.R. Givens), pp.
    15-44. Chicago: Year Book Med. Publishers Inc.
Banister, E.W. and Hamilton, C.L. (1985). Variations in iron status
    with fatigue modelled from training in female distance runners.
    European J. Appl. Physiol. 54:16-23
Bonen, A., Belcastro, A.N. and Simpson, A.A. (1981). Profiles of
    menstrual cycle hormones in teenage athletes. J. Appl.
    Physiol. 50:545-551
Boyden, T.W., Parmenter, R.W., Stanforth, P., Rotkis, T. and
    Wilmore, J.H. (1982a). Evidence for mild thyroid impairment in
    women undergoing endurance training. J. Clin. Endocrinology
    and Metabolism. 54:53-56
Boyden, T.W., Parmenter, R.W., Grosso, D., Stanforth, P., Rotkis,
    T. and Wilmore, J.H. (1982b). Prolactin responses, menstrual
    cycles and body composition of women runners. J. Clin.
    Endocrinology and Metabolism. 54:711-714
Boyden, T.W., Parmenter, R.W., Stanforth, P., Rotkis, T. and
    Wilmore, J. (1983). Sex steroids and endurance running in women.
    Fertility Sterility. 39:629-632
Boyden, T.W., Parmenter, R.W., Stanforth, P. Rotkis, T. and
    Wilmore, J. (1984). Impaired gonadotropin responses to
    gonadotropin-releasing hormone stimulation in endurance-trained
    women. Fertility Sterility 41:359-363
Bullen, B.A., Skrinar, G.S., Beitins, I.Z., von Mering, G.,
    Turnbull, B.A. and McArthur, J.W. (1985). New Engl. J. Med.
    312:1349-1353
Carli, G., Martelli, G. Viti, A., Baldi, L., Bonitazi, M. and Lupo
    di Prisco, C. (1983). The effect of swimming training on hormone
    levels in girls. J. Sport Medicine 23:45-51
Cumming, D.C., Vickovic, M.M., Wall, S.R., Fluker, M.R and
    Belcastro, A.N. (1985). The effect of acute exercise on
    pulsatile release of luteinizing hormone in women runners.
    Amer. J. Obst. & Gyne. 153:482-485
Dixon, G., Eurman, P., Stern, B.E., Schwartz, B and Rebar, R.
    (1984). Hypothalamic function in amenorrheic runners.
    Fertility Sterility 42:377-383
Drinkwater, B., Nilson, K., Chestnut, C.H., Bremner, W.J.,
    Shainholtz, S. and Southward, M.B. (1984). Bone mineral content
    of amenorrheic and eumenorrheic athletes. New England Journal
    of Medicine 311:277-281
Frisch, R.E., Hall, G.M., Aski, T., Birnholz, J., Jacob, R.,
    Landsberg, L., Munro, H., Parker-Jones, K., Tulchinskly, C. and
    Young, J. (1984). Metabolic, endocrine and reproductive changes
    of a woman channel swimmer. Metabolism 33:1106-1111

Frisch, R.E. and McArthur, J.W. (1974). Menstrual cycles: Fatness as a determinant of minimum weight for height necessary for their maintenance or onset. Science 185:949-950

Haynes, S., Wilson, J.D. and Dyke, F.S. (1985). Menstrual dysfunction and running - a case history. Aust. J. Scient. Med. in Sport. 17:12-14

Howlett, T.A., Tomlin, S., Ngahfoong, L., Rees, L.H., Bullen, B.A., Skrinar, G.S. and McArthur, J.W. (1984). Release of β endorphin and met-enkephalin during exercise in normal women: response to training. British Medical Journal. 288:1950-1952

Loucks, A.B. and Horvath, S.M. (1984). Exercise-induced stress responses of amenorrheic and eumenorrheic runners. J. Clin. Endocrinology and Metabolism. 59:1109-1120

McArthur, J.W., Bullen, B.A., Beitins, I.Z., Pagano, M., Badger, T.M. and Klibanski A. (1980). Hypothalamic amenorrhea in runners of normal body composition. Endocrin. Res. Communic. 7:13-25

Magyar, D.M., Boyers, S.P., Marshall, J.R. and Abraham, G.E. (1979). Regular menstrual cycles and premenstrual molimina as indicators of ovulation. Obst. & Gyne. 53:411-414

Metcalf, M.G., Skidmore, D.S., Lowry, G.F. and Mackenzie, J.A. (1983). Incidence of ovulation in the years after the menarche. J. Endocrinol 97:213-219

Nagata, I., Kato, K., Seki, K. and Furuya, K. (1986). Ovulatory disturbances. Causative factors among Japanese student nurses in a dormitory. J. Adolescent Health Care. 7:1-5

Pettersson, F., Fries, H. and Nillius, S.J. (1973). Epidemiology of secondary amenorrhea. Amer. J. Obst. & Gyne. 117:80-86

Prior, J.C., Ho Yeun, B., Clement, P., Bowie, L. and Thomas, J. (1982a). Reversible luteal phase changes and infertility associated with marathon training. Lancet. 1:269-270

Prior, J.C. (1982b). Endocrine 'conditioning' with endurance training: a preliminary review. Can. J. Appl. Sport Sciences. 7:149-157

Prior, J.C., Cameron, K., Ho Yuen, B. and Thomas, J. (1982c). Menstrual cycle changes with marathon training: anovulation and short luteal phase. Can. J. Appl. Sports Sciences. 7:173-177

Prior, J.C., Pride, S., Vigna, Y. and Ho Yuen, B. (1983). Marathon training and reversible luteal phase shortening: a controlled, prospective study. Medicine and Science in Sports and Exercise 15:174 (abstract)

Prior J.C. (1985). Luteal phase defects and anovulation: adaptive alterations occurring with conditioning exercise. In Seminars in Reproductive Endocrinology (edited by R.W. Rebar) 3:27-33

Prior, J.C. and Vigna, Y. (1985). The therapy of reproductive system changes associated with exercise. In The Menstrual Cycle and Physical Activity (edited by J.L. Puhl and C.H. Brown). pp. 105-14. Champaign, Illinois: Human Kinetics Publishers Inc.

Prior, J.C., Vigna, Y. and Alojada, N. (1986). Conditioning exercise decreases premenstrual symptoms - a prospective controlled three month trial. Europ. J. Appl. Physiol. (in press)

Reame, N.E., Sauder, S.E., Case, G.D., Kelch, R.P. and Marshall, J.C. (1985). Pulsatile gonadotropin secretion in women with hypothalamic amenorrhea: evidence that reduced frequency of gonadotropin-releasing hormone secretion is the mechanism of persistent anovulation. <u>J. Clin. Endocrinology and Metabolism.</u> 61:851-858

Ronkainen, H., Pakarenen, A., Kirkenen, P. and Kauppla, A. (1985). Physical exercise-induced changes and season-associated differences in pituitary-ovarian function of runners and joggers. <u>J. Clin. Endocrinology and Metabolism.</u> 60:416-422

Russell, J.B., Mitchell, D.E., Musey, P.I. and Collins, D.C. (1984). The role of β endorphin and catechol estrogens on the hypothalamic-pituitary axis in female athletes. <u>Fertility Sterility</u> 42:690-695

Sampson G.A. and Prescott, P. (1981). The assessment of the symptoms of premenstrual syndrome and their response to therapy. <u>British J. Psychiatry.</u> 138:399-405

Selye, H. (1939). The effect of adaptation to various damaging agents on the female sex organs in the rat. <u>Endocrinology</u> 25:615-624

Shangold, M., Freeman, R., Thysen, B. and Gatz, M. (1979). The relationship between long-distance running, plasma progesterone and luteal phase length. <u>Fertility Sterility</u> 31:130-133

Vigersky, R.A., Loriaux, D.L. and Anderson, A.E. (1976). Anorexia nervosa: behavioural and hypothalamic aspects. <u>Clinical Endocrinology and Metabolism</u> 5:517-535

Vollman, R.F. (1977). The menstrual cycle. In <u>Major Problems in Obst. & Gyne.</u> (edited by E.A. Friedman), Toronto: W.B. Saunders Co.

Warren, M.P. and Van de Wiele, R.L. (1973). Clinical and metabolic features of anorexia nervosa. <u>Amer. J. Obst. & Gyne.</u> 117:435-441

Warren, M.P. (1980). The effects of exercise on pubertal progression and reproductive function in girls. <u>J. Clinical Endocrinology and Metabolism</u> 51:1150-1157

Warren, M.P. (1983). Effects of undernutrition on reproductive function in the human. <u>Endocrine Reviews</u> 4:363-377

Woolf, P.D., Hamil, R.W., McDonald, J.V., Lee, L.A. and Kelly, M. (1985). Transient hypogonadotropic hypogonadism caused by critical illness. <u>J. Clinical Endocrinology and Metabolism</u> 60:444-450

Discussion

Dr Wootton, Southampton

In a recent study by Nelson et al. (<u>Am. J. Clin. Nut.</u> 1986) they compared eumenorrheic athletes with amenorrheic athletes matched for training status, body weight and composition. The amenorrheic athletes had 25% lower energy intakes than eumenorrheic. The authors concluded that the amenorrhea was an adaptive response to the energy deficit.

Would you like to comment, as this would suggest that energy intake rather than decreased body weight is important?

Dr Prior, Vancouver, Canada
I have not seen that study but there are difficulties in using
cross sectional data. It is important to know what happened at the
onset of the amenorrhea. Also, there is a metabolic change that
goes with conditioning exercise that also goes with weight loss.
There may be changes in amino acid metabolism, such as tryptophan
or 5HT. These metabolic changes relate to hypothalmic change and
it is important to investigate them. These women may very well be
in energy balance because they are more efficient at using their
fuel intake. Their T_3 levels may be lower, their macrometabolic
changes, their growth hormone levels higher and prolactin levels
lower. There are many factors which go with the amenorrheic state,
especially if the women are exercising.

Professor Raven, Fort Worth, Texas
In dancers and gymnasts might it not be the stress of the total
event rather than the conditioning exercise or endurance exercise
itself. Gymnasts often starve three days before a competition so
that they can get their strength/body weight ratios up.

Dr Prior
Both of the groups you cited are young and the added factor which I
forgot to put in my summary is that the first nine years of
reproductive life is a time of hypothalamic maturation and often
the young sportswoman has not even established ovulation before she
is under the stress of added exercise and low body weight.

Dr Sutton, Toronto, Canada
What is your favourite hypothesis for the neurotransmitor which
allows the interaction of the psychic, the nutrition, the exercise,
or whatever, which leads to abnormalities of the reproductive
cycle?

Dr Prior
I initially postulated that it might be through some change in the
insulin receptor related to exercise, weight change, energy fluxes
at the hypothalamic level. However, the exact mechanism is not
clear. We need a team of neurochemists, exercise physiologists and
endocrinologists to tackle the question. There are definitely
endorphin changes, probably hypothalamic dopamine changes and
catecholamine changes.

Dr Sutton
Can you appraise the hypothesis?

Dr Prior
Probably dopamine. An increase in central dopamine might be the
common pathway.

Dr Loucks, California, USA
I don't think any of the studies have been well enough controlled
to allow us to say that exercise disrupts the reproductive system.
It may be some aspect of exercise training such as psychological
stress or diet, but it is not possible to say that it is exercise
per se. Do you agree with that?

Dr Prior

I personally believe that exercise does influence the reproductive system and I think it is more than several factors. There is an added stress and obvious changes in the fuel utilisation and percent body fat as they train. I do think there is very strong suggestive evidence that exercise by itself does affect reproduction. I don't think it causes amenorrhea.

Dr Simpson, Glasgow

Chronobiologists regard all living material as having a structure in time as well as a structure in space and with reference to the menstrual cycle I would like to explain how this is seen by chronobiologists. The menstrual cycle can be seen in a circadian domain and in a menstrual domain. This means that a woman, in effect, is a different woman at different points and if she were to undertake an athletic event she would operate, probably, with different efficiency. Temperature correlates with many variables and it is interesting that the circadian role in the first part of the cycle is different from the circadian role in the second part of the cycle, in as much that the peaks of temperature at four hours before midnight form the proliferative phase of the cycle and they occur at midnight in the luteal phase of the cycle.

I would suggest that the menstrual cycle cannot be looked at in isolation but must include consideration of adrenal function.

Dr Prior

That point is very well taken and it is important when considering female performance to identify the phase of the menstrual cycle.

Skeletal demineralization in the amenorrheic athlete

A.B. LOUCKS

This review assesses the evidence indicating that athletic
amenorrhea causes skeletal demineralization, thereby placing
amenorrheic athletes at increased risk of incurring osteoporotic
fractures. In evaluating the studies which provided this evidence
the extent to which several confounding factors were controlled is
considered. The cross-sectional data show that (1) the site at
which to seek effects of hypoestrogenism on bone density of
athletes is the spine not the wrist, (2) hypoestrogenic amenorrheic
runners have less vertebral bone density than cyclic runners, (3)
amenorrheic runners appear to be consuming diets deficient in
calcium, and (4) amenorrheic runners may already be suffering stress
fractures as a result of their condition. Longitudinal data show
that amenorrheic runners are losing bone over time in the same
temporal pattern as has been observed in other groups of
hypoestrogenic women. Preliminary data indicate that bone loss may
be partially reversed by returning steroid levels to normal. These
results emphasize the importance of early treatment of amenorrheic
athletes to prevent bone loss.

1. Introduction: osteoporosis

Osteoporosis is a quantitative deficiency of bone mineral
sufficient to render a bone abnormally susceptible to fracture.
There is no known cure for osteoporotic fractures. Over 50% of
women 55 years and older have some degree of osteoporosis (Larsen,
1985). The total cost of osteoporosis and osteoporotic fractures
in the U.S. alone in 1983 was estimated to be 6.1 billion dollars
(Holbrook et al., 1985).

Four years ago it was not believed that many athletic women were
losing bone. Three years ago, few investigators believed the first
observation of bone loss in 'healthy athletic women'. Now the
results of several studies have been dismayingly consistent.

This review evaluates the evidence indicating that athletic
amenorrhea causes skeletal demineralization, thereby placing
amenorrheic athletes at increased risk of incurring osteoporotic
fractures. In evaluating the studies which provided this evidence,
we must consider whether several factors affecting bone density
besides reproductive system status were controlled.

2. Regulation of bone density

There are two types of bone tissue. Overall the adult skeleton is about 80% cortical and 20% trabecular bone (Gong et al., 1964), with each bone in the body containing its own proportion of cortical and trabecular components. Cortical bone tissue appears solid and hard and is found in the shaft of long bones and exterior of all bones. Long bones such as the shafts of the radius and ulna contain at least 50% cortical tissue (Schlenker and VonSeggen, 1976).

Trabecular bone tissue is a network of voids like a sponge and is found inside bones. Trabecular bone tends to be more sensitive to metabolic influences such as changes in levels of estrogen (Cann et al., 1984). Thus, bone sites which contain predominantly trabecular bone are the most sensitive sites for detecting bone mass changes, the vertebral bodies being a prominent example.

The causal chain of events in osteoporosis is shown in Fig. 1. Involuntary genetic factors include race, frame size, and perhaps sex: blacks have higher bone densities than caucasians (Trotter et al., 1960); the small bone mass of light framed individuals provides little mineral reserve against demineralization; and although the average bone density of men is greater than that of women, the extent to which this is due to genetic or lifestyle factors is not clear.

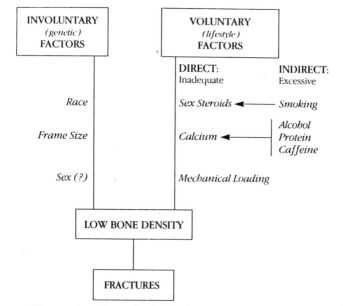

Figure 1. Causal chain for osteoporosis. Reproduced with permission, A. Loucks, Human Kinetics Publishers.

There are two types of voluntary lifestyle factors: deficiencies which have direct effects upon bone density, and excesses which influence bone density indirectly by creating or exaggerating these deficiencies. Excessive smoking (Daniel, 1976), alcohol (Dalen and

Lamke, 1976), protein and caffeine (Heaney and Recker, 1982) intake can indirectly lower bone density.

Deficiencies which have a direct effect upon bone density include sex steroids, dietary calcium, and mechanical loading. Sex steroids have been shown to be essential to the maintenance of skeletal integrity in women. This conclusion is based on studies showing decreased bone mass in women with low estrogen levels compared to age matched controls (Cann et al., 1984; Genant et al., 1982) and on studies showing maintenance of bone mass in women with low endogenous estrogen levels who are placed on estrogen supplements (Ettinger et al., 1985; Genant et al., 1982; Lindsay et al., 1976).

Calcium is a threshold nutrient (Heaney, 1985). When calcium intake is below a certain level, bone mass is proportional to calcium consumption. When calcium intake is above this threshold, however, in the sufficiency range, there is no relationship between the calcium intake and bone mass. Above the threshold there is no evidence that larger intakes of calcium will increase bone mass.

Bone strength depends on both mineral mass and micro-structure; and a bone responds to weight bearing and muscle contraction by both increasing its mass and improving its structure. The skeletal system, like the muscular system, needs the stimulus of mechanical loading for maintenance of size and strength and for hypertrophy. Body composition studies show that while adult women lose 30 to 40% of total body calcium as they age, they also lose an equivalent amount of total body potassium (reflecting cell mass which is largely muscle) (Heaney, 1983). Thus there is a close relation between bone mass and muscle mass.

The studies that have examined bone density in the amenorrheic athletes must be considered with all these factors in mind.

3. Review criteria

The types of experimental designs for clinical research are listed in order of their inferential strength (Table 1) (Dept. of Clinical Epidemiology and Statistics, 1981; Guyatt et al., 1984). Although randomized experiments are scientifically preferable to nonrandomized subexperiments, subexperiments are frequently performed in human research for other overriding reasons: randomized studies may be unethical, impossible, too expensive, or fail to reflect the real situations. Because of their susceptibility to confounding influences all non-randomized studies require precautions to detect and correct for bias in results. One cannot detect and correct for the biasing effects of factors that are not measured. Nor is it sufficient to acknowledge that results may be biased by presenting differences between groups in possible confounding factors and then leaving the reader to guess what the effects of these factors may have been. Means for detecting and reducing the effects of bias are readily available (Anderson et al., 1980).

Table 1. Experimental Designs

I.   Randomized experiments

   A. Prospective

      1. Cohort

      2. Self-controlled

   B. Cross-sectional

II. Nonrandomized subexperiments

   A. Prospective

      1. Cohort

      2. Self-sectional

   B. Cross-sectional

   C. Retrospective case-control

   D. Case

The various sources of error in the published research were evaluated according to the following criteria. The study had to be well controlled, with a clear description of the experimental variable (risk factor). For steroids, measurement of estradiol was required. Confounding factors are those other than the risk factors which may have influenced experimental results. When neglected they are a potential source of bias. If, having been identified, they have been measured and found to differ between groups, they must be further analysed for correlations with outcome variables to allow for correction for their effect. Age, race, calcium consumption, weight and exercise regimen are potentially confounding factors. Age strongly influences bone density results in studies of young women because bone mineral is rapidly deposited during adolescence. To control the effect of calcium intake, dietary records over at least three days were required to show no differences in calcium consumption. For exercise the type and frequency were required.

Bone density outcome variables were evaluated for the precision of the method and the appropriateness of the sites of measurement, which were required to include the vertebral body. Finally type I and type II statistical errors were examined. Type I error was charged when nonsignificant numerical differences were treated as real. A type II error was charged when statistical power was too low to detect a difference of two standard deviations.

4. Demineralization of amenorrheic athletes

In 1982, Cann and colleagues made the first observation of reduced bone density of amenorrheic women whose amenorrhea was not associated with hyperprolactinaemia (Cann et al., 1982; Cann et al., 1984). They found 24% less trabecular bone mineral content in the vertebrae of women with hypothalamic amenorrhea than in those of normal cycling women. Ten of the eleven women in the hypothalamic amenorrheic group were regular participants in exercise.

Although this finding created wide media attention, it drew considerable skepticism amongst investigators, since exercise was thought to be protective against bone loss in postmenopausal women. Several studies were initiated using more highly trained athletes and equally trained menstruating control groups. None of these were randomized or nonrandomized prospective cohort studies. The nonrandomized cross-sectional and before-and-after studies, are reviewed below.

The cross-sectional studies of skeletal demineralization in amenorrheic athletes have attempted to determine the effects of two risk factors, exercise and sex steroids, on bone mass. There are four possible subject groups: cyclic and amenorrheic trained women, and cyclic and amenorrheic untrained women. The effect of sex steroids on bone mass is determined by comparing the bone densities of cyclic and amenorrheic trained women, or cyclic and amenorrheic untrained women. The effect of exercise training on bone mass is revealed, however, by comparing the bone densities of cyclic trained and untrained women, or amenorrheic trained and untrained women. In studies comparing cyclic untrained women to amenorrheic trained women or cyclic trained women to amenorrheic untrained women, the two risk factors are confounded and their effects on bone mass inseparable. Such studies are not considered here. The effect of steroids on women not involved in exercise training is not the focus of this review and these, too, are not reviewed.

Six studies have examined the effect of steroids on bone density in exercise-trained women by measuring bone density in cyclic and amenorrheic athletes (Drinkwater et al., 1984; Linnell et al., 1984; Lindberg et al., 1984; Marcus et al., 1985; Nelson et al., 1986; Snyder et al., in press). Four studies assessed runners; Snyder et al. (in press) examined rowers; and Drinkwater et al. (1984) examined both runners and rowers.

The potential sources of error in these studies are summarized in Table 2. Linnell et al. (1984) and Snyder et al. (in press) did not measure steroids but assumed them to be different in amenorrheic and cyclic subjects. Lindberg et al. (1984) were vague about whether steroid levels differed significantly between their groups. Drinkwater et al. (1984), Marcus et al. (1985) and Nelson et al. (1986) all measured estradiol, all finding a significantly lower estradiol level in their amenorrheic groups.

Table 2. Sources of error in the reviewed cross-sectional studies of the effect of athletic amenorrhea on bone density

	Lindberg et al. (1984)	Snyder et al. (in press)	Linnell et al. (1984)	Drinkwater et al. (1984)	Marcus et al. (1985)	Nelson et al. (1986)
Risk Factor Steroids	-	O	O	+	+	+
Confounding Factors						
Age	+	+	+	+	<	<
Race	O	+	O	O	+	O
Calcium intake	O	O	+	+	+	+
Weight	<	+	+	+	<	+
Exercise	<	+	+	<	+	+
Outcome Variables Bone density						
method	+	+	+	+	+	+
site	O	+	O	+	+	+
Statistical Errors						
Type I	+	+	+	+	+	+
Type II	+	-	+	+	+	+
Score (+)	4	7	7	8	8	8

O: unmeasured or not described for at least one group
-: imprecisely measured or controlled
<: difference detected: potential bias
+: adequately measured or controlled

With regard to the confounding factors, the studies of Marcus et al. (1985) and Nelson et al. (1986) could have been biased by differences in age. Only the studies of Marcus et al. (1985) and Snyder et al. (in press) stated that subjects were of the same race, caucasian. Lindberg et al. (1984) and Snyder et al. (in press) did not measure calcium consumption. The results of Lindberg et al. (1984) and Marcus et al. (1985) could have been biased by their amenorrheic athletes having weighed less than their cyclic athletes. The amenorrheic runners of Lindberg et al. (1984) had been training longer and those of Drinkwater et al. (1984) trained more miles per week than the cyclic runners. This potential source of bias would probably have tended to increase bone density of the amenorrheic runners and to reduce the likelihood of finding differences in bone density between the groups. Therefore, these studies may be conservative in their estimate of the effect of amenorrhea upon bone density.

Regarding outcome variables, all five studies used adequate methods for comparing bone densities in separate groups, but neither Linnell et al. (1984) nor Lindberg et al. (1984) measured bone density at the spine in both groups. The results of Snyder et al. (in press) were susceptible to type II error, since only four amenorrheic rowers were observed.

Thus, the potential sources of error indicate that the studies of Drinkwater et al. (1984), Marcus et al. (1985) and Nelson et al. (1986) provide the most credible results.

Drinkwater et al. (1984), Marcus et al. (1985) and Nelson et al. (1986) confirmed Cann and colleagues' (1982, 1985) original observations of lower vertebral bone density in amenorrheic athletes than in the cyclic athletes. In fact, when plotted against the age-related density changes found by Riggs et al. (1982), the amenorrheic runners and rowers assessed by Drinkwater et al. (1984) had bone densities comparable to 50 year old women. The lack of a significant difference in vertebral density in the data of Snyder et al. (in press) may indicate that rowing, unlike running, protects against the loss of vertebral bone mineral, or it may merely reflect the low statistical power of the experiment. Lindberg et al. (1984) assessed amenorrheic athletes but not cyclic athletes.

Of the five studies measuring bone mineral content at the wrist, only Lindberg et al. (1984) found significant differences. Cortical bone mass has not been measured at weight-bearing sites, however. Marcus et al. (1985) suspect such differences in the mineral density of the tibia or femur might exist, since they observed a higher incidence of cortical stress fractures in the amenorrheic runners (6 of 11) than in cyclic runners (1 of 6). Similarly, Lindberg et al. (1984) reported that in the year before their study, 49% of the amenorrheic runners had incurred stress fractures, while no stress fractures had been incurred in cyclic runners.

Although no statistical differences in calcium intakes have been observed, the apparent effect of estrogen deficiency upon bone density in amenorrheic athletes may still have been biased by calcium intake. The amenorrheic athletes were probably deficient in calcium consumption since their intake of approximately 800 mg/day was less than the 1500 mg/day recommended for hypoestrogenic women (Heaney et al., 1978).

Very little reliable data is available from these studies concerning whether athletic training increases the bone densities of amenorrheic women with estrogen deficiencies. Marcus et al. (1984) reported that the vertebral density of the amenorrheic runners was greater than that previously reported from the same laboratory for women with secondary amenorrhea who were less physically active. Potential confounding variables could not be checked, as the women were not tested with the same protocol.

Amongst other cross-sectional studies, Jones et al. (1985) found amenorrheic athletes to have greater radial bone density than weight-loss-associated amenorrheic women or women with premature menopause. The differences in duration of amenorrhea between the groups combined with the significant correlation between duration of amenorrhea and bone density may have confouded the radial bone density data, even though the difference in duration of amenorrhea was not significant. Rigotti et al. (1984) reported that highly active amenorrheic anorexia nervosa patients have higher radial bone density than less active amenorrheic anorexia nervosa patients.

In summary, the cross-sectional data show that (1) the site at which to seek effects of hypoestrogenism on the bone density of athletes is the spine not the wrist, (2) hypoestrogenic amenorrheic runners have less vertebral bone density than cyclic runners, (3) amenorrheic runners appear to be consuming diets deficient in calcium, and (4) amenorrheic runners may already be suffering stress fractures as a result of their condition. The data do not show whether the bone densities of amenorrheic athletes were changing prior to the experiments, or whether their bone densities were lower before the onset of amenorrhea or even before the onset of athletic training. Nor do the data show whether the observed densities were stable. Longitudinal data are needed to address these issues.

Before-and-after studies for inferring causality are stronger than cross-sectional studies since the temporal relationship between risk factors and outcome variables is observed in subjects utilized as their own controls. Longitudinal data on vertebral bone density in amenorrheic athletes have only recently become available. In May of 1985, Cann and colleagues (1985) reported that amenorrheic runners were losing bone in the same temporal pattern as has been observed in other groups of hypoestrogenic women: that is rapidly (approximately 8% per year) in the first two years after the onset of estrogen deficiency, and more slowly or negligibly in later years (5% per year in the third year, and 1% per year after three years of amenorrhea). These results have disappointed investigators, physicians, coaches, and athletes alike. They contradict both the belief that the differences observed in cross-sectional studies may have been due to differences in bone density which existed before any of the women became athletes and the idea that exercise is effective in counteracting the effect of hypoestrogenism in athletic amenorrhea. They emphasize the importance of early treatment of amenorrheic athletes to prevent bone loss.

The outlook may be more promising for amenorrheic athletes who regain normal sex steroid levels. Drinkwater and colleagues (1986) reassessed the bone mineral density in sixteen of the athletes from their original study (Drinkwater et al., 1984) after 15.5 months. Seven originally amenorrheic athletes whose menstrual cycles had resumed showed a significant increase of 6.3% in vertebral bone mineral density. This contrasted with a further 3.4% loss in two athletes who remained amenorrheic. There was no significant change in the seven cyclic athletes. Drinkwater and colleagues proposed that resumption of menses was the primary factor for the significant increase in the vertebral bone mineral density of the formerly amenorrheic athletes.

Lindberg et al. (1985) reevaluated bone mineral content in seven of their amenorrhoeic runners after 15 months. Four runners took supplementary calcium (775 mg/day), reduced their weekly running distance by 43%, increased their body weight (3%), and experienced a return of regular menses with increased estradiol levels. Mean vertebral bone density in these four runners increased (from (mean

±SD) 0.943 ± 0.106 to 1.070 ± 0.089 g/cm^2), yet still
remained below the normal range (1.10 to 1.38 g/cm^2) for their
age. The three other runners studied during the follow-up period
remained amenorrheic with no change in running mileage or body
weight, and although they took supplementary calcium (1500
mg/day), there was no significant change in their mean vertebral
bone density (from a mean ±SD of 0.894 ± 0.024 to 0.885 ±
0.044 g/cm^2). Although the change in bone mineral overall in
both groups was positively correlated with a change in body weight
($r=0.88$), increased steroid levels again appear to be necessary for
reversing bone losses.

When considering the evidence regarding athletic amenorrhea and
skeletal demineralization, it must be acknowledged that none of the
studies has been fully randomized. The research, therefore, may be
criticized because the observed effects may occur only in certain
subsets of the general population and results may be inadvertently
biased. Nevertheless, the evidence in favor of a causal
relationship between athletic amenorrhea and skeletal
demineralization is strong. This appears to be true despite the
mechanical loading provided by aerobic training. Amenorrheic
runners have less bone density than matched regularly menstruating
runners; they are losing bone over time; and they are at increased
risk, sooner or later, of incurring osteoporotic fractures.

5. Treatment of amenorrheic athletes

Recommendations for treatment of amenorrheic athletes are made
cautiously because of individual variation and because of
inexperience with premenopausal osteoporotic women (Martin, 1985).
Individual prediction of osteoporotic risk is not yet possible.
Therefore, generalizations derived from populations of women are
used to predict average risks and therapeutic benefits. Most of
the available information about osteoporosis has been gained from
studies of older populations. It is not clear that premenopausal
women with amenorrhea will behave in the same way as menopausal
women. Several studies are currently being done to determine the
effectiveness of various treatments on bone density in amenorrheic
athletes.

With these considerations in mind, it must be stressed firstly
that most menopausal women who have lived for more than three or
four years without protective effects of estrogen have already
suffered the loss of a major portion of bone mineral (Ettinger et
al., 1985). Furthermore, these women have not regained these
minerals when subsequently placed on estrogen therapy (Council on
Scientific Affairs, 1983), and there is no cure for the pain,
deformity, and disability of osteoporotic fractures. This strongly
suggests that treatment of the amenorrheic athlete must not be
delayed.

The second point to be stressed is that when amenorrhea occurs
it should not be assumed to be due to athletic training. Diagnosis
should be by exclusion of pregnancy and of pathologies known to
display amenorrhea as a symptom. A full endocrine investigation
is required including a progesterone-withdrawal bleeding test
(Shangold, 1986).

Cyclic estrogen/progesterone therapy is indicated for all amenorrheic athletes confirmed to be hypoestrogenic, with no withdrawal bleeding and without specific contraindications (Martin, 1985 Rebar, 1982 Shangold, 1986). Meanwhile those amenorrheic athletes displaying withdrawal bleeding are experiencing unopposed endometrial stimulation by endogenous estrogens. Cyclic progesterone therapy is indicated to protect these women against endometrial cancer (Martin, 1985; Shangold, 1986). Dosages are equivalent to those in low dose oral contraceptives. It is further recommended that normo-estrogenic women take 1000 mg and hypo-oestrogenic women 1500 mg of elemental calcium daily (Heaney et al., 1978).

In addition, physical activity should be maintained. At the present time, it is not known what aspect of athletic training causes amenorrhea or precisely how much of which specific physical activities a woman must do to prevent osteoporosis. Because the bone strengthening effect of exercise is local, however, an exercise program for preventing osteoporosis needs to be comprehensive in loading the musculature of the entire body. High bone density is the product of a large, strong muscle mass. Low intensity repetitive aerobic activities, such as running, which work only part of the body are not adequate for protecting the entire skeleton. Probably no single traditional game or sport is fully protective.

A mixture of activities which load different body parts is a better exercise program but this may be impractical for the athlete committed to a particular sport. An alternative approach, progressive resistance weight training, has several practical advantages over the mixed sports approach. Firstly, weight-training is systematic: an exercise physiologist can design programs on the basis of a strong foundation of kinesiological knowledge. Secondly, weight-training can be comprehensive: an exercise program which loads every muscle group and bone can be performed. Thirdly, weight-training is quantitative: the load being applied can be measured, recorded, and monitored over years and decades to ensure that its bone-strengthening stimulus is being maintained. Fourthly, weight-training is time efficient: a strenuous comprehensive weight-training workout can be done in less than an hour.

Amenorrheic athletes are usually unwilling to abandon their lifestyles. Unfortunately, physicians have found amenorrheic athletes also frequently resist accepting steroid therapy due to fears of possible side effects, such as weight gain or subjective feelings upon athletic performance. Nevertheless, sufficient levels of sex steroids and calcium consumption are essential if vertebral bone loss is to be prevented in amenorrheic athletes. Physicians, coaches and parents alike are responsible for the health as well as the performance of the athletes in their care. Therefore it is their responsibility to prevail upon amenorrheic athletes to comply with these recommendations.

References

Anderson, S., Anguier, A., Hauck, W.W., Oakes, D., Vandale, W. and
Weisberg, H.I. (1980). Statistical Methods for Comparative
Studies New York; John Wiley & Sons.

Cann, C.E., Martin, M.C., and Genant, H.K (1982). Detection of
premenopausal amenorrheic women at risk for the development of
osteoporosis. Endocrinol Supplement to 110:226

Cann, C.E., Martin, M.C., Genant, H.K., and Jaffe, R.B. (1984).
Decreased spinal mineral content in amenorrheic women. JAMA
251:626-629

Cann, C.E., Martin, M.C., and Jaffe, R.B. (1985). Duration of
amenorrhea affects rate of bone loss in women runners:
implications for therapy. Med. Sci. Sports and Exercise
17:214

Council on Scientific Affairs (1983). Estrogen replacement in the
menopause. JAMA 249:359-361

Dalen, N. and Lamke, B. (1976). Bone mineral losses in alcoholics.
ACTA Orthop. Scand 47:469-71

Daniel, H.W. (1976). Osteoporosis of the slender smoker: vertebral
compression fractures and loss of metacarpal cortex in relation
to postmenopausal cigarette smoking and lack of obestiy. Arch.
Intern. Med. 136:298-304

Department of Clinical Epidemiology and Biostatistics (1981).
McMaster University Health Sciences Centre: How to read clinical
journals: IV. To determine etiology or causation. Can. Med.
Assoc. J. 124:985-990

Drinkwater, B.L., Nilson, K., Chesnut, C.H. III, Bremner, W.J.,
Shainholtz, S., and Southworth, M.B. (1984). Bone mineral
content of amenorrheic and eumenorrheic athletes. N. Eng. J.
Med. 311:277-281

Drinkwater, B.L., Nilson, K., Ott, S., and Chesnut, C.H. III (1986)
Bone mineral density after resumption of menses in amenorrheic
athletes. JAMA 256:380-382

Ettinger, B., Genant, H.K., and Cann, C.E. (1985). Menopausal bone
loss can be prevented by low-dose estrogen combined with
calcium supplements. Drug Therapy. Supplement 63-65

Genant, H.K., Cann, C.E., Ettinger, B., and Gordan, G.S. (1982).
Quantitative computed tomography of vertebral spongiosa: a
sensitive method for detecting early bone loss after
oophorectomy. Ann. Intern. Med. 97:699-705

Gong, J.K., Arnold, J.S., and Cohn, S.H. (1964). Composition of
trabecular and cortical bone. Anal. Rec. 149:325-332

Guyatt, G.H., Webber, C.E., Mewa, A.A., and Sackett, D.L. (1984).
Determining causation -- a case study: Adrenocorticosteroids and
osteoporosis. J. Chron. Dis. 37:343-352

Heaney, R.P. (1983). Prevention of age-related osteoporosis by
women. In The Osteoporotic Syndrome: Detection, Prevention
and Treatment. (edited by L.V. Avioli), pp 123-144. New York:
Grune and Stratton.

Heaney, R. (1985). Dietary and pharmacological maintenance of
skeletal integrity. Symposium Skeletal Integrity: Exercise
and Amenorrhea. American College of Sports Medicine Annual
Meeting, Nashville, Tennessee.

Heaney, R.P. and Recker, R.R. (1982). Effects of nitrogen, phosphorus, and caffeine on calcium balance in women. J. Lab. Clin. Med. 99:46-55

Heaney, R.P., Recker, R.R., and Saville, P.D. (1978). Menopausal changes in calcium balance performance. J. Lab. Clin. Med. 92:953-963

Holbrook, T.L., Grazier, K., Kelsey, J.L. et al. (1985). The frequency of occurence, impact and cost of musculoskeletal conditions in the United States. Chicago: American Academy of Orthopedic Surgeons.

Jones, K.P., Ravnikar, V.A., Tulchinsky, D., and Schiff, I. (1985). Comparison of bone density in amenorrheic women due to athletics, weight loss, and premature menopause. Obstet. Gynecol. 66:5-8

Larsen, L.M. (1985). Osteoporosis facts. The Osteoporosis Report 1(2):2

Lindberg, J.S., Fears, W.B., Hunt, M.M., Powell, M.R., Boll, D., and Wade, C.E. (1984). Exercise-induced amenorrhea and bone density. Ann. Intern. Med. 101:647-648

Lindberg, J.S., Powell, M.R., Hunt, M.M., Ducey, D., and Wade, C.E., (1985). Resolution of exercise-induced amenorrheic osteopenia after decreased exercise, increased body weight, and normal menses. Endocrinol. Supplement 116:245

Lindsay, R., Hart, D.M., Aitken, J.M., MacDonald, E.B., Anderson, J.B. and Clarke, A.C., (1976). Long-term prevention of postmenopausal osteoporosis by oestrogen. Lancet i:1038-1041

Linnell, S.L., Stager, J.M., Blue, P.W., Oyster, N. and Robertshaw, D. (1984). Bone mineral content and menstrual regularity in female runners. Med. Sci. Sports Exerc. 16:343-348

Martin (1985). Medical treatment for athletic amenorrhea. Athletic Amenorrhea Bulletin. 4(1):3-5

Marcus, R., Cann, C., Madvig, P., Minkoff, J., Goddard, M., Bayer, M., Martin, M., Gaudiani, L., Haskell, W., and Genant, H. (1985). Menstrual function and bone mass in elite women distance runners endocrine and metabolic features. Ann. Intern. Med. 102:158-163

Nelson, M.E., Fisher, E.C., Catsos, P.D., Meredith, C.N., Turksoy, R.N. and Evans, W.J. (1986). Dict and bone status in amenorrheic runners. Am. J. Clin. Nutr. 43:910-916

Rebar, R.W (1982). Clinical Assessment of the amenorrheic athlete. Athletic Amenorrhea Bulletin 1:1-8

Riggs, B.L., Wahner, H.W., Seeman, E., Offord, K.P., Dunn, W.L., Mazess, R.B., Johnson, K.A., and Melton, L.J. III (1982). Changes in bone mineral density of the proximal femur and spine with aging: differences between the postmenopausal and senile osteoporosis syndromes. J. Clin. Invest. 70:716-723

Rigotti, N.A., Nussbaum, S.R., Herzog, D.B., and Neer, R.M. (1984). Osteoporosis in women with anorexia nervosa. N. Engl. J. Med. 311:1601-6

Schlenker, R.A. and VonSeggen, W.W. (1976). The distribution of cortical and trabecular bone mass along the length of the radius and ulna and implications for in vivo bone mass measurements. Calcif Tissue Res. 20:41-52

Shangold, M. (1986). How I manage exercise amenorrhea. Phys. and
    Sportsmed. 14(3):113-120
Snyder, A.C., Wenderoth, M.P., Johnston, C.C. Jr., and Hui, S.L.
    (in press). Bone mineral content of elite lightweight
    amenorrheic oarswomen. Hum. Biol.
Trotter, M., Broman, G., and Peterson, R.R. (1960). Densities of
    bone in white and negro skeletons. J. Bone Joint Surg.
    42A:50-58

Discussion

Dr Jacobs, Toronto, Canada
There seems to be a need to establish bone densities of resistance-
trained women who are amenorrheic. Researchers in Stockholm have
published a paper that has compared bone density in different
types of male athletes engaged in different types of sports,
providing good cross sectional data. Indeed, as has been
suggested, those athletes who are weightlifters have more dense
bones as compared to soccer players, endurance trained people and
sedentary individuals. As you pointed out I think resistance
training may be an excellent prophylactic measure to consider for
amenorrheic women.

Professor Åstrand, Stockholm, Sweden
Do you think if those women had not been running they would have
lost more of their bone mineral content? With reference to the
different types of activity one might expect that amenorrheic
female swimmers would be worse off than the joggers. Have you any
comment?

Dr Loucks, California, USA
At this point we do not have the data. All we have is the data of
Snyder et al. showing that the rowers vertebral bone density was
not different from the amenorrheic running athletes but again they
only measured four amenorrheic rowers.

Professor Åstrand
From an educational point of view when newspapers recommend
jogging, they should recommend a mixture of activities.

Dr Frederick, New Hampshire, USA
It is generally known that some women middle and long distance
runners use anabolic steroids. They follow this practice because
they believe it helps them recover from hard training sessions.
Would you comment on the effect of this practice on bone demineralisation, given that many of these women may also be
amenorrheic?

Dr Loucks
No clear mechanism has been shown as to how the steroid interacts
with bone tissue. It may not only be oestradiol. Potentially
androgens and progesterone may have a role in stimulating bone

density. I think there are a couple of studies showing that
androgen supplementation in post-menopausal women is of benefit.
If I were to guess then I would think that anabolic steroids have
a role in stimulating bone density.

Dr Prior, Vancouver, Canada
I would just like to make a comment. You said that the steroid
effect was a direct effect on bone. I would like to ask you in
what way it directly affects bone because that is not my
understanding. It can definitely prevent bone loss or resorption
but it is an indirect factor to the best of my knowledge.

Dr Loucks
That is correct.

Dr Prior
I would like to show some of the initial cross-sectional data from
a study that we are doing now in which we have enrolled
approximately 90 women all of whom are documented to be ovulatory.
A sedentary group, a recreationary active group and a marathon
training group. Bone density was estimated in these women by
computed tomography and showed that marathon runners and the
recreational runners differ from the sedentary group at every
level.
    The tendency is that the sedentary group is lower. Therefore,
the negative factor in amenorrheic athletes seems to be not the
exercise but the anovulation or amenorrhea.

Dr Sutton, Ontario, Canada
It has been emphasised throughout that it is a bone loss mechanism
but bone is a very dynamic tissue of synthesis and degradation. In
many other tissues the limb of the balance equation that is
predominately affected is the synthesis arm not the increased
degradation. Are we actually seeing an impairment in the
resynthesis of bone?

Dr Loucks
Bone is in constant turnover and we do not know whether it is
increased breakdown or decrease in synthesis which is contributing
to this.

Dr Sutton
Finally, why is there this tremendous difference in the recommended
daily intake (RDI) of dietary calcium: 550mg in Britain, 800mg in
the US and then from a therapeutic point of view, you are telling
us that you need twice as much as is recommended if you are going
to treat someone?

Dr Loucks
There is no agreement as to what the exact intake should be. The
therapeutic figure derives from Heaney (1978), which recommended
that hypooestrogenic women should be given 1500mg of calcium. This
study investigated calcium balance in post-menopausal women and
they could reduce the calcium loss from bone by increasing the
calcium intake.

<u>Dr Montoye, Wisconsin, USA</u>
I think in these studies it would be helpful if measurements of
bone density were taken in many of the other bones of the body.
You yourself have alluded to the localised effect of muscular
activity and there is pungent evidence of that. We looked at
amateur tennis players whose age averaged 64. We could show
differences of 6 to 13% between their right and left hand, in their
humerus as well as their meta-carpals. In addition in women taking
exercise primarily involving the lower limbs it has been found that
bone density decreases in the radius and humerus. There may be
shifts of calcium therefore from one place to the other in the
body. In order to really understand the mechanism it is essential
to get total calcium and bone densities in various limbs. I can
only deduce from the studies which you have reported that there was
loss in the lower limbs as well as vertebral bones because you
talked about stress fractures but that's not absolutely clear
unless you get some real measurements.

<u>Dr Loucks</u>
Those studies are currently being undertaken.

The psychological effects of exercise for women

N. MUTRIE

The psychological effect of exercise is an exciting new area in the sports science literature. It is important that psychological effects are documented to the same extent as physiological effects, because it may be that people continue to exercise as a result of the psychological benefits they perceive. To date the research has been poorly designed, but consistent reports of mood elevation, anxiety reduction and improved self-image have been noted as being associated with exercise. Exercise has also been successful in alleviating moderate levels of depression.

In general, both men and women perceive benefits from exercise. There is a possibility that more women than men perceive exercise as improving mood, and that more women than men are psychologically distressed by missing a regular exercise session. Exercise has been used as a treatment for depression more frequently with women.

The mechanisms by which the psychological effects of exercise might be explained have not, as yet, been fully explored. It is suggested that biochemical, physiological, and psychological processes may interact to produce the effects which have been noted in the literature.

1. Introduction

The psychological effect of exercise is an exciting new area in the sports science literature. Increasing interest in this area reflects a growing awareness of the need to consider the whole person and not just his or her physiology during exercise. It is possible that people exercise because they experience psychological benefits. It is important, therefore, for sports scientists to document psychological benefits to the same extent as they have documented physiological benefits. It is timely, therefore, to review the current literature on the psychological benefits of exercise.

As with other sport and exercise sciences, most of the early research was conducted only with male subjects. It is therefore important to review the current literature with particular reference to women.

In this review no specific mention will be made about the psychological effects of high-level training or competition. The population of interest is non-elite. The literature review will cover both descriptive and experimental studies and will point out any sex differences which have been noted.

In reviewing the literature for particular references to women there are two major problems. Firstly, many studies do not include female subjects. Of those studies which do include female subjects, not all of them report analyses by sex. This makes it difficult to make more than speculative conclusions regarding comparisons between men and women. Secondly, very few research designs allow firm conclusions to be drawn; this simply reflects the fact that research in this area has a very short history. Both problems should be overcome as the number of researchers interested in this area expands. It is hoped that this paper might encourage more research projects to include the psychological aspects of exercise involvement.

2. Review of literature

2.1 Descriptive studies

Several large surveys have noted that very high percentages (60-92%) of non-elite runners feel that running provides psychological benefits (Callen, 1983; Carmack and Martens, 1979; Jorgenson and Jorgenson, 1979; Mutrie and Knill-Jones, 1985). These benefits include reports of 'feeling better' (Carmack and Martens, 1979), an increased sense of well-being (Jorgenson and Jorgenson, 1979), anxiety and tension reduction (Callen, 1983; Mutrie and Knill-Jones, 1985), and increased self-image and self-confidence (Callen, 1983). No sex differences have been noted for these effects. However, Callen (1983), noted two interesting sex differences in his survey of American runners; firstly, more women (72%) than men (62%) felt that running improved their mood and secondly, more women (69%) than men (52%) reported that running relieved feelings of depression. This latter finding has been supported by Mutrie and Knill-Jones (1985) who also found that more women (50.6%) than men (37%), in a sample of Scottish non-elite marathon runners, reported that running relieved feelings of depression.

The opposite of a 'feel better' effect has been noted when exercisers miss their regular workout. Glasser (1976) has described symptoms of withdrawal from exercise, which include increased irritability, guilt and tension. Carmack and Martens (1979) and Summers et al. (1982) have also reported that when runners missed their regular exercise they experienced bad moods, guilt, irritability, depression, and sluggishness. Similar findings have been reported by Robbins and Joseph (1985), but they noted that distress from missing a run was more common in the women in their study.

There is a major problem in this descriptive literature when sex differences are being examined. In all studies the number of men in the sample exceeds the number of women. This inequality perhaps leads to sex differences being masked because the standard error of the statistic in question will be higher for women than for men.

There is, of course, a very practical reason for the differences
between the numbers of men and women in these studies; there are
more men than women participating in events or associated with
clubs featured in the surveys. Positive discrimination is required
to recruit more equal numbers so that more valid statistical
comparisons can be made.

An added dimension to descriptive studies is an examination of
the mood states of those involved in different intensities of
exercise. Tooman et al. (1985) found that competitive runners (13
men and 7 women, with an average running speed in training of 6.13
minutes/mile), had more positive mood states than recreational
runners (14 men and 6 women, with an average running speed of 8.31
minutes/mile). The mood states were measured by the Profile of
Mood States (POMS, McNair et al., 1971). Wilson et al. (1980)
compared the POMS scores of a group of marathon runners, a group of
joggers, and a group of non-exercisers. They found that both the
marathon runners (weekly mileage = 36-100 miles) and the joggers
(weekly mileage = 3-10 miles) had lower depression, anger and
confusion scores and higher vigour scores than the non-exercisers.
They also found that the marathon runners had more positive mood
profiles than the joggers. However, only men were included in
this study (10 per group), so it is not certain that this finding
would be true for women.

The suggestion that different intensities of exercise may be
associated with different mood profiles developed from the idea
that athletes may differ from non-athletes. Morgan and Pollock
(1977) have suggested that athletes have more positive mood
profiles (as measured by POMS) than the normal population. The
athletes' mood profiles were characterised by lower than normal
levels of tension, depression, anger, fatigue and confusion and
higher than normal levels of vigour. Morgan (1980) has described
this configuration as the 'iceberg profile'. Morgan's work was
conducted on male athletes only and has not been replicated for
female athletes. However some evidence exists for a similar
'iceberg profile' amongst women exercisers; Gondola and Tuckman
(1982) and Berger and Owen (1983) found that both male and female
recreational exercisers did display an 'iceberg profile' in
comparison to non-exercising controls.

Descriptions do not provide evidence that exercise causes
psychological benefits. There are many alternative explanations
which could be offered to explain the differences in mood profiles
previously described. For example, it could be argued that people
who generally experience positive moods are more likely to exercise
than those who do not. The relationship between exercise and
effect, as described by these studies, remains associative rather
than causal. There is a slight suggestion that more women than men
describe mood elevation and depression relief from exercise and that
more women than men report that missing regular exercise is
distressing. Descriptive studies, despite their limitations, are
valuable because they provide hypotheses which can be tested in
experimental situations.

2.2 Experimental and quasi-experimental studies

There are very few true experimental studies (i.e. those which employ random assignment of subjects to experimental and control conditions) which have examined the psychological effects of exercise. Folkins and Sime (1981) have suggested that as few as 15% of studies in this area qualify as true experiments and most of these have examined clinical populations. Most of the designs are at best quasi-experimental in which a group receiving exercise is compared with a non-equivalent group in a control condition. Alternative explanations of effects, such as local history or selection bias, remain plausible with this design. Other designs do not incorporate control conditions at all. Cook and Campbell (1979) warn that there are several factors which threaten validity in this kind of design, namely, local history, statistical regression and testing effects. This kind of design therefore does not allow causal inference regarding treatment effects. Only when subjects are randomly assigned to treatments can reasonable causal inference be made. The effect of exercise could be more clearly identified in future studies by the use of placebo control groups in which all variables, except the one under investigation, remain constant. With these caveats in mind and with the hope that current research will spawn future work which is more appropriately designed, the experimental and quasi-experimental literature will now be reviewed.

2.2.1 The effects of acute exercise involvement

Several studies have measured the effect of a single exercise session on mood. Nowlis and Greenberg (1979) measured the effects of a 12.5 mile run on mood in 18 (13 men and 5 women) experienced runners. They found that the runners reported increased 'pleasantness' after the run, and that this effect was reported by both men and women.

Berger and Owen (1983) measured the mood profiles of novice (n = 25) and intermediate (n = 33) swimmers before and after one swimming lesson. In this study, gender was included as an organismic variable. They found that, compared to a lecture class control group (n = 42), the swimmers reported greater decrease in levels of tension, depression, anger and confusion and greater increases in vigour after one swimming lesson. These effects were found for both the men and the women. The conclusion that 'swimmers really do report "feeling better"' should, however, be accepted with caution. Swimming in this study was performed as part of a lesson. It is not clear from this design that it was swimming itself which was responsible for mood elevation or whether it was some other aspects of the teaching/learning interaction. A similar problem arose in a study by Reiter (1981) in which the effects of one general exercise session on a group of elderly women were measured. Reiter (1981) found that this kind of exercise had a positive effect on the group's reported sense of well-being while control groups in arts and crafts classes did not report a change in sense of well-being. Again it is not clear if it was the exercise iteslf or some other aspect of the exercise environment, such as the charisma of the exercise leader, which was responsible for the mood elevation.

State anxiety has been a popular dependent measure in examining the acute effects of exercise. Trait anxiety, by comparison, is relatively enduring and would therefore not be expected to change over short periods of time. Several review articles (Folkins & Sime, 1981; Mihevic, 1982; Morgan, 1985) have concluded that acute exercise has a tranquilising effect. This effect (according to Mihevic, 1982) is evident a few minutes after the exercise ends and results in lower levels of state anxiety 20-30 minutes after exercise compared to those recorded before the start of exercise. However, many questions remain regarding these findings. Firstly, it must be considered whether the noted anxiety reduction is simply a return to baseline. Possible reductions in state anxiety after exercise can only be evaluated if several baseline measures are taken at various points prior to exercise. Anxiety may be increased immediately prior to treatment for experimental and control subjects alike because of the effects of anticipation; any reduction which is noted from this point may be a simple return to baseline. This may be particularly true for experiments involving exercise since Morgan et al. (1980) have shown that state anxiety increases during laboratory exercise. Rather than exercise causing the reduction in anxiety it could be argued that the cessation of exercise causes the higher than normal levels of anxiety to drop.

Secondly, the intensity of exercise required to bring about a reduction in state anxiety must be questioned. Morgan (1979a) has suggested that vigorous exercise is required to reduce anxiety levels in both male and female subjects. Morgan (1979a) cites studies which have shown that light exercise has no effect on anxiety, but the intensity of the exercise (in terms of oxygen consumption or heart rate) is not specified. It is clear that exact definitions of the exercise completed, in terms that are comparable across studies (e.g. oxygen consumption) are required to differentiate between light and vigorous exercise.

Finally, a question of whether the effects of exercise on state anxiety are similar for men and women must be raised. Most studies have used male subjects, but Wood (1977) compared the effects of a 12-minute run on male (n = 62) and female (n = 44) students. He found that male and female students who were classified as high-anxious, reduced their levels of state anxiety after the run, while both male and female low-anxious students reported increased levels of state anxiety after the run. Since the pre-run anxiety scores were within the normal range and the classification into high and low categories made on an arbitrary basis, it is likely that these results could be explained by statistical regression to the mean rather than by the effects of exercise.

There is some evidence then that acute involvement in exercise produces a psychological effect, but future studies must rule out the alternative explanations which are plausible in many of the past designs, namely local history, selection bias, testing effects, and statistical regression.

2.2.2 The effect of chronic exercise involvement

Several studies have investigated the effects of a programme of exercise. These programmes typically last between eight and ten weeks with two to four exercise sessions each week. For example, after a ten-week jogging class, Folkins et al. (1972) found that fitness improvements were positively correlated with measures of psychological well-being for a group of college students ($\underline{N}$ = 44). It was noted that this effect was stronger for the women than for the men. Brown et al. (1978) studied the effects of various types of exercise on 71 male and 96 female college and high school students. They found that those who did 30 minutes of exercise (tennis, wrestling, or jogging), three times per week for ten weeks decreased depression scores (although scores were below clinical levels), while a non-exercising control group and a team of softball players did not. No sex differences were noted in this study, but the selection bias involved in using intact groups may have confounded the results. In a more controlled study, Blumenthal et al. (1982) compared mood profiles of 16 exercisers (11 women and 5 men) and 16 sedentary, matched control subjects. The comparisons were made before and after the experimental subjects engaged in a ten-week exercise programme. By the end of the exercise programme the experimental group reduced levels of trait and state anxiety and reported more positive mood profiles than the control group. Blumenthal et al. (1982) acknowledge that selection bias may provide an alternative to exercise as an explanation of the results.

Another topical area in the measurement of chronic exercise effects is that of self-esteem. Sonstroem (1984) has provided a comprehensive review of this area. He concludes that, despite limitations in the designs of studies, 'exercise programs are associated with significant increases in self-esteem scores of participants' and that 'the score increases are particularly pronounced in subjects initially lower in self-esteem' (p.138). The majority of subjects in the 16 studies reviewed by Sonstroem (1984) were male. However, when women were included in the studies the results were similar to those found with male subjects. The only exception to this pattern was in the case of Army recruits (Kowal et al., 1978) where only men increased in self estimation scores after basic training. As with other dimensions of the psychological effects of exercise, the short history of this research has not yet led us to the point of recognising exercise as the causal agent in the reported effects.

Taken together these results provide some support for the idea that chronic involvement in exercise leads to psychological benefits, but they also point out flaws in the research. One study (Folkins et al., 1972) has suggested more benefit for women than men. The complete picture will not be available until designs which incorporate random assignment to treatment groups replicate these findings.

2.2.3 The effects of exercise deprivation

Another way of investigating experimentally the psychological effects of exercise is to deprive regular exercisers of exercise. Baekeland (1970) experimentally deprived 14 regular exercisers of their usual exercise for one month and studied the effects of this on sleep patterns. The sex of the subjects was not stated. Changes in sleep patterns were interpreted as increases in anxiety levels. The subjects also reported increased sexual tension and an increased need to be with others.

One other study has looked at the effects of exercise deprivation. Tooman et al. (1985) measured mood profiles of both competitive and recreational runners after a normal training run and then deprived them of running for two consecutive days. All runners experienced a positive mood swing after running which was maintained into the first day without exercise. However, by the second day without exercise, mood scores had dropped to the level recorded before a regular run. This suggests that the positive effects of one exercise session may last up to one day. There was no sex difference in the pattern of these results.

The experimental paradigm of exercise deprivation is difficult to put into practice because not many runners who experience benefits from exercise are willing to give up their routines. Moreover those runners/exercisers who are willing to stop exercising may be quite different from those who are not willing to comply with this experimental condition. Thus a selection bias is likely to occur in exercise studies using this design.

2.2.4 The use of exercise as a treatment for depression

In contrast to research examining non-depressed populations, studies which have examined the use of exercise as a treatment for depression have almost always included more female than male subjects. While sex differences have not been found in this literature, it is possible that potential differences may have been masked by the invalidity of some statistical comparisons. It is certain that researchers have found it easier or more convenient to recruit female subjects. This trend in itself is of interest. It has been noted that the number of women reporting symptoms of depression out-number men by 5:2 (Weissman and Klerman, 1977). It is not surprising therefore that studies using exercise as a treatment for depression have included more female than male subjects. The reasons for this sex difference encompass sociological, psychological and cognitive factors and the reader is referred to Weissman and Klerman (1977) and Brown and Harris (1978) for more comprehensive reviews.

The idea that running (or something associated with the running) could alleviate depression was first introduced by Kostrubala (1976) and quickly led to experimental research. Greist et al. (1979a) were among the first therapists to use an experimental design to quantify the effects of exercise (in this case running) on depression. They randomly assigned 28 subjects to one of three treatment groups:

(a) ten sessions of time-limited, behaviourally
    focused, psychotherapy;
(b) time-unlimited psychotherapy which was
    insight oriented;
(c) running, with a group leader, for 30-65
    minutes, three times each week.

All treatments lasted for ten weeks. The subjects were 13 men
and 15 women, from a private clinic, who scored above the 50th
percentile of the SCL-90 depression scale. The results indicated
that the eight subjects assigned to the running treatment had at
least as much improvement as those in the other two treatments. No
sex differences were noted in the treatment effects.

While Greist et al. (1979a) had made an important step in
beginning the experimental research in this area, they acknowledged
that the design had several flaws which limited the validity of the
findings. The internal validity was limited by the presence of a
single running leader but several psychotherapists and by the fact
that the running group had more contact than the other two groups
with the therapist and other patients. In addition, it was not
clear which aspects of the running treatment were related to
improvement; social interaction, mastery of a task, or fitness
improvements are all possible agents in the observed changes.

To eliminate some of these problems Greist and his associates
(Klein et al., 1985) conducted a second study which equated the
time that subjects had in contact with the therapist and provided a
comparison condition (meditation-relaxation). In this second
study, 74 subjects (21 men and 53 women) were randomly assigned to
either group psychotherapy, meditation therapy, or running therapy.
Comparisons between the three groups, after twelve weeks of
treatment and at a nine-month follow-up, led to the conclusion that
the three treatments were equally effective in reducing depression.
There were no sex differences noted in these treatment effects.

The findings of Greist et al. (1979a) and of Klein et al. (1985)
have been supported by other research. Rueter (1979) randomly
assigned 18 students (2 men and 16 women), who had sought help for
depression at a university mental health clinic, to one of two
treatment groups. One group received counselling therapy for ten
weeks; the other group received the same counselling therapy, but,
in addition, ran three times per week with a running leader. The
results indicated that the group receiving both running and
counselling improved significantly more, on scores on the Beck
Depression Inventory (BDI), than the group receiving counselling
alone. This conclusion must be interpreted with caution, as the
running and counselling group had more time in treatment each week
than the counselling-only group.

Fremont (1983) expanded on the design used by Reuter (1979). In
a study conducted with 49 volunteers (13 men and 36 women), Fremont
(1983) randomly assigned subjects to one of three treatments:

(a) cognitive therapy only for one hour per week;
(b) running with a group leader for 20 minutes three times each week;
(c) both cognitive therapy (one hour per week) and running therapy (20 minutes three times per week).

The volunteers, who had responded to media advertisements for depression therapy, met standardised screening criteria for depression. The results indicated that all three treatments caused equal improvements in depression, as measured by the BDI. Again, there were no sex differences in treatment effects.

One major criticism of the studies examined so far is that comparisons have not been made to groups which receive no-treatment. Creating a no-treatment group presents the researcher with an ethical dilemma but the comparison is needed to test whether or not people recover from moderate depression without treatment. The following studies have tried to counteract this problem. Moreau (1982) compared cognitive therapy, jogging therapy, and a programme of nature study with a waiting-list control group. All programmes provided a total of 19 hours of treatment over an eight-week period. The results showed that, after treatment, the groups did not differ from each other, nor from the waiting-list control group, on depression scores. However, the subjects (47 housewives) were not randomly assigned to the treatment conditions, which makes it difficult to draw conclusions about the causal factors underlying these results.

Mutrie (1986) examined the effects of three different eight-week exercise programmes on depression, mood and fitness. The subjects ($\underline{N}$ = 24, 4 men and 20 women) were diagnosed as depressed by general practitioners, and then referred to a physical educator. The general practitioners were working within the National Health Service of the United Kingdom. Subjects were randomly assigned to three groups. Group A ($\underline{n}$ = 9) received eight weeks of aerobic exercise, with strengthening and stretching exercise introduced after four weeks. Group B ($\underline{n}$ = 8) received eight weeks of strengthening and stretching exercise, with aerobic exercise introduced after four weeks. Group C ($\underline{n}$ = 7) had no treatment for four weeks, and then received eight weeks of exercise which included aerobic, strengthening, and stretching exercise. Each subject met individually with a physical educator every two weeks. The physical educator taught the fitness programmes, set appropriate exercise goals, and conducted fitness tests. The dependent measures were the Beck Depression Inventory (BDI), the Profile of Mood States (POMS), a step test, and a sit-up test.

After four weeks of aerobic exercise group A had lower scores on the BDI ($\underline{M}$ = 9.46) than at intake ($\underline{M}$ = 22.44), $\underline{p}$<.01. Reductions on the BDI were not evident after four weeks of non-aerobic exercise (group B) nor after four weeks of no-treatment (group C). It is therefore more likely that the reduction in depression was caused by aerobic exercise itself, rather than by spontaneous remission or by peripheral effects of the experimental situation.

After eight weeks of exercise all subjects reported lower levels
of depression, more positive moods and were found to be fitter.
These improvements were maintained 20 weeks after the eight-week
programmes. Again, no sex differences were noted.

The findings of this study both confirm the generalisability of
North American research, which has shown that exercise can have an
antidepressant effect and also show that aerobic exercise can be
used within a National Health Service as a treatment for
depression. It also shows that moderate depression does not remit
spontaneously over four weeks and that effects associated with
aerobic exercise were not due to social interaction or other
peripheral effects of the experimental situation.

Finally, Martinsen et al. (1985) randomly assigned hospitalised
depressives ($\underline{N}$ = 43) to an aerobic exercise group or a control
group. The exercise group increased fitness and reduced depression
scores more than the control group, again suggesting that exercise
is a causal agent.

The studies involving the use of exercise as a treatment for
moderate depression consistently show a positive effect across
various subject populations and no sex differences have been
noted. Experimental designs must continue to build on previous
findings and include larger groups of subjects. Most of the
previous studies have had too few subjects to provide appropriate
statistical power for testing the between-groups effects. Thus
results which indicate no difference between groups may simply have
too little power to show the treatment effects. In addition, an
effort should be made to include comparisons between equal numbers
of men and women. Finally, the next wave of research in this area
must investigate the mechanisms by which the antidepressant effect
of exercise takes place.

3. Mechanisms

The mechanisms by which the psychological effects of exercise can
be explained are not, as yet, well-documented. Human beings are
complex organisms and it is likely that a particular behaviour will
have more than one explanation. Thus beneficial effects from
exercise are likely to be created by several mechanisms operating
in a synergistic fashion. In this section, three processes which
provide possible mechanisms will be reviewed.

3.1 Biochemical processes
Changes in biochemical activity during and after exercise may
provide mechanisms through which the psychological benefits of
exercise are perceived. Firstly, Morgan (1985) has suggested that
exercise-induced changes in the sympathetic nervous system and
monoamines in particular might mediate the affective benefits which
have been associated with exercise. Secondly, acute bouts of
exercise appear to cause increases in the plasma levels of
endorphins which are endogenous, morphine-like chemicals (Carr et
al., 1981; Colt et al., 1981; Farrel et al., 1982; Gambert et al.,
1981; Howlett et al., 1984). It has been speculated that these
increases are associated with mood-elevation (Gambert et al.,
1981), runner's high (Pargman & Baker, 1980; Sachs, 1984),

decreased pain perception in injured athletes (Moore, 1982), addiction to exercise (Trotter, 1984), and with the antidepressant effect of exercise (Greist et al., 1979b). These speculations provide an endorphin hypothesis for the affective benefits associated with exercise. This hypothesis is appealing because morphine (a similar chemical substance to endorphin) has well known analgesic and euphoric properties. The major problem for this hypothesis is that while increases in endorphin levels due to exercise have been noted in blood plasma, the psychological effects speculated to be associated with endorphins are mediated in the CNS. However, this remains a tenable hypothesis to be tested by future research technology. Harber and Sutton (1984) provide and excellent review of this area.

3.2 Physiological processes
Two possible physiological mechanisms which might explain the psychological benefits of exercise have been noted. The first relates to muscle tension levels and the second to work capacity.

Reductions in electromyographic (EMG) recordings of muscle tension after exercise have been noted by deVries (1968, 1981). The modality, intensity, frequency and duration of exercise required to produce this tranquilising effect have been described by deVries (1981, p.53) as 'rhythmic exercise such as walking, jogging, cycling, and bench stepping from 5 to 30 minutes at 30% to 60% of maximum intensities'. This reduction in muscle tension may indicate a mechanism for reported decreases in anxiety and tension levels after exercise.

Increased work capacity should be associated with chronic involvement in exercise. The effects of this increased capacity might be experienced as an increase in energy available for daily tasks, thus decreasing feelings of fatigue. In this way, exercise may provide a mood elevating effect. Increased capacity for work may also assist the individual in coping with stress (Schafer, 1978; Warshaw, 1979). In order to test this mechanism all future studies of the psychological effects of exercise must measure fitness improvements. This particular mechanism may be important in explaining the psychological benefits of exercise for women. Since women have traditionally been less active than men (Boutilier and SanGiovanni, 1983) it could be that they can make greater fitness improvements than men from a programme of exercise.

3.3 Psychological processes
Three possible psychological sources of the reported benefits of exercise will be examined.

Firstly, exercise may be beneficial because it provides a mastery experience. Robbins and Joseph (1985) hypothesised that one cause of the negative affect which accompanies exercise deprivation is the loss of predictable feelings of success and self-fulfillment associated with running. Sonstroem (1984) suggested that one way in which exercise might improve self-esteem was by providing situations in which participants could master a task. Greist et al., (1981) made specific reference to mastering the skills of running as an important aspect of the antidepressant effect of running. This potential mechanism may be particularly important for women for the following reason. The stereotypical female image has reflected frailty rather than physical prowess. By gaining physical strength and ability, women may come to realise that they are not frail, but competent. Rindskopf and Gratch (1982) describe this process as 'resocialization of body perceptions', and believe it to be central to women's mental health.

A second psychological process which may provide explanations for perceived benefits is that exercise provides a distraction for the participant (Mobily, 1982; Morgan, 1985). This suggestion has been supported by studies which show that meditation and relaxation (Bahrke and Morgan, 1978) and eating lunch (Wilson et al., 1981) are as effective as exercise in reducing levels of state anxiety, although serious flaws in the designs of these studies make the findings rather tentative. However, this hypothesis has intuitive appeal, in that exercise usually provides a 'time-out' from other daily tasks, and is usually undertaken away from home or work.

The third psychological process to be examined is that of exercise addiction. It is possible that people can experience long term benefits from regular exercise because they become positively addicted to it (Glasser, 1976). Positive addiction is defined as regular involvement in an activity which provides pleasure and satisfaction, allowing the participant to gain an increased sense of self-confidence or 'strength', as Glasser (1976) suggested. Furthermore, the activity affords the individual an opportunity to experience a euphoric mental state or, to put it in Glasser's (1976) terms, the brain has a chance to 'spin free'. It is this pleasurable state to which the participant becomes addicted. Carmack and Martens (1979) have developed a scale which measures positive addiction and found that many runners (both competitive and recreational) are positively addicted to running.

A note of caution must be sounded regarding the potential benefits of positive addiction to exercise; there is the possibility that negative addiction and consequent psychological harm may also occur. Morgan (1979b) suggested that if running becomes the most important aspect of a person's life, there are three signals which suggest the addiction is negative rather than positive:

(a) relationships with family and friends come lower on the priority list than running;
(b) responsibilities at work are not fulfilled because of running commitments;
(c) running continues even when it is medically contraindicated.

Sachs (1982) suggested that negatively addicted runners are no longer in control of their behaviour and may need help, from educators and counsellors, in reorganising their priorities.

The three processes reviewed provide several possible mechanisms for the psychological benefits of exercise. Future research must systematically test and eliminate competing hypotheses. This will not be an easy task as several mechanisms may operate together to produce an overall effect.

4. Conclusions

This paper has reviewed the current literature on the psychological effects of exercise, with particular regard to women. Conclusions must be tentative because the history of the research in this area is too short to provide complete answers.

4.1 Summary of the psychological effects of exercise

(1) Descriptive studies show that exercise (mainly running) provides benefits such as improved mood, decreased anxiety and improved self-image. Descriptions of distress have also been noted by regular exercisers when they miss their workouts. There is a suggestion that regular exercisers may have a more positive mood profile than that expected from a normal population.

(2) Experimental studies have shown that acute effects from an exercise session include mood elevation and anxiety reduction. However, studies in this area have, in general, been poorly designed and it is not clear that exercise is the causal mechanism in the effects which have been reported.

(3) Experimental studies have shown that chronic effects from a programme of exercise include an increased sense of well-being, decreased depression levels and increased self-esteem. Again, it is not clear from the research, whether the exercise programme itself causes these effects. However, depriving exercisers of their regular sessions does seem to reverse the reported benefits of regular exercise involvement.

(4) Studies which have used aerobic exercise as a treatment for moderate depression consistently show positive effects across various subject populations. However, the mechanisms by which this effect takes place have not, as yet, been directly investigated.

(5) There is a need for future research to specify the modality (e.g. aerobic exercise, weight training), duration, intensity, and frequency of exercise which is required to provide psychological effects.

4.2 Summary of sex differences
Specific effects for women were difficult to discern from the literature for several reasons:

(a) some studies did not include female subjects;
(b) most studies had unequal numbers of men and women, thus making valid statistical comparisons difficult;
(c) some studies did not provide an analysis by sex.

The following conclusions must therefore be seen as tentative.

(1) In general both men and women perceive psychological benefits from exercise.

(2) There is a suggestion that more women than men describe improved moods and depression relief as benefits of exercise and that more women than men experience psychological distress if regular exercise is prevented.

(3) There is a suggestion that physiological benefits and psychological benefits are more closely related for women than for men.

(4) The effects of exercise as a treatment for moderate depression appear to be similar for men and women. However, it should be noted that the validity of this comparison is questionable because all of the studies in this area have included more women than men in the samples.

4.3 Summary of possible mechanisms

The mechanisms which might explain how the psychological effects of exercise take place are not, as yet, well described. Three processes, namely biochemical, physiological, and psychological, were suggested as providing several hypotheses which may operate together to produce the effects described in the literature.

References

Baekeland, F. (1970). Exercise deprivation. Sleep and psychological reactions. Archives of General Psychiatry 22:365-369

Bahrke, M.S. and Morgan, W.P. (1978). Anxiety reduction following exercise and meditation. Cognitive Therapy and Research 2:323-333

Berger, B.G. and Owen, D.R. (1983). Mood alterations with swimming - swimmers really do 'feel better'. Psychosomatic Medicine 45(5):425-433

Blumenthal, J.A., Williams, S., Needels, T.L. and Wallace, A.G. (1982). Psychological changes accompany aerobic exercise in healthy middle-aged adults. Psychosomatic Medicine 44(6):529-536

Boutilier, M.A. and San Giovanni, L. (1983). The sporting woman. Illinois: Human Kinetics.

Brown, G.W. and Harris, T. (1978). Social origins of depression London: Tavistock Publications.

Brown, R.S., Ramirez, D.E. and Taub, J.M. (1978). The prescription of exercise for depression. The Physician and Sportsmedicine, December:35-45

Callen, K.E. (1983). Mental and emotional aspects of long-distance running. Psychosomatics 24(2):133-151

Carmack, M.A. and Martens, R. (1979). Measuring commitment to running: A survey of runners' attitudes and mental states. Journal of Sport Psychology 1:25-42

Carr, D.B., Bullen, B.A., Skrinar, G.S., Arnold, M.A., Rosenblatt, M., Beitens, I.Z., Martin, J.B. and McArthur, J.W. (1981). Physical conditioning facilitates the exercise-induced secretion of beta-endorphin and beta-lipoprotein in women. The New England Journal of Medicine 305(10):56-563

Colt, E.W., Wardlaw, S.L. and Frantz, A.G. (1981). The effect of running on plasma β-endorphin. Life Science 28:1637-1640

Cook, T.D. and Campbell, D.T. (1979). Quasi-experimentation. Design and analysis issues for field settings. Chicago: Rand McNally.

deVries, H.A. (1968). Immediate and long term effects of exercise upon resting muscle potential level. The Journal of Sports Medicine and Physical Fitness 8:1-11

deVries, H.A. (1981) Tranquilizer effect of exercise: A critical review. The Physician and Sportsmedicine 9(11):47-53

Farrell, P.A., Gates, W.K., Morgan, W.P. and Maksud, M.G. (1982). Increases in plasma β-EP and β-LPH immunoreactivity after treadmill running in humans. J. Appl. Physiol: Respiratory, Environmental and Exercise Physiol 52:1245-1249

Folkins, C.H., Lynch, S. and Gardiner, M.M. (1972). Psychological fitness as a function of physical fitness. Archives of Physical Medicine and Rehabilitation 53:503-508

Folkins, C.H. and Sime, W. (1981). Physical fitness training and mental health. Americal Psychologist 36:373-389

Fremont, J. (1983). The separate and combined effects of cognitively based counseling and aerobic exercise for the treatment of mild and moderate depression. Unpublished doctoral dissertation. The Pennsylvania State University.

Gambert, S.R., Garthwaite, T.L., Hagen, T.L., Tristani, F.E. and McCarty, D.J. (1981). Exercise increases plasma beta-endorphins (EP) and ACTH in untrained human subjects. Clinical Research 29(2):429a

Glasser, W. (1976). Positive addiction New York: Harper and Row.

Gondola, J.C. and Tuckman, B.W. (1982). Psychological mood states in 'average' marathon runners. Perceptual and Motor Skills 55:1295-1300

Greist, J.H., Eischens, R.R., Klein, M.H. and Faris, J.W. (1979a) Antidepressant running. Psychiatric Annals 9:134-140

Greist, J.H., Klein, M.H., Eischens, R.R., Faris, J., Gurman, A.S. and Morgan, W.P. (1979b). Running as a treatment for depression. Comprehensive Psychiatry 20:41-54

Greist, J.H., Klein, M.H., Eischens, R.R., Faris, J., Gurman, A.S. and Morgan, W.P. (1981). Running through your mind. In M.H. Sacks, and M.L. Sachs, (Eds.), Psychology of Running (pp.5-26). Champaign, IL: Human Kinetics.

Harber, V.J. and Sutton, J.R. (1984). Endorphins and exercise. Sports Medicine 1:154-171

Howlett, T.A., Tomlin, S., Ngahfoong, L., Rees, L.H., Bullen, B.A., Skrinar, G.S., McArthur, G.W., (1984). Release of β-endorphin and met-enkephalin during exercise in normal women: response to training. British Medical Journal. 288:1950-1952.

Jorgenson, C.B. and Jorgenson, D.E. (1979). Effects of running on perception of self and others. Perceptual and Motor Skills 48:242

Klein, M.H., Greist, J.H., Gurman, A.S., Neimeyer, R.A., Lesser, D.P., Bushnell, N.J. and Smith, R.E. (1985). A comparative outcome study of group psychotherapy vs. exercise treatments for depression. International Journal of Mental Health 13:148-177

Kostrubala, T. (1976). The joy of running New York: Lippincott Company.

Kowal, D.M., Patton, J.F. and Vogel, J.A. (1978). Psychological states and aerobic fitness of male and female recruits before and after basic training. Aviation Space Environmental Medicine 49:603-606

Martinsen, E.W., Medhus, A. and Sandvik, L. (1985). Effects of aerobic exercise on depression: A controlled study. British Medical Journal 291:100

McNair, D.M., Lorr, M. and Droppleman, L.F. (1971). Manual for the profile of mood states. San Diego: Educational and Industrial Testing Service.

Mihevic, P.M. (1982). Anxiety, depression, and exercise. Quest 33(2):140-153

Mobily, K. (1982). Using physical exercise and recreation to cope with stress and anxiety: A review. American Corrective Therapy Journal 36(3):77-81

Moore, M. (1982). Endorphins and exercise. The Physician and Sportsmedicine 10(2):111-119

Moreau, M.E. (1982). The effectiveness of jogging as a treatment for depression. Dissertation Abstracts International 42(10):4202B

Morgan, W.P. (1979a). Anxiety reduction following acute physical activity. Phychiatric Annals 9:141-147

Morgan, W.P. (1979b). Negative addiction in runners. The Physician and Sportsmedicine 7(2):56-63, 67-70

Morgan, W.P. (1980). Test of champions: The iceberg profile. Psychology Today 14:92-99, 101, 108

Morgan, W.P. (1985). Affective benefit of vigorous physical activity. Medicine and Science in Sports and Exercise 17:94-100

Morgan, W.P. and Pollock, M.L. (1977). Psychological characterization of the elite distance runner. Annals of the New York Academy of Sciences 301:382-403

Morgan, W.P., Horstman, D.H., Cymerman, A. and Stokes, J. (1980). Exercise as a relaxation technique. Primary Cardiology August:48-57

Mutrie, N. (1986). Exercise as a treatment for depression within a national health service. Unpublished doctoral dissertation. The Pennsylvania State University.

Mutrie, N. and Knill-Jones, R. (1985, June). Reasons for running: 1984 survey of the Glasgow People's Marathon Paper presented at the congress of the International Society for Sports Psychology, Copenhagen, Denmark.

Nowlis, D.P. and Greenberg, N. (1979). Empirical description of effects of exercise on mood. Perceptual and Motor Skills 49:1001-1002

Pargman, D. and Baker, M.C. (1980). Running high: Enkephalin indicted. Journal of Drug Issues 10:341-349

Reiter, M.A. (1981). Effects of a physical exercise program on selected mood states in a group of women over age 65. Dissertation Abstracts International 42(5):1974a

Robbins, J.M. and Joseph, P. (1985). Experiencing exercise withdrawal: Possible consequences of therapeutic and mastery running. Journal of Sport Psychology 7:23-39

Rindskopf, K.D. and Gratch, S.E. (1982). Women and exercise: A therapeutic approach. Women and Therapy 1(4):15-26

Rueter, M.A. (1979). The effect of running on individuals who are clinically depressed Unpublished master's thesis, the Pennsylvania State University.

Sachs, M.L. (1982). Positive and negative addiction to running. In J.T. Partington, T. Orlick and J.H. Salmela (Eds.), Sport in perspective (pp.154-155) Ottowa: Sport in Perspective Inc.

Sachs, M.L. (1984). The runner's high. In M.L. Sachs, and G.W. Buffone, (Eds.). Running as therapy (pp.273-287). Nebraska: University of Nebraska Press.

Schafer, W. (1978). Stress, distress and growth Davis, CA: Responsible Action.

Sonstroem, R.J. (1984). Exercise and self-esteem. Exercise and Sport Reviews 12:123-155

Summers, J.J., Sargent, G.I., Levey, A.J. and Murray, K.D. (1982). Middle-aged, non-elite marathon runners: a profile. Perceptual and Motor Skills 52:963-969

Tooman, M.E., Harris, D.V. and Mutrie, N. (1985). The effect of running and its deprivation on muscle tension, mood and anxiety Paper presented at the congress of the International Society for Sports Psychology, Copenhagen, Denmark.

Trotter, R.J. (1984). Rethinking the high in runner's high. Psychology Today May:8

Warshaw, L.J. (1979). Managing stress Reading, MA: Addison-Wesley Publishing Company.

Weissman, M.M. and Klerman, G.L. (1977). Sex differences in the epidemiology of depression. Archives of General Psychiatry 34:98-111

Wilson, V.E., Morley, M.C. and Bird, E.I. (1980). Mood profile of marathon runners, joggers, and non-exercisers. Perceptual and Motor Skills 5:117-118

Wilson, V.E., Berger, B.G. and Bird, E.I. (1981). Effects of running and of an exercise class on anxiety. Perceptual and Motor Skills 53:472-474

Wood, D.T. (1977). The relationship between state anxiety and acute physical activity. American Corrective Therapy Journal 31(3):67-69

Discussion

Dr Harrison, Farnborough, Hants
What was the background of the patients who volunteered for the depression study? Is it not possible that the sample was biased towards those already keen on exercise?

Dr Mutrie, Glasgow
The subjects had to be sedentary. They had not previously been exercising.

Dr Sutton, Ontario, Canada
Did the control group of the depression study have any contact with the supervisors? A number of studies have been able to show improvements merely with this contact. It would be advantageous to have a control group and exercise group with the same number of consultant contact hours.

Dr Mutrie
The control group had no contact of any kind with the consultants. I think it is important to remember that this is a small study and is only a start. I agree a further step forward in the design would be to have the control group contacted. The two different exercise groups however did have a different response while having the same amount of contact with the supervisor.

Professor Åstrand, Stockholm, Sweden
If people who exercise regularly feel better, why is there not a greater percentage of people taking exercise? Only about 10% or less of middle aged American males and 5% of females take regular exercise.

Dr Mutrie
As a physical educator I would say that many of our programmes in schools have been to blame. In order to reap the benefits of exercise it is important to experience exercise and to enjoy the experience.

Professor Åstrand
Irrespective of what type of physical activity they have in the school I think the statistics are very similar in all of the industrialised countries. So I think that one should not blame the curriculum in schools for what is wrong in adult life.

Dr Prior, Vancouver, Canada
In investigating the benefits of exercise it is important to control the group interaction of exercisers.

Dr Mutrie
We need to compare individual exercise with group exercise. In this depression study exercise was carried out individually because previously all the depression studies have used groups. It is not clear whether it is the exercise effect or the interaction effect. That study needs to be done.

Dr Nagle, Wisconsin, USA
You saw the change in depression after four weeks but was that the
first time you re-assessed them? If it was a response to aerobic
training, then physiological changes can occur before that time.

Dr Mutrie
There was very little correlation in this study between the
psychological and physiological changes. I do agree however that
the psychological changes may have occurred earlier.

Physiological profiles of the male and the female

E. NYGAARD and K. HEDE

Previous studies often exaggerated sex-differences in the cardiovascular dimensions, as evaluated from recent studies where subjects were matched for training background. Lower haemoglobin concentrations in females may account for still-remaining sex-differences in aerobic capacity. Lower blood pressures in females at rest and during exercise were consistent findings in many studies, along with a lower activity of the sympathetic nervous system. the reason remaining unclear. Several studies showed lower values of respiratory exchange ratios during exercise, and higher endurance capacity in females, indicative of a higher degree of lipid oxidation. Morphological and enzymatical studies of skeletal muscle also seem to agree upon a higher potential for oxidative phosphorylation in females. The relative body fat content is 50% higher in females than in males, and the pattern of plasma lipoproteins differs markedly between sexes. Also intramuscular lipid stores were higher in females. A higher degree of fat mobilisation in females was further substantiated by higher levels of plasma glycerol and free fatty acids, lower levels of lactate, and less decrease of muscle glycogen. Basal and maximally catecholamine-stimulated lipolysis of adipocytes from peripheral fat was similar in females and males. Plasma insulin levels at rest and during exercise were higher in females, with similar levels of glucose. Also growth hormone levels were higher at rest and during mild exercise. At identical levels of lipolysis-stimulating hormones, the higher body fat content in females will lead to higher levels of lipolytic metabolites. A lower peripheral resistance resulting from a lower adrenergic reactivity provides a better blood supply to exercising muscle. Thus, in females a high degree of free fatty acid oxidation can occur. Oestrogens have been shown to influence many of these physiological manifestations of a high capacity for fat mobilisation and oxidative phosphorylation in females.

1. Circulatory and respiratory reactions to exercise

1.1 Maximal aerobic capacity
In males and females with similar training background, maximal
oxygen uptake capactiy in females amounts to 70% of that in males
(Åstrand and Rodahl, 1977 Sparling, 1980), primarily due to gender-
related differences in muscle mass and in the dimensions of the
oxygen-transport system. When related to body weight this
difference is reduced, the capacity of males being 15-20% higher
than in females. This is primarily due to the higher body fat
content in women (Cureton and Sparling, 1980), and when related to
lean body mass, the difference is negligible - around 5%. This final
differential figure is closely related to the gender-related
difference in haemoglobin concentrations (Åstrand and Rodahl, 1977).
   According to Astrand (1960) two criteria should be fulfilled
when evaluating a person's maximal level for oxygen uptake:
Firstly, oxygen uptake should not increase despite a rising work
load, but should reach a plateau. Secondly, lactate concentrations
should be above 10mmol/l after work of at least 4 min duration. In
24 of 44 women, 20-65 years of age, oxygen uptake did not plateau
(Åstrand, 1960). In age group 20-29 years, mean plasma lactate
concentration was 13.4 mmol/l, and in age group 50-65 years 8.7
mmol/l, or 36% higher, in the younger women (Åstrand, 1960). Plasma
lactate concentrations were 10-15% higher in males than in females,
all sedentary, 30-60 years of age (Nygaard et al., 1983). In male
and female groups of young students, 25 years of age, matched on
maximal oxygen uptake in relation to lean body weight and training
background, no such difference was seen (Hede and Raa Andersen,
1985). These studies show that determination of maximal oxygen
uptake capacity according to the criteria of Åstrand (1960) may be
more complicated in women than in men, especially in sedentary and
elderly women.

1.2 Circulatory responses to sub-maximal exercise
The magnitude of gender-related differences in circulatory responses
to submaximal exercise appeared to be smaller than previously
thought. In groups of equally trained men and women, differences
in cardiac output, arterio-venous O_2-differences, and heart rate
responses to sub-maximal bicycle exercise were less (Zwiren et al.,
1983) than in previous research in which subjects were not equated
on habitual physical activity (Åstrand et al., 1964): Sex
differences for cardiac output and arterio-venous O_2-
differences at an O_2-demand of 1.5 l/min were non-significant
and smaller than the significant differences reported by Åstrand et
al. (1964). For heart rate the difference of 45 beats/min found
by Åstrand et al. (1964) was almost twice as large as that found
by Zwiren et al. (1983). The difference for stroke volume was
similar in the two studies. Åstrand and co-workers argued that the
lower cardiac performance in women combined with the lower
concentrations of haemoglobin were the basic reasons for the lesser
aerobic capacity seen in women, especially at maximal work-loads.
The significance of haemoglobin has been questioned, since its
effect upon blood viscocity should also be considered (Rost, 1981).

1.3 Blood pressure

Blood pressure at rest is lower in females than in males (Petrofsky et al., 1975; Hagerup et al., 1981; Gleerup Madsen et al., 1985; Andersen, 1986). In children and in post-menopausal women this sex-difference was not observed (Shroll and Hollnagel, 1982).

A lower blood pressure in women was also observed during isometric muscle conctractions, both during hand-grips at 30% of maximal voluntary contraction force (MVC) (Ewing et al 1974), and at 40% MVC (Petrofsky et al., 1975; Sanchez et al., 1980), and during contraction of the knee extensors at 20% MVC (Gleerup-Madsen et al., 1985). The same sex-difference was observed during dynamic exercise (Shroll and Hollnagel, 1982; Kobryn et al., 1986).

The explanation of the lower mean arterial pressure in women aged 15-55 years is not clear. Obviously, peripheral resistance will be affected by the lower adrenergic reactivity with females than with males (see 3.3). Identical arterio-venous O_2-differences with males and females at the same absolute O_2-uptake (Zwiren et al., 1983), also supports the notion of a lower peripheral resistance with the females, considering their lower concentration of haemoglobin.

It has also been suggested that the lower pressure may be associated with the 'protective' effect of oestrogens: in post-menopausal women treated with oestrogens against osteoporosis a lowering of the blood pressure was observed. Another possible explanation could be attached to the relatively lower blood volume and less red blood cells in women, partly explained through the menstrual flow. Thus lower blood volume and lower viscocity, primarily due to lower concentrations of haemoglobin, may be important determinants for blood pressure levels in women.

1.4 Isometric endurance

Female subjects were able to maintain an isometric contraction for a longer period of time than the males (Petrofsky et al., 1975; Petrofsky and Phillips,1980; Byrd and Jeness, 1982; Harmon et al., 1984), while in other studies isometric endurance was similar in males and females (Ewing et al., 1974; Sanchez et al., 1980; Gleerup-Madsen et al., 1985). Also in dynamic exercise, a higher endurance was observed in females (Nygaard, 1981b; Froberg and Pedersen, 1984).

Byrd and Jeness (1982) argued that female subjects were less motivated than male subjects; therefore they do not exert a 'true' maximal voluntary contraction force and thus perform at a comparatively lower relative load than males leading to a longer endurance time.

Wilmore (1977) stated that 'while strength training does produce large increases in the female's total body strength, it does not appear to result in concomitant gains in muscle bulk.' Milner-Brown et al. (1975) found that strength training led to an increased motor unit synchronisation of trained muscles. Thus a role of neural adaptations in the 'local' component of the response to strength training cannot be excluded (Lewis et al., 1984).

1.5 Blood pressure and the quality of skeletal muscle
The quality of skeletal muscle has been pointed at as a factor
which may co-influence the circulatory reactions to exercise:
in cats, at any proportion of the muscles' maximal tension, the
intramuscular pressure and resistance to flow in the medial
gastrocnemius muscle (predominantly fast twitch fibres) was about
twice that of the soleus muscle (slow twitch fibres) (Petrofsky and
Hendershot, 1984; Bonde-Petersen and Robertson, 1981).

Juhlin-Dannfelt et al. (1979) and Frisk-Holmberg et al. (1983)
showed that blood pressure at rest correlated negatively with the
relative proportion of slow twitch fibres in the lateral vastus
muscle of 22 male subjects, and 11 males and 6 females,
respectively. No such correlations were seen in the study by
Gleerup-Madsen et al. (1985).

2. Metabolic reactions to submaximal exercise

2.1 Respiratory exchange ratio
An estimation of the relative contribution of carbohydrates and fat
to the oxidative metabolism can be obtained by measurements of the
respiratory exchange ratio (RER), which under steady-state conditions
equals the metabolic respiratory quotient (RQ) (Christensen and
Hansen, 1939).

Lower RER-values were observed in females during tread-mill
walking at 35% of maximal aerobic capacity (Blatchford et al.,
1985) and during bicycle exercise at various intensities (Jansson
1980; Nygaard et al., 1984a; Froberg and Pedersen, 1984). Other
studies did not confirm to this finding on RER (Costill et al.,
1979; Powers et al., 1980; Favier et al., 1983).

Inclusion criteria introduce some confusion as to the
interpretation of results from studies comparing males and females.
Cardio-respiratory capacity and background physical activity are
important criteria to consider as previously discussed.

2.2 Energy stores
Fat deposits in the adult female constitute 25-30% of total body
weight, and in the male 15-20% (Novak, 1972; Durnin and Womersley,
1974; Hede and Raa Andersen, 1985). Von Döbeln (1956) found 10%
body fat in well-trained males and 20% in well-trained females.
An extensive review on body composition of athletes and changes
with training has been presented by Wilmore (1983). Body fat
content in female athletes ranged from 9.6% in gymnasts to 28% in
shot putters. The range for male athletes was 3.7% in distance
runners and 19.6 in shot putters.

More intra- and extracellular lipid is found in female than in
male skeletal muscle (Prince et al., 1977; Sjøgaard, 1979). No sex-
difference has been demonstrated in the glycogen storage capacity
of skeletal muscle, the capacity being similar for slow and fast
twitch fibres (Essén et al., 1975).

2.3 Substrate utilisation

Observed sex-differences in RER and in endurance time were best explained as a result of sex-differences in substrate utilisation (Froberg and Pedersen, 1984). Muscle glycogen of the thigh was reduced by 45mmol/kg in five men, and by only 25mmol/kg in five women during a day of recreational down-hill skiing (Nygaard et al., 1978). Initial values were identical in the two groups, around 80mmol/kg, and the groups were comparable in terms of the amount of skiing, food intake during the day and technical skill.

During endurance exercise the working muscle utilises fatty acids which originate from the hydrolysis of triglycerides stored within the muscle cell (Carlson et al., 1971; Galbo, 1983), and from extramuscular triglyceride stores (Newsholme and Leech, 1983). The concentration of plasma glycerol is often used as indicator of the mobilisation of triglycerides from extramuscular fat deposits. Fatty acids are hydrolysed from the glycerol component and transported to the working muscle attached to albumin molecules. Uptake is believed to occur passively across the cell membrane. Since fat tissue does not contain the enzyme glycerokinase, free glycerol cannot be reesterified into triglycerides and is therefore transported to the liver for further metabolism. Some recycling of fatty acids takes place in the fat tissue, since the free fatty acids can be incorporated in the triglycerides of the peripheral fat tissue (Bülow, 1982). The plasma concentration of free fatty acids is considered a reasonable measure of muscular uptake of fatty acids, since the rate of turnover is proportionate to the concentration (Armstrong et al., 1961)

Lower plasma concentrations of lactate and higher plasma concentrations of glycerol and free fatty acids along with less decrease of muscle glycogen were observed along with the lower RER-values in females (Nygaard et al., 1984; Blatchford et al., 1985).

The general trend from these studies is that sedentary adult women are on average capable of utilising more fat as a substrate during prolonged sub-maximal exercise than men.

2.4 Lipolysis of peripheral fat

Basal hydrolysis of triglycerides to glycerol and free fatty acids is complete and therefore of higher significance for the understanding of human energy metabolism than the maximal catecholamine-stimulated lipolysis, the latter being incomplete and leading to net-accumulation of mono- and di-glycerides (Arner et al., 1981). Studies on lipocyte concentrations of cAMP during basal conditions supported this (Engfeldt et al., 1982). Mean cell volume of lipocytes from various parts of the human body exhibited no sex-difference (Sjöström et al., 1972; Chumlea et al., 1981) and lipocyte volume correlated positively with basal lipolysis (Ostman et al., 1973; Jacobsson et al., 1976; Melander et al., 1985) in contrast with the findings by Deprés et al. (1982).

Deprés et al. (1984) and Melander et al. (1985) did not find any difference between sexes in basal lipolysis before or after a training period. However, five months of endurance training increased suprailiac adipocyte adrenalin maximal stimulated lipolysis in both men and women (Deprés et al., 1984). This finding was not confirmed by Melander et al. (1985) in a study of lipolysis of adipocytes from the upper gluteal region. However, a

left-ward shift of the dose-response curve for adrenalin showed
that the sensivity to adrenalin had increased with training
(Melander et al., 1985). It should be noted that there are
metabolic differences between the various fat deposits of the body
(Smith et al., 1979), and also that adipose tissue metabolism is
influenced by sex-hormones, especially the oestrogens (Hansen et
al., 1980).

2.5 Plasma triglycerides.
The depleted intramuscular triglycerides after prolonged exercise
are restored by means of free fatty acids from adipose tissue and
with plasma triglycerides (Essén, 1977; Lithell et al., 1979). This
restoration process is mediated by an increased activity of the
enzyme lipoproteinlipase (LPL), as shown after vigorous exercise
(Lithell et al., 1979; Taskinen and Nikkilä 1980). Plasma
triglycerides do not contribute quantitatively to energy production
during exercise (Dufaux et al., 1982).
  Compared to sedentary subjects endurance trained athletes have
high LPL activities in muscle and in adipose tissue (Nikkilä et
al., 1978; Peltonen et al., 1981) and low low levels of
triglycerides (Haskell, 1984), supporting the concept of an
increased capacity to degradation of triglycerides in endurance
trained athletes.
  Women at all ages after puberty have significantly higher plasma
levels of HDL (high density lipoprotein) (Gordon et al., 1977). An
extensive review of the plasma lipoprotein profile in relation to
sex hormones in premenarcheal athletes has been presented by
Zonderland (1985).
  Women have a higher LPL activity in adipose tissue than men
(Nikkilä et al., 1978). This might influence the sex difference
seen in HDL. Also oestrogens have been shown to affect lipoprotein
triglyceride and cholesterol in adult females (Knopp et al., 1981).

3. Hormonal reactions to submaximal exercise

3.1 Plasma concentrations of hormones during exercise
A change from rest to muscular exercise increases the activity of
the sympathetic nervous system, which with nor-adrenalin as
transmittor facilitates lipolysis and inhibits insulin secretion.
This change induces mobilisation of glucose and free fatty acids
from liver and adipose tissue and reduces glucose uptake by
skeletal muscle. As muscle activity continues, and plasma glucose
concentration is reduced, secretion of adrenalin, growth hormone
and glucagon will be stimulated (Galbo, 1983). Adrenalin is
considered a more potent lipolytic hormone than nor-adrenalin in
adipose tissue, indicating that lipolysis is sensitive to
stimulation of the β_2-receptors (Clutter et al., 1980; Galster
et al., 1981; Hjemdahl and Linde,1983). The function of nor-
adrenalin as a circulating hormone is limited to very high plasma
concentrations, as seen during prolonged severe exercise (Sjöström
et al. 1983).

3.2 Insulin
Higher plasma concentrations of insulin at rest (Boyns et al.,
1969; Nygaard et al., 1984b; Hale et al., 1985) and during exercise
(Nygaard et al., 1984b), and a greater insulin response to a glucose
load were observed in women (Hale et al. 1985). Plasma glucose
levels were similar in males and females indicating that the
insulin sensitivity is different between the sexes (Hale et al.,
1985). Yki Järvinen (1984) also noted a sex-difference in
insulin sensitivity, but having considered the sex-difference in
muscle mass, concluded that the sensitivity to insulin was higher
in females. A greater number of insulin receptors in males than in
females has been indicated (Bertoli et al., 1980; Hendricks et al.,
1981). This difference in insulin sensitivity seems to be related
to the female sex hormones, since in animals insulin levels were
increased with administration of physiologic amounts of oestrogens
(Baily and Matty, 1972; Baily and Ahmed-Sorour, 1980).

3.3 Catecholamines
A lower adrenergic reactivity was observed in females during
psychoemotional or physical stress. The female responds less
intensely and later than the male and at times she may not respond
at all (Johansson et al., 1974; Frankenhaeuser et al., 1976, Claustre
et al., 1980). In addition during muscle contraction at the same
relative load, lower adrenergic rectivities were observed in
females (Vendsalu, 1960; Sanchez et al., 1980). In other studies no
sex-related differences were seen in cathecholamine levels during
exercise (Favier et al., 1983 and Lehmann et al., 1986). A sex-
related difference in the behaviour of the adrenergic system may
result from the effects of sexual hormones (Ball et al., 1972).
    A mild activation of the sympathetic nervous system in women
under a glycaemic stress may be related to a more active lipid
mobilisation in females (Claustre et al., 1980).

3.4 Growth hormone
After light exercise higher plasma concentrations of growth hormone
were demonstrated in women than in men (Franz and Rabkin, 1965).
Plasma concentrations in women during the menstrual cycle and in
men after administration of oestrogens, led to the conclusion that
oestrogens are partly responsible for the sex-differences in
plasma concentrations of growth hormone. In agreement with Franz
and Rabkin (1965) we found that plasma concentrations of growth
hormone during the initial 30 min of 60 min bicycle exercise were
significantly higher in females than in males (Nygaard et al.,
1984b).

4. Morphology and enzymatic profiles of skeletal muscle

4.1 Muscle fibre composition
Fibre composition of skeletal muscle in healthy subjects has been
widely studied through the past 25 years. Reviews on muscle fibre
characteristics were presented by Saltin and Gollnick (1983), and by
Drinkwater (1984) with special focus upon the female. These reviews,
however, were not quite complete, since they did not include observed
sex-differences, some of which will be presented below.

The incidence of one fibre type in repeated needle biopsies, or as evaluated from autopsy material, in tissue samples comprising 200-400 fibres differed by 15% to 20% (coefficient of variation) (Gollnick et al., 1972; Thorstensson 1976; Nygaard and Sanchez, 1982; Elder et al., 1982; Blomstrand and Ekblom, 1982; Lexell et al., 1983). Since sampling of 3-5 sites as suggested by Elder et al. (1982) to reduce the variation to ± 5% is not possible on a large scale, and since most studies include very few subjects, conclusions on differences between groups should be carefully considered because of the large variability of the measurements.

A recent study of histochemical and metabolic characteristics of human skeletal muscle included 31 female subjects and 34 male subjects aged 20-70 years (Essén-Gustavsson and Borges, 1986). Two other Scandinavian studies included 48 female subjects aged 16 years (Hedberg and Jansson, 1976), and 54 adult females aged 20-40 years (Nygaard, 1981a). A Canadian study included 38 females aged 25 years (Simoneau et al., 1985).

The relative occurrence of slow and fast twitch fibres of the vastus lateralis muscle was similar in sedentary males and females, around 50% of each type. Similarity between the sexes is also apparent when fast twitch fibres were subclassified into the more oxidative and the more glycolytic fast twitch fibres. Details on fibre type classifications were described by Saltin et al. (1977). Trained skeletal muscle of endurance athletes, males and females, has a high proportion of slow twitch fibres (Nygaard, 1981a; Saltin and Gollnick, 1983). Another characteristic feature of endurance trained muscles is the lack of fast twitch glycolytic fibres which constitutes 15-20% in sedentary subjects. In the gastroc nemius muscle of world class sprinters, males and females, slow twitch fibres constituted only 20-30% (Costill et al., 1976). Thus a certain relative proportion of fibre types seems to favour successful participation at an international level in some athletic events.

4.2 Muscle fibre area
A difference between the sexes appeared in the cross-sectional areas of muscle fibres: Fibres in general were smaller in females than in males. In the lateral vastus of sedentary females slow twitch fibres were larger than fast twitch fibres. This was in contrast to findings in age-matched male subjects in whom the fast twitch fibres were significantly larger than the slow twitch fibres (Hedberg and Jansson, 1976; Nygaard, 1981a; Simoneau et al., 1985; Essén-Gustavsson and Borges, 1986). The same sex-difference was observed in some groups of athletes (Saltin and Gollnick, 1983). Thus in the lateral vastus muscle the fractional volume of slow twitch fibres was larger in females than in males. Considering the metabolic profile of the slow twitch fibres (Saltin et al., 1977), a relatively greater potential for oxidative phosphorylation was indicated in females.

4.3 Muscle enzyme activities

In parallel with the histochemical observations, it was demonstrated that the ratio of oxidative to glycolytic enzyme activities was higher in females than in males (Bass et al., 1975; Nikkilä et al., 1978; Komi and Karlsson, 1978; Nygaard, 1981a; Simoneau et al., 1985). This was further suggestive of oxidative phosphorylation as the preferred metabolic pathway in sedentary females.

5. Activity patterns in males and females

Considering the prevailing theories on fibre type involvement in various types of muscular activity, based upon histochemical and electrophysiological data (see Saltin and Gollnick, 1983), and the close relationship between intensity and type of activity and muscle fibre size, the higher relative slow twitch fibre volume observed in skeletal muscle of female subjects may reflect a predominance of specific types of muscular activities in females compared to males. This was commented upon by Brooke and Engel (1969) who observed that the fast twitch fibres of the brachial biceps muscle were larger than the slow twitch fibres in mothers of severely disabled children with Duchenne muscular dystrophy, but not in other females. The authors suggested that this might be due to lifting the disabled children. The general finding of a high relative volume of slow twitch fibres in females is consistent with observed differences between boys and girls in their choice of spare-time physical activities: Girls give a high priority to recreational activities such as walking, light bicycling, and dancing, whereas boys prefer vigorous and competitive activities (Engström, 1975). Ilmarinen and Rutenfranz (1980) in a longitudinal qualitative study of the participation in sport activities by boys and girls from the age of 14 to 17 years found that boys' participation was four times as high as that of girls.

Heart rate determinations during the day supported the notion of various activity patterns in males and females. Gilliam et al. (1981) studied boys and girls 6-7 years of age; Spady (1980) boys and girls 8-14 years of age; Verschuur et al. (1983) studied teen-agers using heart rate monitoring and pedometers; Honnens and Tungelund (1983) students aged 25 years. These studies agreed upon differences between sexes in levels of physical activity there being both lower mean levels in females and less bursts of high activity in females than in males.

It thus appears that the observed differences between sexes in some of the physiological variables may well be explained by various modes of muscular activity typical of every-day life of males and females.

6. Dietary intervention

6.1 Fat-rich diet

Intensity and duration of work, degree of training, and diet are important factors to consider when evaluating the respiratory exchange ratio. The two former factors have often been controlled.

Krogh and Lindhard (1920) demonstrated that a diet rich in carbohydrate and poor in fat led to a relatively high oxidation of carbohydrates, while a diet rich in fat and poor in carbohydrate induced a favouring of fat as a fuel, as evaluated from the respiratory exchange ratio.

Bergström et al. (1967) showed that muscular stores of glycogen were dependent upon the preceding diet. A fat-enriched diet poor in carbohydrate lowered the stores of muscle glycogen and led to increased utilisation of fat as a substrate compared to the situation after a carbohydrate-enriched diet, where muscle glycogen stores were optimally replenished. A lower dependence upon oxidation of carbohydrates after a fat-rich diet was further supported by a changed composition of plasma metabolites: Plasma concentrations of glycerol and free fatty acids during exercise after diets rich in carbohydrate and fat, respectively, were higher in the latter situation (Rennie and Johnson, 1974; Maughan et al., 1978; Galbo et al., 1979; Phinney et al., 1983).

After a fat-enriched diet females were better adapted to utilisation of fat: After a normal mixed diet, during exercise at a load equivalent to 60% of maximal aerobic capacity, mean fat oxidation contributed 50% of total energy production in females, and 47% in the males; after a fat-enriched diet the corresponding values were 77% in the females and 64% in the males (Hede and Raa Andersen, 1985). These changes had previously been indicated by Jansson (1980).

The mechanisms behind the observed changes in substrate mobilistion with changed dietary regimens are not clear. A fat-rich diet induced at rest and during exercise lower plasma concentrations of insulin when compared to normal (Galbo, 1983). Besides the vital significance for carbohydrate metabolism, insulin plays a major role as anti-lipolytic hormone through inhibition of the mobilisation of triglycerides from the adipose tissue. Adrenaline - the catecholamine with the higher stimulatory effect upon lipolysis - was increased in fat experiments (Galbo et al., 1979).

6.2 Fat utilisation in long-lasting exercise

Increased fat-oxidation may be advantageous, since at the same time glycogen is spared. Stores of liver- and muscle-glycogen amount to 400-500g. In human maximally 5.4g of glycogen can be oxidised per min (Newsholme and Leech, 1983). In long-lasting physical performances (marathon, cross-country skiing, bicycling) the athlete will often experience symptoms of hypoglycemia. The capacity to utilise fat as a substrate obviously is a beneficial adaptation. While at rest the skeletal muscle is able to utilise fat as energy source almost exclusively (Felig and Wahren, 1975), the activities mentioned above will demand a certain contribution of carbohydrates as energy source, since the maximal exercise intensity of exclusive

fat oxidation is less than 50% of maximal aerobic capacity
(Gollnick, 1985).

7. Conclusion

Based on the available evidence - when groups were equated for
cardiovascular capacity and training background-sex-differences
seem to remain: females functionally have a higher endurance in
dynamic and isometric exercise; physiologically: a higher body
fat content; in the cardiovascular system a lower arterial
pressure, lower haemaglobin concentration, and higher concentration
of high density lipoprotein; in the muscular system more
intramuscular lipid, a higher relative volume of slow twitch (high
oxidative) muscle fibres, and enzymatically a higher potential for
oxidative phosphorylation; in the metabolic and hormonal reactions
to submaximal exercise a lower respiratory exchange ratio, less
decrease of muscle glycogen, lower lactate production, higher
concentrations of plasma glycerol and free fatty acids, higher
concentrations of plasma insulin and growth hormone and a lower
adrenergic reactivity. Most of these differences point to the
females' favouring of fat as a fuel, which according to the present
state of evidence is based on the following physiological events in
females as compared to males:

(1) Lower activity of the sympathetic system leading to lower
peripheral resistance (lower blood pressure and more blood to
exercising muscle.

(2) Larger amounts of total body fat can (even at a lower
adrenergic reactivity) supply higher plasma concentrations
of free fatty acids.

(3) Thinner muscle fibres give a larger diffusion surface per
unit muscle; and high potential of skeletal muscle for
oxidative phosphorylation.

References

Andersen, L.B. (1986). Physical profile of Danish Adolescents,
    16-19 years. Thesis, University of Copenhagen.
Armstrong, D.T., Steele, R., Altszuler, N., Dunn, A., Bishop, J.S.
    and de Bodo, R.C. (1961). Regulation of plasma free fatty acid.
    Amer. J. Physiol. 210:9-15
Arner, P., Bolinder J., Engfeld, P. and Östman, J. (1981). The
    antilipolytic effect of insulin in human adipose tissue in
    obesity, diabetes millitus, hyperinsulinemia and starvation.
    Metabolism. 30:753-760
Åstrand, I. (1960). Aerobic capacity in men and women with special
    reference to age. Acta Physiol. Scand. Suppl. 169:49:3-92

Åstrand, P.O., Cuddy, T., Saltin, B. and Steenberg, J. (1964).
Cardiac output during submaximal and maximal work. J. Appl.
Physiol. 19:268-274

Åstrand, P.O. and Rodahl, K. (1977). Textbook of Work
Physiology. New York: McGraw-Hill.

Ball, P., Knuppen, R., Haupt, M. and Breuer, H. (1972).
Interactions between oestrogens and catecholamines. III. Studies
on the methylation of catechol oestrogen, catechol amines and
other catechols by the catechol-O-methyl-transferase of human
liver. J. Clin. Endocrinol. Metab. 34:736-746

Bailey, C.J. and Matty, A.J. (1972). Glucose tolerance and plasma
insulin of the rat in relation to the oestrous cycle and sex
hormones. Horm. Metab. Res. 4:266-270

Bailey, C.J. and Ahmed-Sorour, H. (1980). Role of ovarian hormones
in the long-term control of glucose homeostasis.
Diabetologia. 19:475-481

Bass, A., Vondra, K., Rath, R. and Vitek, V. (1975). M. quadriceps
femoris of man, a muscle with an unusual enzyme activity pattern
of energy supplying metabolism in mammals. Pflügers Arch.
354:249-255

Bergström, J., Hermansen, L., Hultman, E. and Saltin, B. (1967).
Diet, muscle glycogen and physical performance. Acta Physiol.
Scand. 71:140-150

Bertoli, A., De Pirro, R., Fusco, A., Greco, A.V., Magnatta, R. and
Lauro, R. (1980). Differences in insulin receptors between men
and menstruating women and influence of sex hormones on insulin
binding during the menstrual cycle. J. Clin. Endocrinol.
Metab. 50:246-250

Blatchford, F.K., Knowlton, R.G. and Schneider, D.A. (1985).
Plasma FFA responses to prolonged walking in untrained men and
women. Eur. J. Appl. Physiol. 53:343-347

Blomstrand, E. and Ekblom, B. (1982). The needle biopsy technique
for fibre type determination in human skeletal muscle - a
methodological study. Acta Physiol. Scand. 116:437-442

Bonde-Petersen, F. and Robertson Jr, C.H. (1981). Blood flow in
'red' and 'white' calf muscles in cats during isometric and
isotonic exercise. Acta Physiol. Scand. 112:243-251

Boyns, D.R., Crossly, J.N., Abrams, M.E., Jarrett, R.J. and Keen,
H. (1969). Oral glucose tolerance and related factors in a
normal population sample. B.M.J. 1:595-598

Brooke, M.H. and Engel, W.K. (1969). The histographic analysis of
human muscle biopsies with regard to fibre types. 1. Adult male
and female. Neurology. 19:221-233

Bülow, J. (1982). Adipose tissue blood flow during exercise.
Thesis. Copenhagen: Laegeforeningens Forlag.

Byrd, R. and Jenness, M.E. (1982). Effect on maximal grip strength
and initial grip strength on contraction time and on areas under
force-time curves during isometric contractions. Ergonomics.
25:387-392

Carlson, L.A., Eklund, L.G. and Fröberg, S.O. (1971).
Concentration of triglycerides, phospholipids and glycogen in
skeletal muscle and of free fatty acids and betahydroxy butyric
acid in blood in men in response to exercise. Eur. J. Clin.
Invest. 1:248-254

- 300 -

Christensen, E.H. and Hansen, A. (1939). Arbeitsfähigkeit und
Ernärung. Skandinav. Archiv. für Physiologie. 81:160-171
Chumlea, C., Knittle, J.L. Roche, A.F. Siervogel, R.M. and Webb, P.
(1981). Adipocytes and adiposity in adults. Am. J. Clin.
Nutr. 34:1798-1803
Claustre, J., Peyrin, L., Fitoussi, R. and Mornex, R. (1980). Sex
differences in the adrenergic response to hypoglycemic stress in
human. Psychopharmacology. 67:147-153
Clutter, W.E., Bier, D.M., Shah, S.D. and Cryer, P.E. (1980).
Adrenalin plasma metabolic clearance rates and physiologic
thresholds for metabolic and haemodynamic actions in man.
J. Clin. Invest. 66:94-101
Costill, D.L., Daniels, J., Evans, J., Fink, W., Krahenbuhl, G. and
Saltin, B. (1976). Skeletal muscle enzymes and fibre
compositions in male track athletes. J. App. Physiol.
40:149-154
Costill, D.l., Fink, W.J., Getchell, L.H., Ivy, J.L. and Witzmann,
F.A. (1979). Lipid metabolism in skeletal muscle of endurance-
trained males and females. J. Appl. Physiol. 47:787-791
Cureton, K.J. and Sparling, P.B. (1980). Distance running
performance and metabolic responses to running in men and women
with excess weight experimentally equated. Med. Sci. Sport
Exerc. 12:288-294
Deprés, J.P., Bouchard, C., Bukowiecki, L., Savard, R. and
Lupien, J. (1982). Effects of sex, fatness and training status
in human fat cell lipolysis. Arch. Int. Physiol. Biochem.
90:329-335
Deprés, J.P. Bouchard, C., Savard, R., Tremblay, A., Marcotte, M.
and Thériault, G. (1984). The effect of a 20-week endurance
training program on adipose tissue morphology and lipolysis in
men and women. Metabolism. 33:235-239
von Döbeln, W. (1956). Human standard and maximal metabolic rate
in relation to fatfree body mass. acta Physiol. Scand.
Suppl. 126
Drinkwater, B.L. (1984). Women and exercise: Physiological
aspects. Exerc. Sport Sci. Rev. 12:21-51
Dufaux, B., Assmann, G., and Hollmann, W. (1982). Plasma
lipoproteins and physical activity: a review. Int. J. Sports
Med. 3:123-136
Durnin, J.V.G.A. and Womersley, J. (1974). Body fat assessed from
total body density and its estimation from skinfold thickness:
Measurements on 481 men and women aged from 16-72 years.
Br. J. Nutr. 32:77-97
Elder, G.C.B., Bradbury, K., and Roberts, R. (1982). Variability
of fibre type distributions within human muscles. J. Appl.
Physiol: Respirat. Environ. Exercise Physiol. 53:1473-1480
Engfeldt, P., Arner, P. and Ostman, J. (1982). Changes in
phosphodiesterase activity of human subcutaneous adipose tissue
during starvation. Metabolism. 31:910-915
Engström, L.M. (1975). Physical activity during adolescence.
Thesis. Stockholm: Lärarhögskolan.
Essén, B., Jansson, E., Henriksson, J., Taylor, A.W. and Saltin, B.
(1975). Metabolic characteristics of fibre types in human
skeletal muscle. Acta Physiol. Scand. 95:153-165

Essén, B. (1977). Intramuscular substrate utilisation during prolonged exercise. Ann. N.Y. Acad. Sci. 301:30-44

Essén-Gustavsson, B. and Borges, O. (1986). Histochemical and metabolic characteristics of human skeletal muscle in relation to age. Acta Physiol. Scand. 126:107-114

Ewing, D.J., Irving, J.B., Kirr, F., Wildsmith, J.A.W. and Clarke, B.F. (1974). Cardiovascular responses to sustained handgrip in normal subjects and in patients with diabetes mellitus: A test of autonomic function. Clin. Sci. 46:295-306

Favier, R., Pequignot, J.M., Desplanches, D., Mayet, M.H., Lacour, J.R., Peyrin, L. and Flandrois, R. (1983). Catecholamines and metabolic responses to submaximal exercise in untrained men and women. Eur. J. Appl. Physiol. 50:393-404

Felig, P. and Wahren, J. (1975). Fuel homeostasis in exercise. New Engl. J. Med. 293:1078-1084

Frisk-Holmberg, M., Essén, B., Fredrikson, M., Ström, G. and Wibell, L. (1983). Muscle fibre composition in relation to blood pressure response to isometric exercise in normotensive and hypertensive subjects. Acta Med. Scand. 213:21-24

Frantz, A.G. and Rabkin, M.T. (1965). Effects of oestrogen and sex difference on secretion of human growth hormone. J. Clin. Endocr. 25:1470-1480

Frankenhaeuser, M., Dunne, E. and Lundberg, U. (1976). Sex differences in sympathetic-adrenal medullary rections induced by different stressors. Psychopharmacology. 47:1-5

Froberg, K. and Pedersen, P.K. (1984). Sex differences in endurance capacity and metabolic response to prolonged, heavy exercise. Eur. J. Appl. Physiol. 52:446-450

Galbo, H., Holst, J.J. and Christensen, N.J. (1979). The effect of different diets and of insulin on the hormonal response to prolonged exercise. Acta Physiol. Scand. 107:19-32

Galbo, H. (1983). Hormonal and metabolic adaptation to exercise. Stuttgart. New York. Georg Thieme Verlag

Galster, A.D., Clutter, W.E. Cryer, P.E., Collins, J.A. and Bier, D.M. (1981). Adrenalin plasma thresholds for lipolytic effects in man. J. Clin. Invest. 67:1729-1738

Gilliam, T.B., Freedson, P.S., Greenen, D.L. and Shahraray, B. (1981). Physical activity patterns determined by heart rate monitoring in 6-7 year-old children. Med. Sci. Sports. Exerc. 13:65-67

Gleerup-Madsen, A., Christensen, H., Melander, L., Lützhøft, J. and Nygaard, E. (1985). Cardiovascular reactions to isometric contractions in relation to muscle characteristics in males and females. Clin. Phys. 5:Suppl 4,168

Gollnick, P.D., Armstrong, R.B., Saubert IV, C.W., Piehl, K. and Saltin, B. (1972). Enzyme activity and fibre composition in skeletal muscle of untrained and trained men. J. Appl. Physiol. 33:312-319

Gollnick, P.D. (1985). Metabolism of substrates. Energy substrate metabolism during exercise and as modified by training. Fed. Proc. 44:353-357

Gordon, T., Castelli, W.P., Hjortland, M.C., Kannel, W.B. and
Dauber, T.R. (1977). High density lipoprotein as a protective
factor against coronary heart disease. The Framingham Study.
Am. J. Med. 62:707-714

Hagerup, L., Eriksen, M., Schroll, M., Hollnagel, H., Agner, E. and
Larsen, S. (1981). Glostrup Population Studies. Collection of
epidemiologic tables. Scand. J. Soc. Med. 20:5-112

Hale, P.J., Wright, J.V. and Nattrass, M. (1985). Differences in
insulin sensitivity between normal men and women. Metabolism
12:1133-1138

Hansen, F.M., Fahmy, N. and Nielsen, J.H. (1980). The influence of
sexual hormones on lipogenesis and lipolysis in rat fat cells.
Acta Endocrin. Copenhagen. 95:566-570

Harmon, M., Leifer, J.B., Litchfield, P.E. and Maughan, R.J.
(1984). Isometric endurance capacity in untrained males and
females. J. Physiol. 357:103P

Haskell, W.L. (1984). The influence of exercise on the
concentrations of triglyceride and cholesterol in human plasma.
Exerc. Sport Sci. Rev. 12:205-244

Hedberg, G. and Jansson, E. (1976). Skeletal muscle fibre
distribution, capacity and interest in different physical
activities among students in high school. Umeå, Sweden.
Pedagogiska rapporter no. 54

Hede, K. and Raa Andersen, V. (1985). Energistofskiftet hos maend
og kvinder. Effekt af diaet med højt fedtindhold på
substratvalg under arbejde. Specialerapport. University of
Copenhagen.

Hendricks, S.A., Lippe, B.M., Kaplan, S.A., Landaw, E.M., Hertz, D.
and Scott, M. (1981). Insulin binding to erythrocytes of normal
infants, children and adults: Variation with sex and age.
J. Clin. Endocrinol. Metab. 52:969-974

Hjemdahl, P. and Linde, B. (1983). Influence of circulating NE and
Epi on adipose tissue vascular resistance and lipolysis in
humans. Am. J. Physiol. 245:H447-H452

Honnens de Lichtenberg, B. and Tungelund, K. (1983). Forskel i
kvinders og maends substratvalg under arbejde. Specialerapport.
University of Copenhagen.

Ilmarinen, J. and Rutenfrantz, J. (1980). Longitudinal studies of
the change in habitual physical activity of school children and
working adolescents. Exerc. Sport Sci. Rev. 10:166-174

Jacobsson, B., Holm, G., Björntorp, P. and Smith, U. (1976).
Influence of cell size on the effects of insulin and
noradrenaline on human adipose tissue. Diabetologica
12:69-72

Jansson, E. (1980). Diet and muscle metabolism in man. Acta
Physiol. Scand. Suppl. 487

Johansson, G. and Post, B. (1974). Catecholamine output of males
and females over a one year period. Acta Physiol. Scand.
92:557-565

Juhlin-Dannfelt, A., Frisk-Holmberg, M., Karlsson, J. and Tesh, P.
(1979). Central and peripheral circulation in relation to
muscle-fibre composition in normo- and hypertensive man.
Clin. Sci. 56:335-340

Knopp, R.H., Walden, C.E., Wahl, P.W., Hoover, J.J., Warnick, G.R., Albers, J.J., Ogilvie, J.T. and Hazzard, W.R. (1981). Oral contraceptive and postmenopausal oestrogen effect on lipoprotein triglyceride and cholesterol in an adult female population: Ralationships to oestrogen and progestin potency. J. Clin. Endocrin. Metab. 53:1123-1132

Kobryn, U., Hoffmann, B. and Ransch, E. (1986). Sex- and age-related blood pressure response to dynamic work with small muscle masses. Eur. J. Appl. Physiol. 55:79-82

Komi, P.V. and Karlsson, J. (1978). Skeletal muscle fibre types, enzyme activities and physical performance in young males and females. Acta Physiol. Scand. 103:210-218

Krogh, A. and Lindhard, J. (1920). The relative value of fat and carbohydrate as sources of muscular energy. Biochem. J. 14:290-363

Lehmann, M., Berg, A. and Keul, J. (1986). Sex-related differences in free plasma catecholamines in individuals of similar performance ability during graded ergometric exercise. Eur. J. Appl. Physiol. 55:54-58

Lewis, S., Nygaard, E., Sanchez, J., Egeblad, H. and Saltin, B. (1984). Static contraction of the quadriceps muscle in man: Cardiovascular control and responses to one-legged strength training. Acta Physiol. Scand. 122:341-353

Lexell, J., Henriksson-Larsén, K. and Sjöström, M. (1983). Distribution of different fibre types in human skeletal muscles. 2. A study of cross-sections of Whole m. vastus lateralis. Acta Physiol. Scand. 117:115-122

Lithell, H., Örlander, J., Schele, R., Sjödin, B. and Karlsson, J. (1979). Changes in lipoprotein-lipase activity and lipid stores in human skeletal muscle in man. Acta Physiol. Scand. 107:257-261

Maughan, R.J., Williams, C., Campbell, D.M. and Hepburn, D. (1978). Fat and carbohydrate metabolism during exercise: Effects of the availability of muscle glycogen. Eur. J. Appl. Physiol. 39:7-16

Melander, L.S., Galbo, H., Markvardsen, K., Nygaard, E. and Vinten, J. (1985). Lipolytic activity of isolated cells from subcutaneous adipose tissue in male and female subjects. Effect of muscular activity. Acta Physiol. Scand. 123:45A

Milner-Brown, H.S., Stein, R.B. and Lee, R.G. (1975). Synchronisation of human motor units. Possible roles of exercise and supraspinal reflexes. Electroencephalogr. Clin. Neurophysiol. 38:245-254

Newsholme, E.A. and Leech, A.R. (1983). Biochemistry for the medical sciences. London: J. Wiley and Sons.

Nikkilä, E.A., Taskinen, M.-R., Rehunen, S. and Härkonen, M. (1978). Lipoprotein lipase activity in adipose tissue and skeletal muscle of runners: relation to serum lipoproteins. Metabolism. 27:1661-1671

Novak, L.P. (1972). Ageing, total body potassium, fat-free mass, and cell mass in males and females between ages 18 and 85 years. J. Geront. 27:438-443

Nygaard, E., Andersen, P., Nilsson, P, Eriksson, E., Kjessel, T. and Saltin, B. (1978). Glycogen depletion pattern and lactate accumulation in leg muscles during recreational downhill skiing. Eur. J. Appl. Physiol. 38:261-269

Nygaard, E. (1981a). Skeletal muscle fibre characteristics in young women. Acta Physiol. Scand. 112:299-304

Nygaard, E. (1981b). Morphology and function of the human brachial biceps muscle. Thesis. University of Copenhagen.

Nygaard, E. and Sanchez, J. (1982). Intramuscular variation of fibre types in the brachial biceps and the lateral vastus muscles of elderly men: How representative is a small biopsy sample? Anat. Rec. 203:451-459

Nygaard, E., Jørgensen, K. and Nicolaisen, T. (1983). Work capacity and health in postmen and -women. (In Danish). Copenhagen: Generaldirektoratet for Post- og telegrafvaesenet.

Nygaard, E., Honnens, B., Tungelund, K., Christensen, T. and Galbo, H. (1984a). Fat as a fuel in energy-turnover of man and woman. Acta Physiol. Scand. 120:51A

Nygaard, E., Christensen, T., Hvid, K., Juel-Christensen, N. and Galbo, H. (1984b). Metabolic and hormonal characteristics associated with the choice of fat as a fuel in humans. Acta Physiol. Scand. 123:42A

Östman, J., Backman, L. and Hallberg, D. (1973). Cell size and lipolysis by human subcutaneous adipose tissue. Acta Med. Scand. 193:469-475

Peltonen, P., Marniemi, J., Hietanen, E., Vuori, I. and Ehnolm, C. (1981). Changes in serum lipids, lipoproteins and heparin releasable lipolytic enzymes during moderate physical training in man: a longitudinal study. Metabolism. 30:518-526

Petrofsky, J.S., Burse, R.L. and Lind, A.L. (1975). Comparison of physiological responses of women and men to isometric exercise. J. Appl. Physiol. 38:863-868

Petrofsky, J.S. and Phillips, C.A. (1980). The effect of elbow angle on the isometric strength and endurance of the elbow flexors in men and women. J. Human Ergol. 9:125-131

Petrofsky, J.S. and Hendershot, D. (1984) The interrelationship between blood pressure, intramuscular pressure, and isometric endurance in fast and slow twitch skeletal muscle in the cat. Eur. J. Appl. Physiol. 53:106-111

Phinney, S.D., Bistrian, B.R., Wolfe, R.R. and Blackburn, G.L. (1983). The human metabolic response to chronic ketosis without caloric restriction: Physical and biochemical adaptation. Metabolism. 32:757-768

Powers, S.K., Riley, W. and Howley, E.T. (1980). Comparison of fat metabolism between trained men and women during prolonged aerobic work. Res. Quart. Exerc. Sport. 51:427-431

Prince, F.P., Hikida, R.S. and Hagerman, F.L. (1977). Muscle fiber types in women athletes and nonathletes. Pflügers Arch. 371:161-165

Rennie, M.J. and Johnson, R.H. (1974). Effects of an exercise-diet programme on metabolic changes with exercise in runners. J.Appl. Physiol. 37:821-825

Rost, R. (1981). An passungserscheinungen im Herzkreislaufbereich bei Frauen als Folge von Ausdauertraining. In: Beiheft zur Leistungssport (edited by Sabine Wedekind) pp.27-37. Sportwissenschaftliche Beitrage zum Leistungssport der Frau.

Saltin, B., Henriksson, J., Nygaard, E., Andersen, P. and Jansson, E. (1977). Fibre types and metabolic potentials of skeletal muscles in sedentary man and endurance runners. Ann. N.Y. Acad. Sci. 301:3-29

Saltin, B. and Gollnick, P.D. (1983). Skeletal muscle adaptability: Significance for metabolism and performance. In Handbook of Physiology. Section 10: Skeletal Muscle (edited by L.D. Peachy), pp. 555-631

Sanchez, J., Pequinot, J.M., Peyrin, L. and Monod, H. (1980). Sex differences in the sympatho-adrenal response to isometric exercise. Eur. J. Appl. Physiol. 45:147-154

Shroll, M. and Hollnagel, H. (1982). Blood pressure response during exercise. Acta Med. Scand. 670:49-53

Simoneau, J.A., Lortie, G., Boulay, M.R., Thibault, M.C., Thériault, G. and Bouchard, C. (1985). Skeletal muscle histochemical and biochemical characteristics in sedentary male and female subjects. Can. J. Physiol. Pharmacol. 63:30-35

Sjöström, L., Smith, U., Krotkiewski, M. and Björntorp, P. (1972). Cellularity in different regions of adipose tissue in young men and women. Metabolism. 21:1143-1153

Sjöström, L., Schutz, Y., Gudinchet, F., Hegnell, L., Pittet, P.G. and Jéquier, E. (1983). Adrenalin sensitivity with respect to metabolic rate and other variables in women. Am. J. Physiol. 245:E431-E442

Sjøgaard, G. (1979). Water spaces and electrolyte concentrations in human skeletal muscle. Thesis. University of Copenhagen.

Smith, U., Hammersten, J., Björntorp, P. and Kral, J.G. (1979). Regional differences and effects of weight reduction on human fat cell metabolism. Eur. J. Clin. Invest. 9:327-332

Spady, D.W. (1980). Total daily energy expenditure of healthy, free ranging school children. Am. J. Clin. Nutr. 33.766-775

Sparling, P.B. (1980). A meta-analysis of studies comparing maximal oxygen uptake in men and women. Res. Quart. Exerc. Sports. 51:542-552

Taskinen, M.R. and Nikkilä, E.A. (1980). Effect of acute vigorous exercise on lipoprotein lipase activity in adipose tissue and skeletal muscle in physically active men. Artery. 6:471-483

Thorstensson, A. (1976). Muscle strength, fibre types and enzyme activities in man. Acta Physiol. Scand. Suppl. 443:1-45

Vendsalu, A. (1960). Studies on adrenaline and nor-adrenaline in human plasma. Acta Physiol. Scand. Suppl. 173

Verschuur, R., Kemper, H.C.G., Dekker, H., Ootjers, G., Post, B., Ritmeester, J.W., Snel, J., Splinter, P. and Storm van Essen, L. (1983). Growth and health of teenagers - a multiple longitudinal study in Amsterdam. The Netherlands

Wilmore, J.H., (1977). Athletic training and physical fitness. Boston: Allyn and Bacon, Inc. p. 182

Wilmore, J.H. (1983). Body composition in sport and exercise: directions for future research. Med. Sci. Sports Exerc. 15:21-31

Yki-järvinen, H. (1984). Sex and insulin sensitivity. Metabolism. 33:1011-1015

Zonderland, M.L. (1985). Lipid and apolipoprotein profiles in premenarcheal athletes. The relation with training, nutrition and biological maturation. <u>Thesis</u>. University of Utrecht.

Zwiren, L.D., Cureton, K.J. and Hutchinson, P. (1983). Comparison of circulatory responses to submaximal exercise in equally trained men and women. <u>Int. J. Sports. Med</u>. 4:255-259

Discussion

Professor Williams, Loughborough

You have already mentioned that you observed functional differences between males and females in terms of isometric contraction. I would like to ask two questions. Firstly, were there any differences in dynamic work and secondly, have you carried out any open-ended studies where for example you asked males and females to exercise to exhaustion at the same percentage of $\dot{V}O_2$max to see if the metabolic differences carry over into the functional reality of exercise?

Professor Nygaard, Copenhagen, Denmark

Yes: we carried out exercise on bicycle ergometers at 80% $\dot{V}O_2$max. Males and females bicycled to exhaustion. The female group continued significantly longer.

Professor Williams

We have carried out experiments, at 70% $\dot{V}O_2$max in males and females running to exhaustion. When males (n=15) and females (n=15) run to exhaustion the females don't run any longer than the males. I wonder whether your results might be attributed to the use of a bicycle ergometer which uses a different muscle mass. Obviously the males run further because of the higher running speed at the same percentage of $\dot{V}O_2$max. Therefore there is no difference in endurance capacity and they have similar respiratory exchange ratios (RER). In addition there are no differences in the maximal heart rates that males and females achieve. Consequently, we wonder whether an exercise intensity factor may be responsible for the differences observed at lower exercise intensity in the female capacity for endurance.

Professor Nygaard

This may be true. My hunch is that the differences we see in sedentary subjects appear more obvious during bicycling than during running because treadmill running is more stressful to the female body.

Professor Williams

That is possible. All that I would say is that when selecting male and female subjects for our biopsy work the majority of females coming into the laboratory have a higher percentage of Type 11A fibres than the male subjects we recruit. It may be that the female volunteers are already exercise orientated.

Professor Nygaard
There is always a problem of selection and it is probably more
likely that the females seen in the laboratory are better trained.

Professor Åstrand, Stockholm, Sweden
In introducing Dr Nygaard the question was posed as to whether it
was possible that women could beat men. There have also been
reports in the literature that suggest that women will probably
eventually run a marathon faster than men. This is nonsense in my
opinion. It is interesting when comparing male and female world
records that they vary in various events betwen 6 and 10%. In the
marathon the difference is the same, if not a little larger than in
sprinting events. The gap is narrower in swimming.

  The body density of females is lower which is one possible
contributing factor and their shape and body composition is more
reminiscent of a little seal. The differences in high jump and
long jump is for some reason greater, around 20% However, from
your data if strength/unit cross sectional area is compared then it
is the same in men and women.

Dr Nygaard
Yes: in our own study of 1983 we calculated the percentage tension
of the elbow flexors and actualy found no significant difference
between males and females but the groupings were small with only
three males and two females leading to large variation within the
data. However, the actual values were lower in females than in
males and this is confirmed by reports in the literature. Also in
the studies of Maughan et al. a 20% lower force output was reported
in females, than in males when related to cross sectional area of
the muscles. Ikai and Fukunaga's studies (1968) reported these
differences as not significant but that the differences were real.
I don't know what this means. In our own studies I was happy to
find that the differences were not significant. Consequently, we
can say that the quality of muscle and the contractile machinery
works in the same way, thus, letting us rule out differences in
force output.

Dr Jacobs, Toronto, Canada
You showed that during your ramp test at various percentages of
$\dot{V}O_2$max the females began exercise with significantly higher
free fatty acid concentrations in blood. If we presume that free
fatty acid uptake is a function of both arterial concentration and
blood flow then it would make sense for females to use fat to a
greater extent. This need not necessarily be a function of
peripheral capacity to utilise that fat. In that light is there
any data that you are aware of that mucles or adipose tissue
lipoprotein lipase activity differs in the two sexes?

Dr Nygaard
Yes: studies in 1978 indicated that lipoprotein lipase activity in
adipose tissue is much higher in females than in males but in
muscle the values are identical.

Dr Jacobs
Would you agree therefore that the lower RER is probably a function
of the elevated FFA concentration to start off with?

Dr Nygaard
In this study, yes.

Dr Newsholme, Oxford
I am concerned about the use of succinate dehydrogenase over many
years as an index of the capacity of the aerobic metabolism. In
our experience it has no correlation or at least very little, with
aerobic capacity. Of all the enzymes available we have found that
the only enzyme to give quantitive information is oxaglutarate
dehydrogenase.

Dr Nygaard
I agree with you on the use of succinate dehydrogenase. These were
the enzymes that we were using at the time. However if you refer
to the literature and look at the comparability studies analysing
enzyme activities you will find further evidence to support my
conclusion.

Dr Brooks, California, USA
You mentioned longevity; do these studies help explain why women
live longer?

Dr Nygaard
I don't know. Perhaps it is related to the lower blood pressure.

PART V ENVIRONMENTAL FACTORS

Athletic performance differs from laboratory studies of exercise in
many ways. Perhaps one of the major differences is that the former
is influenced by a wide variety of environmental factors, whereas
in the laboratory most, if not all of these are kept constant.
This systematic approach to the study of exercise performance is a
necessary part of the scientific method, which involves keeping all
variables with the exception of the one under study as constant as
possible. Thus experiments are normally carried out in air-
controlled laboratories, at a fixed time of day and with subjects
in the post-absorptive state. The athlete, however, may find
himself competing in extreme environmental conditions, with heat
or cold, wind and rain to contend with; he may find this contest
scheduled for the middle of the night because it is half-way round
the world from home, or because this suits the television
companies; he may come from a country with no mountains and find
that he is expected to compete at an altitude of over 2000 metres:
alternatively he may find that a major championship event he is
aiming for is to take place in a heavily industrialised big city
where levels of air pollution are considered hazardous even for
those not taking exercise. All these situations have occurred
more or less regularly over the last few years, and will continue
to do so.

The aim of the final session of this symposium was to look at
how some of these environmental factors affect performance. We
know that moderate altitude can have deleterious effects on
performance in endurance events due to the decreased oxygen
availability and at the same time can improve performance in
sprints, jumps and throws as a consequence of reduced air
resistance. The effects have been fairly extensively investigated
in the 20 years since the decision to hold the 1968 Olympic Games
in Mexico City first drew attention to the possible effects of
altitude on performance. John Sutton chose instead to describe the
effects of extreme altitude, equivalent to the summit of Mount
Everest; at these altitudes, exercise is still possible, but only
at relatively low levels. Another Olympic Games, those of 1984 in
Los Angeles, focused attention on problems of training and
competing in a city notorious for its poor air quality. The
presence of high levels of pollutants has major implications for
health as well as for performance; the great London smog of 1952
precipitated 4000 deaths, and led to the Clean Air Act of 1956.

Sulphur dioxide was the main culprit, but other pollutants such as carbon monoxide and ozone may be equally dangerous. For a number of reasons air pollution did not prove to be a major factor in the Los Angeles Games, but in his review of the subject Peter Raven warned that competitors and spectators at the 1988 Games in Seoul may not be so fortunate. It has been agreed that we should not include a discussion of the effects of time of day on performance in a discussion of environmental factors, but we all demonstrate a circadian rhythm in various physiological functions, and anything which disturbs this rhythm or which demands peak performance at sub-optimal times can be considered as an external or environmental factor affecting exercise capacity. Tom Reilly reviewed those aspects of function which demonstrate a circadian rhythm and examined the implications for performance. The final paper in this session, by Mike Harrison, looked at the associated problems of temperature regulation and fluid balance in endurance exercise. Dehydration consequent upon sweat loss can seriously impair exercise performance, and even pose a risk to life. The role of fluid ingestion before and during exercise in minimising these risks is obviously of major importance.

It is important, therefore, that we remember that laboratory studies carried out under ideal conditions may not always reflect the real-life situation. The impact of environmental factors on exercise performance has implications not only for the elite sportsman but for all who engage in exercise whether for competition, for enjoyment or in the belief that it will improve health. Exercise prescription must be tailored to suit the individual but must also take account of local conditions.

Dr Ron Maughan

Exercise at extreme altitude

J.R. SUTTON

Mount Everest has now been climbed many times without the use of supplementary oxygen - a feat placing the climber on the very brink of survival. Components of the oxygen transport-extraction process are examined and their contribution which enables this feat are quantified. A four-fold increase in alveolar ventilation and maximal oxygen extraction by the tissue are the most important responses. By contrast, increases in hemoglobin are minor and changes in cardiac output trivial. Final adaptations occur in the tissue.

1. Introduction

When Edmund Hillary and Tenzing Norgay stood on the summit of Mount Everest on May 29, 1953, they settled forever the question of whether Mt. Everest could be climbed by man. They used supplementary oxygen to achieve their feat and this had been part of the mountaineers' equipment for most of the previous half-century. When Mallory and Irvine disappeared on the North side of Everest in 1924, they were transporting heavy loads of oxygen. Using oxygen and depending on the flow rate, this could lower the effective physiological altitude by several thousand feet. So the real physiological question became whether the summit could be reached without the use of supplementary oxygen. This was finally settled almost 25 years after Hillary and Tenzing's climb when, on May 8, 1979, Peter Habeler and Reinhold Messner reached the summit breathing only the air about them. Two years later Messner returned alone and again without the use of supplementary oxygen, reached the summit from the north.

We have much physiological information on Hillary and Tenzing (Pugh, 1958; Pugh et al., 1964), but very little such information exists about Messner and Habeler. This caused Pugh and Sutton to examine some of the likely physiological prerequisites for climbing to extreme altitudes (Pugh and Sutton, 1983; Sutton, In Press).

Of the important physiological variables, that of a high sea level $\dot{V}O_2$max, received considerable attention as the authors argued that starting with a high $\dot{V}O_2$max would be quite an asset as the reduction in $\dot{V}O_2$max with increasing altitude would occur in proportion to the initial level. Cerretelli (In Press) and Oelz (In Press) have independently measured Messner and found a $\dot{V}O_2$max which is in the high 40ml/kg range, Table 1, much below the original estimate (Pugh and Sutton, 1983). Furthermore, the most recent studies in 'Operation Everest II' by Cymerman and colleagues (In Press) have demonstrated that almost irrespective of the sea level $\dot{V}O_2$max, the $\dot{V}O_2$max will decrease to a final common level as altitude increases. In Operation Everest II, the mean decreased from a $\dot{V}O_2$max of 50ml/kg/min to 15ml/kg/min and while the range varied from 42 to 64ml/kg/min at sea level, there was almost no variation in the $\dot{V}O_2$max at the simulated 'summit' of Mt. Everest.

Other important physiological characteristics are seen in Table 2 and include a high power/weight ratio, considerable strength, a high ventilatory responsiveness and also on the climb, to minimize the weight carried, as in vertical work the total weight to be lifted is crucial.

Table 1. Measurement of maximal oxygen uptake in elite high altitude climbers, measured in two separate laboratories.

	10% Grade (Magglingen)	35% Grade (Geneva)
RM 39 A	48.8	46.6
PH 41 A	65.9	55.4
Mean (N=6)	57.0 ± 7.1	56.7 ± 6.5

Table 2. Characteristics considered important determinants in climbing Mt. Everest without supplementary oxygen

1. Climbing and technical skill
2. Strength
3. Power/weight ratio
4. High sea level $\dot{V}O_2$max, which remains relatively high with ascent
5. Low ventilatory response to hypoxia
6. Cerebral tolerance of hypoxia
7. Psychological status of extreme motivation

2. Physiology

A decrease in the barometric pressure and the resultant decrease of the partial pressure of inspired oxygen in air are the most important environmental variables which occur with increasing altitude. Pugh (1957) suggested that the barometric pressure on the summit of Everest was approximately 250 ± 3 Torr which is 15 Torr higher than the International Civil Aviation Organization's (ICAO) standard atmosphere. However, it was not until 1981 that Chris Pizzo on the American Medical Research Expedition to Everest made the first reading - a figure of 253 Torr was confirmed (West et al., 1983c). This results in an inspired oxygen pressure when

fully saturated with water vapour at 37°C of 43 Torr. Using a
device to sample alveolar gas, Pizzo obtained the first alveolar
samples on the summit of Everest and revealed a somewhat higher
than expected alveolar PO_2 of 35 Torr. This was due, in part, to a
marked degree of hyperventilation with an alveolar PCO_2 of 7.5 Torr.

More recently on Operation Everest II, Malconian using alveolar
gas samples, measured an alveolar PCO_2 of 12.4 ± 1.9 Torr and an
alveolar PO_2 of 29.8 ± 3.4 Torr (Malconian et al., In Press).
These differences can be accounted for totally on the basis of
increased alveolar ventilation and subsequently, also in Operation
Everest II, one subject had a measured arterial PCO_2 of 8.2 Torr
(Sutton et al., In Press)

It is well known that exercise capacity decreases dramatically
with increasing altitude (Dempsey, 1971; Grover et al., 1967;
Milledge et al., 1983; West et al., 1983a) and many of the
adaptations to altitude have been studied in detail including the
ventilatory, cardiovascular and hematological changes. Nevertheless,
until recently it has been impossible to study each component of the
oxygen transport system up to and including extreme altitude. The
opportunity to do this in detail presented itself in the project,
Operation Everest II, (OEII) conducted in the autumn of 1985.
OEII was a simulated climb of Mt. Everest where eight subjects were
decompressed gradually over 40 days in a hypobaric chamber eventually
reaching the equivalent of the summit of Mt. Everest P_1O_2 43 Torr.
This was 40 years after the original 'Operation Everest' studies of
Houston and Riley in 1946. Considerable technical advances had been
made in the intervening years and in the 1985 study, it was possible
to examine all components of the oxygen transport and extraction
process. Although they are detailed elsewhere, I will briefly
review some of these findings.

3. Ventilation

Increases in ventilation with acute hypoxia are well demonstrated
but Rahn and Otis (1949) have shown that sea level residents do not
immediately increase ventilation to a maximum and an optimum time
for acclimatisation is necessary for maximum ventilation to be
achieved. As the ventilatory response to increasing altitude is
probably the most important single determinant of survival at
extreme altitude, allowing an adequate time for acclimatisation
cannot be over emphasized. During exercise, this response is
augmented and for example, at the equivalent of the summit of Mt.
Everest at a power output of 120 W, ventilation of 184 l/min (BTPS)
was required whereas the equivalent workload at sea level demanded
a ventilation of only 47 l/min (BTPS). This marked increase in
ventilation was associated with a profound decrease in arterial
PCO_2 to a mean of 9.6 Torr (range 8.2-13.5 Torr) (Sutton et al.(b)
In Press). There was considerable inter-individual variation in
ventilatory responsiveness and Schoene and co-workers (1984) have
suggested that the ventilatory response to hypoxia may be an
important determinant of climbing success at extreme altitudes.
The marked hyperventilation will, of course, be the determinant of
alveolar oxygen which in the case of Pizzo was extremely high
because of the marked alveolar ventilation (West et al., 1983b).

4. Pulmonary gas exchange

The transfer of oxygen from the alveolus to the arterial blood will depend on three factors: the ventilation/perfusion relationships (V_A/Q), the diffusion characteristics of the lung and the presence of a post-pulmonary shunt. Although resting alveolar-arterial oxygen tension differences $[(A-a)DO_2]$ may often widen even at rest with increasing altitude (Reeves et al., 1969), on exercise as at sea level, this difference becomes much greater (Gale et al., 1985; Gledhill et al., 1977; Sutton et al., (b) In Press). On Operation Everest II, the $(A-a)DO_2$ appeared to be altitude-independent and related solely to the intensity of exercise (Sutton et al., (b) In Press). Thus, as maximum exercise capacity decreased, so did the $(A-a)DO_2$ at maximal exercise. Wagner et al. (In Press), using the multiple inert gas technique, were able to quantify the contribution of V_A/Q to the widened $(A-a)DO_2$ on exercise and showed that at higher altitudes above 6,000m, diffusion limitation became progressively more important. Marked arterial desaturation on exercise at altitude caused West to make the same prediction (West et al., 1962).

5. Oxygen transport in blood

An increase in hemoglobin with increasing altitude exposure was first demonstrated by Viault in 1891 when he studied animals living in the Andean Altoplano (Viault, 1891). These observations have been confirmed in man many times and in the well-acclimatised human who is not dehydrated, this may amount to 4-6g/100ml of hemoglobin (Pugh, 1964a). Nevertheless, at extreme altitude, there is profound arterial hypoxemia and thus, the arterial oxygen content is considerably reduced and on exercise, augments the arterial oxygen desaturation (West, 1962). Thus, at extreme altitude, the increase in hemoglobin can in no way offset the decreased oxygen-carrying capacity of blood because of the arterial desaturation.

6. Oxyhemoglobin dissociation curve

Ansel Keys and co-workers (1936) were the first to demonstrate a right shift in the oxyhemoglobin dissociation curve at altitude, caused by an increase in the erythrocyte 2,3diphosphoglycerate (Lenfant et al., 1968). Nevertheless, the in vivo position of the oxyhemoglobin dissociation curve will depend on the influence of both pH and 2,3-DPG and throughout the increasing altitude exposure, arterial pH becomes progressively more alkaline (Sutton et al., (6) In Press) and thus, oxygen loading in the lungs will be favoured. By contrast, in the exercising muscle pH will be less alkaline and the oxyhemoglobin dissociation curve will be relatively right-shifted and favour unloading of oxygen in the tissues.

7. Oxygen delivery to tissues

On acute exposure to altitude, there is an increase in cardiac
output (Klausen, 1966; Vogel and Harris, 1967), primarily due to an
acceleration in heart rate without any significant change in
stroke volume. With acclimatisation, cardiac output returns to
normal; however, with exercise, although the relationship of cardiac
output to oxygen uptake is maintained, the maximum cardiac output
is significantly reduced (Hartley et al., 1967; Pugh, 1964b; Groves
et al., In Press).

8. Oxygen extraction

With increasing exercise, arterial mixed venous oxygen tension
difference widens. Muscle oxygen extraction is best appreciated
during exercise by sampling femoral venous blood draining the
exercising muscle. Technical considerations have prevented direct
measurements of femoral venous and mixed venous blood at extreme
altitude until Operation Everest II when Swan-Ganz catheters were
inserted into the pulmonary artery and direct mixed venous blood
samples were obtained at rest and during exercise at extreme
altitude. Although at sea level during maximum exercise there was
a marked increase in the oxygen extraction with a mixed venous PO_2
of approximately 20 Torr, at the equivalent of 6198m, mixed venous
PO_2 was reduced to approximately 15 Torr and decreased only a
further 2 Torr with an increase in altitude to the 'summit' (Sutton
et al., (b) In Press). Thus, it would seem that at extreme
altitude, oxygen extraction is maximal although femoral venous
blood studies remain to be done and that it is not possible to
decrease the minimum mixed venous PO_2 further.

9. Tissue metabolism

With exercise under conditions of acute hypoxia, there is an
increase in blood lactate for the equivalent power output (Hughes
et al., 1968; Sutton, 1977). Nevertheless, with acclimatisation,
maximum lactate has been shown to be reduced significantly
(Edwards, 1936), a finding confirmed on Operation Everest II
(Sutton et al., (a) In Press). More detailed studies of muscle
metabolism reveal that the decrease in blood lactate is due also to
a reduced rate of glycogenolysis and muscle lactate generation
(Sutton et al.,(a) In Press).

Conclusions

With adaptation, man is capable of considerable exercise,
equivalent to more than 1 litre of oxygen uptake, at the highest
altitudes on earth, where the inspired oxygen is reduced to 43 Torr.
Principal adaptations which make this feat possible are the marked
increase in alveolar ventilation and the near maximal tissue oxygen
extraction. Although not addressed in this paper, there are
further important adaptations at the tissue level.

References

Cerretelli, P., di Prampero, P.E., Bruckner, J.-C., Ferretti, G.,
Capelli, C., Howald, H. and Oelz, O. (In Press). In Hypoxia
and Cold (edited by J.R. Sutton, C.S. Houston and G. Coates).
Philadelphia: Praeger Publishers.

Cymerman, A., Rock, P., Young, P., Sutton, J. and Malconian M.
(In Press). Operation Everest II: maximum oxygen uptake at
extreme altitude. Journal of Applied Physiology.

Dempsey, J. (1971). Quality and significance of pulmonary
adaptation to work in adolescent altitude residents.
Acta Pediatr. Scand. (Suppl. 217):99-104.

Edwards, H.T. (1936). Lactic acid in rest and work at high
altitude. American Journal of Physiology 118:367-75.

Gale, G.E., Torre-Bueno, J.R., Moon, R.E., Saltzman, H.A. and
Wagner P.D. (1985). Ventilation-perfusion inequality in normal
humans during exercise at sea level and simulated altitude.
Journal of Applied Physiology 58:978-88, 1985.

Gledhill, N., Froese A.B. and Dempsey, J.A. (1977). Ventilation to
perfusion distribution during exercise in health. In Muscular
Exercise and the lung (edited by J.A. Dempsey and C.E. Reed),
pp 325-43. Madison: University of Wisconsin Press.

Grover, R.F., Reeves, J.T., Grover, E.B and Leathers, J.E. (1967).
Muscular exercise in young men native to 3,100m altitude.
Journal of Applied Physiology 22:555-64.

Groves, B.M., Reeves, J.T., Sutton, J.R., Wagner, P.D., Cymerman,
A., Malconian, M.K., Rock, P.B., Young, P.M. and Houston C.S.
(In Press). Operation Everest II: high altitude pulmonary
hypertension unresponsive to oxygen. Journal of Applied
Physiology.

Hartley, L.H., Alexander, J.K., Modelski, M. and Grover, R.F.
(1967). Subnormal cardiac output at rest and during exercise in
residents at 3,100m altitude. Journal of Applied Physiology
23:839-48.

Hughes, R.L. Clode, M., Edwards, R.H.T., Goodwin, T.J. and Jones,
N.L. (1968). Effect of inspired O_2 on cardiopulmonary and
metabolic responses to exercise in man. Journal of Applied
Physiology 24:336-47.

Keys, A., Hall, F.G. and Barron, E.S. (1936). The position of the
oxygen dissociation curve of human blood at high altitude.
Americal Journal of Physiology 115:292-307.

Klausen, K. (1966) Cardiac output in man in rest and work during
and after acclimatization to 3,800m. Journal of Applied
Physiology 21:609-16.

Lenfant, C., Torrance, J., English, E., Finch, C.A., Reynafarje,
C., Ramos, J. and Faura, J. (1968). Effect of altitude on
oxygen binding by hemoglobin and on organic phosphate levels.
Journal of Clinical Investigation 47:2652-56.

Malconian, M.K., Rock, P.B., Reeves, J.T., Cymerman, A., Sutton,
J.R., Groves, B.M., Wagner, P.D., Donner, H., Young, P.M. and
Houston, C.S. (In Press). Operation Everest II: alveolar and
arterial blood gases at extreme altitude. Journal of Applied
Physiology.

Milledge, J.S., Ward, M.P., Williams, E.S. and Clarke, C.R.A.
(1983). Cardiorespiratory response to exercise in men
repeatedly exposed to extreme altitude. Journal of Applied
Physiology: respiratory, environmental and exercise physiology
55:1379-85.

Oelz, O., Howald, H., Jenni, R., Hoppeler, H., Claassen, H.,
Bruckner, J.C., di Pramper, P.E. and Cerretelli, P. (In Press).
In Hypoxia and Cold (edited by J.R. Sutton, C.S. Houston and
G. Coates). Philadelphia: Praeger Publishers.

Pugh, L.G.C.E. (1957). Resting ventilation and alveolar air on
Mount Everest; with remarks on the relationship of barometric
pressure to altitude in mountains. Journal of physiology
(London) 135:590-610.

Pugh, L.G.C.E. (1958). Muscular exercise on Mount Everest.
Journal of Physiology 141:233-61.

Pugh, L.G.C.E. (1964a). Blood volume and hemoglobin concentration
at altitudes above 18,000ft (5,500m). Journal of Physiology
(London) 170:344-53.

Pugh, L.G.C.E. (1964b). Cardiac output in muscular exercise at
19,000ft (5,800m). Journal of Applied Physiology 19:441-447.

Pugh, L.G.C.E. and Sutton, J.R. (1983). Everest then and now. In
Hypoxia, Exercise and Altitude (edited by J.R. Sutton, C.S.
Houston and N.L. Jones), pp 415-28. New York: Alan R. Liss, Inc.

Pugh, L.G.C.E., Gill, M.B., Lahiri, S., Milledge, J.S., Ward, M.P.
and West, J.B. (1964). Muscular exercise at great altitudes.
Journal of Applied Physiology 19:431-40.

Rahn, H. and Otis, A.B. (1949). Man's respiratory response during
and after acclimatization to high altitude. American Journal
of Physiology 157:445-62.

Reeves, J.T., Halpin, J., Cohn. J.E. and Daoud, F. (1969).
Increased alveolar-arterial oxygen difference during simulated
high-altitude exposure. Journal of Applied Physiology
27:658-61.

Schoene, R.B., Lahiri, S., Hackett, P.H., Peters, Jr., R.M.,
Milledge, J.S., Pizzo, C.J., Sarnquist, F.H., Boyer, S.J.,
Graber, D.J., Maret, K.H. and West J.B. (1984). Relationship of
hypoxic ventilatory response to exercise performance on Mount
Everest. Journal of Applied Physiology: respiratory,
environmental and exercise physiology 56:1478-83.

Sutton, J.R. (1977). The effect of acute hypoxia on the hormonal
response to exercise. Journal of Applied Physiology
42:587-92.

Sutton, J.R. (In Press) Physiological prerequisites of elite
climbers. In Hypoxia and Cold (edited by J.R. Sutton, C.S.
Houston and G. Coates). Philadelphia: Praeger Publishers.

Sutton, J.R., Cymerman, A., Rock, P., Young, P., Young, A.,
Balcomb, A. and Houston, C.S. (In Press -a). Maximum
ventilation, lactate and perceived exhaustion at extreme
simulated altitude - 'Operation Everest II' Journal of
Applied Physiology.

Sutton, J.R., Reeves, J.T., Wagner, P.D., Groves, B.M., Malconian,
M.K., Rock, P., Cymerman, A., Young, P. and Houston, C.S. (In
Press -b). Severe arterial hypoxemia at rest and during
exercise at extreme simulated altitude - 'Operation Everest II'.
Journal of Applied Physiology.

- 319 -

Viault, E. (1891). Sur la quantite d'oxygene contenue dans le sang des animaux des hauts plateaux de l'Amerique du Sud. C.R. Acad. Sci. (D) (Paris) 112:295-8.

Vogel, J.A. and Harris, C.W. (1967). Cardiopulmonary responses of resting man during early exposure to high altitude. Journal of Applied Physiology 22:1124-28.

Wagner, P.D., Sutton, J.R., Reeves, J.T., Cymerman, A., Groves, B.M. and Malconian, M.K. (In Press). V$_A$/Q inequality at rest and during exercise throughout a simulated ascent of Mt. Everest. Journal of Applied Physiology.

West, J.B., Boyer, S.J., Graber, D.J., Hackett, P.H., Maret, K.H., Milledge, J.S., Peters, Jr., R.M., Pizzo, C.J., Samaja, M., Sarnquist, F.H., Schoene, R.B. and Winslow, R.M. (1983a). Maximal exercise at extreme altitudes on Mount Everest. Journal of Applied Physiology: respiratory, environmental and exercise physiology 55:688-98.

West, J.B., Hacket, P.H., Maret, K.H., Milledge, J.S., Peters, Jr., R.M., Pizzo, C.J. and Winslow, R.M. (1983b). Pulmonary gas exchange on the summit of Mount Everest. Journal of Applied Physiology: respiratory environmental and exercise physiology 55:678-87.

West, J.B., Lahiri, S., Gill, M.B., Milledge, J.S., Pugh, L.G.C.E. and Ward M.P. (1962). Arterial oxygen saturation during exercise at high altitude. Journal of Applied Physiology 17:617-21.

West, J.B., Lahiri, S., Maret, K.H., Peters, R.M. and Pizzo, C. (1983c). Barometric pressures at extreme altitudes on Mt. Everest: physiological significance. Journal of Applied Physiology: respiratory, environmental and Exercise Physiology 54:1188-94.

Discussion

Dr Gleeson, Aberdeen, Scotland
In the real world, climbers on the summit of Everest face a number of problems apart from hypoxia. Have you considered the interactions between cold, exercise, diet and the hypobaric environment?

Dr Sutton, Ontario, Canada
The whole purpose of the study was to eliminate factors other than hypoxia. We did have the capacity to change temperature, humidity, ultraviolet light and other environmental conditions but we wanted to maintain these at constant levels. The question of diet is particularly important and Dr Griffith Pugh showed that climbers on Everest are undernourished and grossly dehydrated. We tried to ensure that our subjects were well nourished but all developed loss of appetite at altitude.

Dr Saltin, Copenhagen, Denmark
How well did your subjects maintain body weight?

Dr Sutton
Subjects suffered severe loss of appetite above 20000ft. There
was a substantial weight loss, averaging about 5kg, with the
greatest loss being about 10kg.

Dr Raven, Texas, USA
Do you think that 40 days is long enough for complete renal
compensation, or do you think that your subjects were still
relatively hypoventilating for that altitude?

Dr Sutton
The ascent profile was based on successful Everest expeditions and
on a previous study by Dr Charles Houston in 1946. We ascended
more slowly and descended each evening to allow subjects to sleep
better. I cannot completely answer your question but we do have
alveolar gas samples on a daily basis, and if we compare our values
with the Rahn-Otis diagram, they correspond precisely.

Dr Saltin
Did you record blood pressure on these subjects?

Dr Sutton
Blood pressure responses were almost normal up to about 20,000ft
but at 25000ft and above, subjects displayed gross orthostatic
hypotension. One of the most significant observations of this
study was that standing resulted in a fall in blood pressure to as
low as 50mmHg. The only way that we were able to get some of these
subjects to the summit was to make them exercise on a cycle
ergometer.

Dr Legg, Farnborough, England
Did your subjects exercise regularly as they would during climbing
or did they rest?

Dr Sutton
We tried to maintain each subject's normal activity levels in the
chamber. Three exercise modes were available; a cycle ergometer, a
treadmill and a Versi-climber, which allows a climbing-type
exercise. Subjects exercised for a few hours per day up to about
20000ft but above about 25000ft on average their activity
levels declined.

Dr Legg
Can we select, on the basis of sea level tests, those individuals
who will perform best at altitude, perhaps on the basis of hypoxic
ventilatory drive or anaerobic capacity?

Dr Sutton
We originally thought that measurements like $\dot{V}O_2$max and ventilatory
responsiveness would be important preductions but when we look at
data on climbers like Meissner and Habeler who reached the top of
Everest without the use of supplementary oxygen, they do not have a
high $\dot{V}O_2$max - measured values were in the region of $50ml.kg^{-1}.min^{-1}$,
although it must be said that at the time of these measurements
they were not as fit as they had been. In our group of subjects,

sea-level values for $\dot{V}O_2$max ranged from 42-65ml.kg^{-1}.min^{-1} but with increasing altitude, $\dot{V}O_2$max of the fittest subjects fell most as you might expect. I should point out that we lost two subjects on the way; the subjects who dropped out were those who began with the highest $\dot{V}O_2$max. Again, although we have data on only a limited number of subjects it is interesting to note that the subject with the lowest ventilatory response was the one who dropped out at only 18000ft. From out studies on Mount Yukon in the early 1970s, we concluded that ventilatory responsiveness was an important predictor of who would develop sickness. The problem is whether a sea-level test lasting only a few minutes can predict how an individual will respond when exposed to hypoxia for periods of hours or days.

Dr Prior,Vancouver, Canada
The postural hypotension observed at the 'summit' could be postulated to be due to weight-loss related to decreased central catecholamines and diuresis of saline (and ?water).

   Did you measure urinary volume; sodium loss and/or any plasma or urine cathecholamine levels?

Dr Sutton
Urinary volumes were well maintained; no dehydration occurred and plasma catecholamines, both at rest and during exercise, were higher at the higher altitudes.

Dr Prior
We have shown that men with obstructive sleep apnoea had lower testosterone levels in a consecutive case series versus snorers and that testosterone increased when nocturnal hypoxia was corrected in a prospective study.

   Did you measure any reproductive parameter as overtime in the Everest chamber studies?

Dr Sutton
Results of the reproductive hormones are not yet available.

Dr Poortmans, Brussels, Belgium
You mentioned less muscle lactate content during exercise at altitude as compared to sea level. Would you comment on the mechanisms which would be involved?

Dr Sutton
The most likely reason muscle lactate was reduced during exercise at altitude was because of the reduced glycogenolysis.

Dr Poortmans
Did you observe any changes in substrate's utilisation at altitude as compared to sea level?

Dr Sutton
Preliminary information suggests an increased fat utilisation?

<u>Dr Poortmans</u>
Do you have data on myoglobin content since one knows that, at least in rats, training at altitude does increase the O_2 intramuscular transport to the mitochondria?

<u>Dr Sutton</u>
Myoglobin data are not yet available.

Air pollution and exercise: physiological effects

P.B. RAVEN

Since World War II, many major athletic events, such as the Olympic and World Games and World Cup Soccer Finals, have been held in large urban environments built around major industrial complexes. When such games are scheduled the question always arises as to whether the air quality of the urban environment will affect the athlete's performance. This review identifies the major pollutants that are known to affect physiological functions. Ozone is the major constituent of oxidant type air pollution while carbon monoxide is present in both oxidant and reductant air quality. Specifically, both ozone and carbon monoxide have been documented to detrimentally affect exercise performance and physiological functions at ambient levels usually found in metropolitan centers. At current ambient levels it is unlikely that sulphur dioxide affects athletic performance. However, asthmatics and exercise induced asthmatics appear more susceptible to the sulphur dioxide induced bronchoconstriction at levels of $\angle 1.00$ parts per million (ppm). It is generally accepted that, if an athletic event occurs during a time of significantly high air pollutant levels, events requiring exercise endurance will be most affected. However, very little information is available concerning the effects of air pollutants on the anaerobic power events such as sprinting or field events.

1. Air pollution and exercise: physiological effects

1.1 The problem

With an increasing population throughout the world and the continued urbanization of the population, it is inevitable that air quality surrounding major cities of the industrialized nations will deteriorate. The problems of air pollution would have undoubtedly worsened, due to our increasing dependency on fossil fuel as a source of energy generation, if significant legislative action had not been initiated in an attempt to improve air quality. However, ambient air surrounding large metropolitan cities still contains small amounts (in the parts per million range) of gases and particulates (pollutants) other than its normal constituents of oxygen, carbon dioxide, nitrogen, inert gases and water vapour. Air pollutant episodes (smog alerts) generally represent a build up of two or more of the common air pollutants. The resultant smog can be classified according to its chemical reactive properties these being: (1) reductant, consisting mainly of carbon monoxide (CO), sulphur oxides (SO_x) and particulates usually in combination with high humidities and high or low temperatures; (2) oxidant or photochemical, consisting mainly of carbon monoxide, ozone (O_3), nitric oxides (NO_x) peroxyacylnitrates, and particulates usually in combination with high temperatures and low humidities. Ozone approximates some 90% of oxidant pollutants.

The continued migration of the industrialized population to urban surroundings results in recreational and spectator sports activities occurring within the areas where air pollutant levels are found to be at their highest. In addition, many of the world's major athletic competitions (Olympic Games, World Cup Soccer Finals, etc.) are being held within the limits of major cities, for example, the last World Cup Soccer finals were be held in Mexico City, a city of 16 million people at an altitude of 2200 meters and with one of the worst air pollutant histories of recent years. Hence, the question 'What effect do air pollutants have on performance?' Until recently relatively few athletic performance related studies had been conducted, indeed the primary investigations carried out since 1970 have focused on health related effects of the common air pollutants. It is the intent of this review to summarize the health related data and by extrapolation from the data from the few performance related investigations present an overview of the effects of some common air pollutants upon the human's capacity to perform work.

1.1.1. Carbon monoxide

Carbon monoxide (CO) is a gas that is not easily detected by human senses, yet it is readily absorbed from inspired air (when present in very low quantities) and combines with hemoglobin to interfere with tissue oxygenation. Theoretical predictions of resultant COHb levels in the blood, based on physical and physiologic data, have been practically verified by many excellent experiments (Forbes et al., 1945; Coburn et al., 1965; Peterson and Stewart, 1970; Peterson and Stewart 1975; Stewart, 1975). Unfortunately, this work concentrated primarily on relating COHb levels to decrements in cognitive function. McCafferty (1981) documents the wide variation in ambient levels of CO that occur within an urban environment. The air quality standard (AQS) of the United States was set with regard for individuals with cardio respiratory disease, chronic obstructive pulmonary disease, pregnant women or anyone with a reduced oxygen carrying capacity and is based upon blood carboxyhemoglobin (COHG) levels not to exceed 2.5 to 3%. The AQS of 9ppm for an 8hr time average and 35ppm for a 1hr average has been set to meet the blood COHG levels. However, on any given city street the levels of CO can vary from 0 to 100ppm within a matter of 10 feet and in enclosed situations, such as tunnels, levels as high as 500ppm have been recorded.

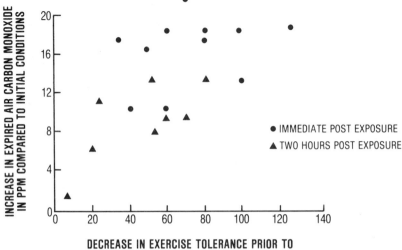

Figure 1. The relationships between time to onset of angina and the
level of end-expired CO from angina patients exposed to freeway
air. (Reprinted with permission of Aronow and Goldsmith, 1975)

(a) Health related effects
Indications of the effect of CO in exacerbation of a pre- existing
disease can be seen in the cardiovascularly impaired patient
(Aronow et al., 1972; Aronow and Isbell, 1973) and highlights the
problems to be encountered by the urban resident who exercises
outdoors.   Aronow et al.(1972) studied ten angina patients after
they had driven for 90 minutes in heavy freeway traffic in Los
Angeles while inhaling outside ambient air (experimental) and again
while breathing compressed purified air (control). The arterial
COHb level was significantly elevated (3.90%) immediately after
the experimental condition to a mean level of 5.08%. Control
conditions showed a decrease in arterial COHb of 0.18% to a mean
level of 0.65%. There was a significant decrease in exercise time
to angina (from 249.4 to 174.3 seconds) on a cycle erogometer test
using progressive increase in load (Fig.1). In addition,
decreases in heart rate, systolic blood pressure, and rate
pressure product (systolic blood pressure times heart rate) at
angina were noted after the breathing of freeway air. Subsequent
double-blind laboratory studies were conducted on ten angina
patients breathing 50ppm CO for two hours (Aronow and Isbell, 1973)
and on ten angina patients breathing 50 and 100ppm CO for four
hours (Anderson et al., 1973). Mean COHb levels after 50ppm
breathing of COHb were 2% and 2.9% for each study, respectively,
and after 100ppm COHb breathing, reached 4.5%. After breathing
purified air for similar periods, the patients' COHb levels were
reduced. Again, excercise time to angina was significantly reduced
after 50 and 100ppm CO breathing. The duration of pain after
100ppm CO breathing was more prolonged. Ischemic ST-segment
changes were worse and were more prevalent with the earlier onset
of angina. Hence, low levels of ambient CO resulting in low levels

of COHb (2.7 - 4.5%) can cause angina to develop sooner after less cardiac work and cause a worsening of myocardial ischemia in diseased coronary patients. Aronow and Cassidy (1975) subsequently demonstrated that in clinically normal people, a significant ST-segment depression greater than 1.00 mm may occur in 10% of the population after CO loading of the blood (3.95% COHb) - indicative of latent coronary artery disease.

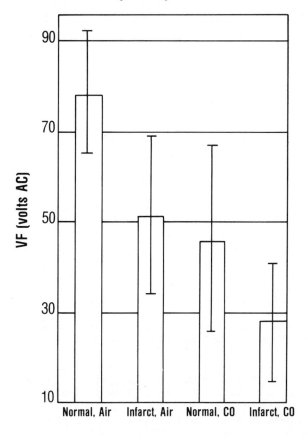

Figure 2. The decrement in voltage required to fibrillate normal and infarcted dogs exposed to carbon monoxide, resulting in COHb levels of 9.3% (Reprinted with permission from Debias, D.A. Effects of carbon monoxide inhalation on ventricular fibrillation. Arch. Environ. Hlth. 31:38-42, 1976, Heldorf Publications).

The susceptibility of the coronary vasculature to oxygen deficiencies has been observed in severe anaemia and arterial hypoxaemia (Bartlett, 1963), and acute elevations of COHb levels (Ayres et al., 1970). In healthy animals a progressive increase in COHb level results in a progressive increase in coronary flow until 15-20% COHb additional increases in COHb level maximize the myocardial arteriovenous oxygen difference without causing additional increases in coronary flow. Hence, in patients with coronary atherosclerosis, the increased flow response to COHb is compromised

to the extent that adequate compensation does not occur even at
levels as low as 6% COHb (Gregg and Fischer, 1963). Debias et al.
(1973) have shown that after a six-hour exposure to 100ppm
(resultant COHb level of 9.3%), the myocardium of the monkey was
more susceptible to fibrillation that the non-CO- exposed animals,
whereas those monkeys that were postinfarcted and then exposed to
CO were even more susceptible than the healty CO- exposed animals
(Fig. 2). It would appear that the cardiac- impaired patients were
at an increased risk of incurring additional coronary events if
ambient levels of CO in the inspired air are capable of causing a
rise in blood COHb levels above 1.5 - 2.0%.

(b) Performance effects
All the previous evidence indicates that the maximal aerobic
capacity ($\dot{V}O_2$max) of healthy men will be reduced linearly in
relation to increased blood levels of COHb (Pirnay et al., 1971;
Vogel et al., 1972; Vogel and Gleser, 1972; Ekblom and Huot, 1972;
Raven et al., 1974; Drinkwater et al., 1974; Raven et al., 1974;
Horvath et al., 1975; Nielsen, 1971) in the 5 - 35% COHb range (Fig.3).
The reduction in $\dot{V}O_2$max was not statistically significant until
levels greater than 4.3% were obtained (Horvath et al., 1975).
However, lower levels (2.7%) have been shown to decrease maximal
performance time on the treadmill significantly (Raven et al.,
1974a; Drinkwater et al., 1974; Raven et al., 1974b). However,
whether these low levels of circulating COHb are sufficient to
interfere with anaerobic metabolism, and hence curtail performance,
has yet to be answered. It has been found that COHb levels of 5%
significantly increase the oxygen debt of acute work, although what
portion of the debt is altered, alactacid or lactacid, was not
identified (Chevalier et al., 1963). During sub maximal work of
short duration at $\dot{V}O_2$ levels below 1.5 liters/min (40 - 60%
$\dot{V}_2$max), COHb levels of less than 15% had little effect on energy
production and ventilation in the healthy person, but the
submaximal heart rate was significantly increased (Pirnay et al.,
1971; Vogel et al., 1972; Vogel and Gleser, 1972). Hence, the
efficiency of muscular exercise during CO inhalation was unaffected
at levels below 15% COHb, because the CO desaturation of hemoglobin
was overcome by a hyperkinetic circulation (i.e., cardiac output
was increased by an increase in heart rate alone). As the work
levels increased relative to the person's maximal capacity,
ventilation volume was increased by means of an increased
respiratory rate similar to the changes observed during altitude
hypoxia (Vogel et al., 1972; Vogel and Gleser, 1972). During more
prolonged work (3.5 - 4.0 hours) at approximately 35% $\dot{V}O_2$max
with exposure to 50ppm CO resulting in COHb levels of 4.6 - 6.8%,
only the heart rate was increased above that observed during
filtered-air exposures (Gliner et al., 1975). Additional exposures
to levels of 75 and 100ppm for similar pariods of time and at
similar levels of exercise resulted in COHb levels of 10.7% and
13.2%, respectively, and failed to alter the cardiopulmonary
response significantly (Gliner et al., 1975). It would appear that
in the healthy, non-cardiovascularly compromised person, ambient CO
levels resulting in COHb levels of 15% do not alter physiologic
responses to low levels of work (35 - 60% $\dot{V}O_2$max). In view of
the physiologic requirements of aerobic exercise, the inroads into

the cardiopulmonary reserved incurred by CO loading will likely
prove detrimental to the elite performer. Specifically, when the
elite performer (a miler or a soccer player) is performing
maximally only slight degrees of CO loading would prove detrimental
to optimum cardiac function, and oxygen delivery and may impair
anaerobic energy production.

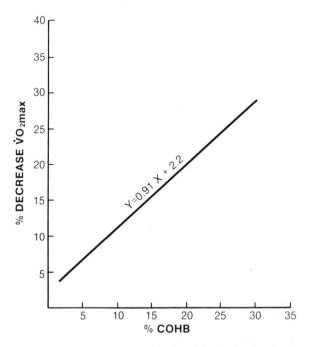

Figure 3. The linear relationship between increasing levels of
carboxyhemo-globin (COHb) and the decrement in maximal aerobic
power ($\dot{V}O_2$max), r = 0.84, P < 0.05. (Reprinted with permission
from Raveñ, P.B., et al. Effect of carbon monoxide and
peroxyacylnitrate on man's maximal aerobic capacity. J. Appl.
Physiol. 36:288-293, 1974. Published by the American Physiological
Society).

1.1.2. Ozone
Ozone is formed by a reaction cycle involving nitrogen monoxide,
nitrogen dioxide, oxygen, hydrocarbons, and energy from ultraviolet
radiation. The term photochemical oxidant is used to refer to the
pollutant mixture generated in this process. Peak levels typically
occur near midday although this varies with the particular location
and the existing meteorologic conditions. Ozone (O_3) is a
potent airway irritant capable of causing airway irritation in
resting or moderately active individuals at concentrations as low
as 0.3ppm, Folinsbee et al.(1978), Higgins et al. (1979). At
higher concentrations (>1ppm) ozone can cause pulmonary edema and
ultimately death. In many cities throughout the world (Los Angeles,
New York Mexico City and London) the levels of ozone exceeds 0.2 to
0.3ppm in the summer months. The AQS for the United States has
been revised upwards from 0.08 to 0.12ppm for a 1hr averaging period.

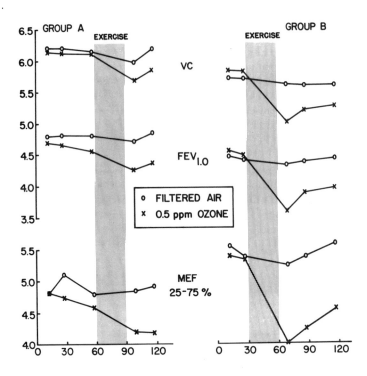

Figure 4. The change in vital capacity (VC), forced expired volume (FEV$_{1.0}$ in liters, maximal midexpiratory flow (MEF 25-75%) in $1 \cdot s^{-1}$ during exposure to filtered air or ozone (0.5 ppm) for 2h. Exercise at 45% $\dot{V}O_2$max was performed between 60 and 90 mins for group A and between 30 and 60 mins for group B. Note the decrease lung measurements during exercise and ozone exposure. These begin to return baseline following the exercise period despite continued resting ozone exposure. (Reprinted with permission from Folinsbee, L.J., et al. Influence of exercise and heat stress on pulmonary function during ozone exposure. J. Appl. Physiol. 43:409-413, 1977. Published by the American Physiological Society).

(a) Health related effects
Early research on the effects of ozone on lung functions in man dealt with concentrations which were unrealistically high in terms of ambient levels (Bates et al., 1972; Clamann and Bancroft, 1959; Hallet, 1965; Young et al., 1964). These studies demonstrated that ozone decreased maximum expiratory flow, increased tracheal irritation and decreased pulmonary diffusing capacity.

Of the greatest interest in terms of potential impact on the populations who may be exposed to elevated ambient ozone levels are those investigations which deal with concentrations of 0.30ppm and less. The primary consensus of those studies carried out with subjects at rest and O_3 concentrations of <0.30ppm was that this type of exposure had minimal, if any, impact on lung function. In contrast to these few studies on resting subjects, numerous investigations have been reported using exercising subjects exposed to ozone levels up to 0.30ppm. One particularly interesting observation was that subjects who exercised during ozone exposure exhibited markedly greater responses and significantly greater decrements in lung function than resting subjects (Bates et al., 1972). Subsequent studies (Hazucha et al., 1973; Hackney et al., 1975b; Folinsbee et al., 1977b) confirmed this observation (Fig.4).

Savin and Adams (1979) found no effects following a progressive exercise test lasting approximately 30 mins with average ventilation of 50 - 60 l/min while subjects breathed either 0.15 or 0.30ppm O_3. On the other hand, McDonnell et al. (1983) observed marked decreases in forced expired volume in 1 sec. (FEV_1) and specific airway resistance (SRaw) in subjects performing intermittent exercise at ventilation volumes of 65 l/min while exposed to one of these same concentrations (0.30ppm). Lategola (1980a) found significant but modest lung function changes in men and women performing light exercise while exposed for three hours to 0.30ppm at ventilation volumes of 20 l/min at 6000 feet simulated altitude. At ozone concentrations between 0.20 and 0.30 ppm, significant lung function effects in man have been observed only in heavily exercising subjects. Folinsbee et al. (1980) studied subjects exposed for three consecutive days to 0.28ppm O_3. Significant decreases in FVC, FEV_1, and maximal mid-expiratory flow (FEF25 - 75%) were observed on the first two exposure days. In a prior study, Folinsbee and colleagues (1978) observed a significant decrease in FEV_1 following a two-hour exposure to 0.24ppm at each of three exercise intensities (average mean ventilation volumes of 30, 49 and 67 l/min, respectively). McDonnell and co-workers (1983) found decreased FVC, FEV_1, FEF25 - 75%, and SRaw in men exposed to 0.24ppm for two hours with heavy intermittent exercise. However, at 0.20ppm several groups of investigators found no significant effects (Higgins et al., 1979; Gliner et al., 1983). Gliner et al. (1983) did report significant changes in FEV_1 in a sensitive subgroup of the exposed subjects. Therefore, for individuals performing moderate to heavy exercise during exposure, decrements in lung function can be expected following exposure to 0.30ppm O_3 for at least one hour (continuous exercise) or two hours (intermittent exercise). The FEV_1 decreases ranged from 2.5% (Lategola et al., 1980a) to 16.8% (McDonnell et al., 1983). This considerable range of response reflects the wide range of exercise intensities and durations employed as well as the broad variation in subject sensitivity (Fig.5) and confirms an earlier finding of differences in subject sensitivity by DeLucia and Adams (1977).

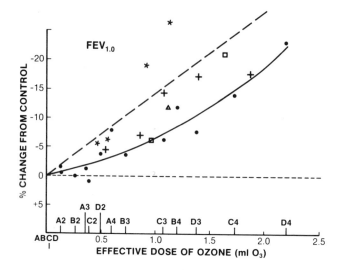

Figure 5. This figure describes the expected decrease in $FEV_{1.0}$ following inhalation of a given effective dose of ozone. Data are included from studies using 2hr intermittent exercise exposures (solid line) and 1hr continuous exercise exposures (dashed line). A-D refer to exercise levels classified by ventilation (A = 10 $1.min^{-1}$, B = 30 $1.min^{-1}$, C = 49 $1.min^{-1}$, D = 67 $1.min^{-1}$; 2-4 refer to ozone concentrations (2 = 0.01, 3 = 0.30 and 4 = 0.50 ppm). All intermittent exercise exposures lasted 2hr and included four 15 min exercise periods. Effective dose = (mean $\dot{V}_E$ x ozone concentration x exposure duration). Solid dots from Folinsbee et al. (1978); +, data from McDonnell et al. (1983); intermittent exercise ($\dot{V}_E$ = 67 $1.min^{-1}$. The solid line is from the original figure (W% $FEV_{1.0}$ =0.19 + 0.38 x + 0.03x^2, where x = effective dose in ml O_3 x 10) (Folinsbee et al., 1978)). Data from studies in which 1hr of continuous exercise was performed include: Adams and Schlegle (1983), $\dot{V}_E$ 80 $1.min^{-1}$, Bedi et al. (1983), $\dot{V}_E$ 90 $1.min^{-1}$; *Avol et al. (1983), $\dot{V}_E$ = 57 $1.min^{-1}$. Dashed line is the linear regression of percent change in $FEV_{1.0}$ on effective dose in ml) (W% $FEV_{1.0}$ = 14.2x + 0.05, r = 0.76; x = ml O_3. (Reprinted with permission from Folinsbee, L.J. and Raven P.B. Exercise and air pollution. Journal of Sports Sciences. 2:57-75, 1984, published by E&FN Spon Ltd. London).

(b) Ozone and exercise performance
Although it has not been clearly established that modest impairment in pulmonary function is associated with impaired endurance performance, a significant number of studies linking individual subjective reports of not being able to perform maximally have been documented. Adams and Schlegle (1983) exposed ten athletes to 0.20 ppm while simulating a 30 minute competitive endurance race preceded by a 30 minute warm-up period (60 min total exposure). Four subjects indicated that they could not have performed maximally during such exposure. At a higher concentration (0.35 ppm), only six of ten subjects were able to complete the exposure

- 332 -

at all. In another study of competitive cyclists exercising at 75%
$\dot{V}O_2$max for 60 mins in 0.21ppm O_3, Bedi et al. (1983)
queried the cyclists regarding their past experiences while
competing in the Los Angeles area. The major complaint was of
chest discomfort associated with the increased ventilation when
attempting to break away from the 'pack'. Three of the seven
subjects studied by Folinsbee et al. (1984) reported that they
would have been unable to perform maximally under the conditions of
the study (1 hr exposure to 0.21ppm O_3. This observation
confirms the previous reports of Adams and Schlegle (1983).

Earlier reports of the effects of ambient air pollutants on
athletes exercising outdoors, although limited, support these
data. One study showed a decrease in FVC following two-hour
outdoor American football practices at the first stage alert level
(0.20ppm O_3 and higher (McCafferty, 1981). Prior to this, a
group of high school cross-country runners had been studied (Wayne
et al., 1967) over a period of six years to determine if there was
a relationship between running performance and oxidant pollution
(ozone) levels. A deterioration of running performance, which was
defined as a failure to improve race times as the season
progressed, was correlated with the oxidant pollution levels one
hour prior to the race. The lower correlation with the ozone
concentration during the race may be related to the fact that the
runners had been exposed to more ozone during their pre-race warm-
up period than during the actual race, which required only 12
minutes to run. When the oxidant level exceeded 0.25ppm, as many
as 50% of the members of the team had a decreased performance time
in their particular running event. In contrast, when the oxidant
level was below 0.10ppm, fewer than 20% of the team members had
decreased performance. Nevertheless, it must be noted that
elevation of ambient ozone levels is typically associated with
increased ambient temperature, primarily because of the
temperature inversion and stagnant air that produces a pollution
episode. The effect of the combined heat and ozone exposure may be
difficult to differentiate. Experimental studies of combined heat
and ozone exposure (Folinsbee et al., 1977b) have shown an additive
effect on lung function changes, i.e. both stresses are associated
with diminished performance on lung function tests. More recently
Gibbons and Adams (1984) using ten female athletes exposed to 0.15
and 0.30ppm O_3 for one hour at 66% $\dot{V}O_2$max confirm the
interaction between heat (35°C) and O_3^2. Subjective
discomfort increased during combined exposures to heat and O_3,
while pulmonary function decrements were similar to those observed
following 2 hr intermittent exercise exposures to 0.24ppm. In a
follow-up investigation (Lauritzen and Adams, 1985), it was
observed that females had greater decrements in lung function for a
given effective ozone level than did males (Fig. 6). Further
analysis suggested that anthropometric differences related to lung
size were the primary factor in this sex-related difference in
response.

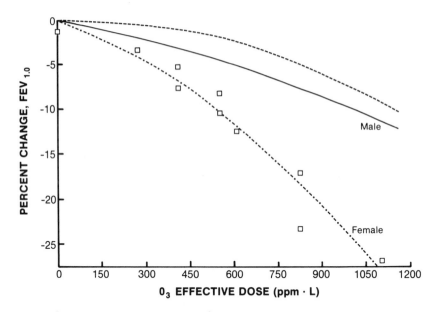

Figure 6. Comparison of females' percent change in forced
expiratory volume in 1s $(FEV_{1.0})$ as function of O_3
effective dose (dashed line with intermittent dots) to that of
males studied in previous investigation (dashed line) (1). Solid
line, response observed in 2-hr intermittent exercise chamber
exposures (9); open squares, females' mean responses for each
protocol, Lauritzen and Adams, 1985. (Reprinted with permission
from Lauritzen, S.K. and Adams, W.C. Ozone inhalation effects
consequent to continuous exercise in females: comparison to males.
J. Appl. Physiol. 59:1601-1601, 1985. Published by the American
Physiological Society).

(c) Mechanism of effect
The effect of ozone exposure on maximum oxygen uptake has been
evaluated to ascertain whether oxygen delivery was compromised by
ozone exposure. Folinsbee et al. (1977a) exposed intermittently
exercising subjects to 0.75ppm O_3 for two hours following
which the subjects performed a maximum exercise test on a cycle
ergometer. A 10% reduction in $\dot{V}O_2$max was observed which was
associated with a 16% decrease in maximal exercise ventilation and
a decrease in the mean maximal workload; FEV_1 decreased by an
average of 23%. While expxosure to 0.75 ppm is unrealistic in
terms of ambient ozone levels, a similar effect on FEV_1 has
been observed in heavily exercising subjects at much lower ozone
concentrations (e.g., McDonnell et al., 1983; Adams and Schlegle,
1983). Thus, it is reasonable to expect that the subjective
reports of being able to perform maximally at ozone levels between
0.20 and 0.35ppm may also be associated with a decline in maximal
oxygen uptake. The two other studies which tested $\dot{V}O_2$max in
conjunction with ozone exposure used either briefer (Savin and
Adams, 1979) or resting (Horvath et al., 1979) exposure and the
investigators were unable to discern any effect of these milder
ozone exposures $\dot{V}O_2$max. These studies found minimal if any

effect on pulmonary function following exposure. These studies
would suggest that mild pulmonary function impairment resulting
from ozone exposure (i.e., $<$10% reduction in FEV_1) will probably
not result in impairment of oxygen delivery capacity (i.e., $\dot{V}O_2$max).
Subsequently, Folinsbee et al. (1986) and Horstman et al. (1986),
by using arterial lines and measures of PaO_2 and $A-aO_2$
gradients and measures of respiratory effort have shown that
exercise related arterial desaturation was not affected by O_3
exposure nor was respiratory effort, yet lung function and
endurance performance decreased following ozone exposure. Beckett
et al. (1985) and Gertner et al. (1982a; 1982b; 1984) have
indentified an O_2 induced vagally mediated bronchoconstriction
as the reason for an increased airway resistance. However,
decrements in maximal lung performance, as determined from lung
volume measures, appear to be more related to an acute inflammatory
reaction to ozone (Holtzman et al., 1983) probably mediated by
thromboxane A_2 (Aizawa et al., 1985).

   In summary, pronounced responses have been shown in heavily
exercising subjects (who consequently breathe more), whereas little
response has been seen in lightly exercising individuals. As would
be expected, short exposures have elicited smaller functional
changes than longer exposures. Thus, athletes competing in events
lasting from 30 minutes to two or more hours while exposed to 0.20
to 0.30ppm O_3 could experience alteration in lung function
with potential consequences for ventilatory performance and
endurance performance (Folinsbee and Raven, 1984).

1.1.3. Sulphur dioxide
Sulphur dioxide (SO_2) is a more ubiquitous pollutant than ozone but
at equivalent concentrations has far less impact on lung function.
The threshold level for SO_2 effects on lung function probably
lies between 1 and 2 ppm whereas for ozone a threshold level near
0.2 ppm is well supported experimentally. However, AQS for the
United States has been established at 0.14ppm SO_2 for a 1 hr
average. This standard was developed from epidemiologic data on
urban smog episodes and the subsequent sequelae to those
individuals with cardiorespiratory disease and asthma. However,
many cities throughout the world including London, Seoul, Munich
and Mexico City exceed this level on a daily basis.

(a) Health effects
Sulphur dioxide is generally regarded as an upper-airway
and bronchial irritant. Exposure to different levels of SO_2
while at rest produces strikingly similar responses; airway
resistance increases rapidly, reaching a maximum after 4-10 minutes
of exposure. Subsequently, a decrease in resistance occurs with
continued exposure, regardless of SO_2 concentrations. The
probable cause of the increase resistance is reflex bronchospasm
initiated by irritation of the bronchial receptors in the smooth
muscle (Lewis et al., 1973; Lehmann, 1908; Sim and Puttle, 1957;
Frank et al., 1961; Frank, 1964; Lawther, 1955; Speiger and Frank,
1966; Snell and Luchsinger, 1969). Investigation suggests that
SO_2 stimulates the subepithelial receptors in the larynx, trachea,

and bronchi and, via the vagus nerve, causes increased tension in the tracheobronchial tree (Nadel et al., 1959; Nadel et al., 1965; Ogura and Harvey, 1971).

Haldane had suspected that the choking effect of dense fog results mainly from sulphate rather than from SO_2 (Haldane and Priestly, 1935), and it has been shown that sulphuric acid and particulate sulphates cause greater air-way obstruction than equivalent amounts of SO_2 was potentiated when a liquid droplet aerosol was administered with SO_2; this result may be explained by the conversion of SO_2 to sulphuric acid within the droplets. Aerosol interaction and high humidity appear to be necessary components of SO_2 reactivity. Recently, it has been shown that lung penetration of particulates and subsequent total lung burden increased during exercise (Bennett et al., 1985). This finding would suggest that aerosolized sulphur dioxide (as droplets of sulphuric acid) may be more affective of lung function that pure gaseous SO_2.

(b) Performance effects
Few experiments have been done on maximal working capacity and submaximal work performance during SO_2 exposures. It was shown that pulmonary function was not affected by two hours of intermittent exercise exposure (ventilations of 20 l/min to 0.37 ppm SO_2; however, no further functional aspects of the human were investigated (Bedi et al., 1979, 1982). It is certain, however, that ambient levels of SO_2 above 1.0 ppm will cause significant discomfort and will prove detrimental to performance.

When inhaled in combination with dry cold air, SO_2 induces bronchoconstriction at even lower concentrations (0.25 ppm) (Sheppard et al., 1983a) and cold exacerbates the effect of a higher concentration (Bethel et al., 1983). It should be noted, however, that there is a fairly broad range of sensitivity to SO_2 in asthmatics with the least sensitive asthmatics being no more sensitive than the most sensitive normal subjects (Rojer et al., 1985).

The major concern with SO_2 is that it affects asthmatic individuals at concentrations lower than 1 ppm (Sheppard et al., 1981a,b; Kirkpatrick et al., 1982). At concentrations as low as 0.50 ppm SO_2, exercising asthmatics may experience marked changes in airway resistance. Two reports (Kirkpatrick et al., 1982; Linn et al., 1983) have demonstrated at least 100% increases in air-way resistance in asthmatics after only 5 min of exercise with SO_2 concentrations in the range of 0.5 ppm. However, with repeated exposures within the same day, the responses become much less severe (Sheppard et al., 1983b).

Another factor which was formerly of concern with exposure to SO_2 in conjunction with ozone was the possibility that the pulmonary function response to the combination of SO_2 plus O_3 would be worse than the sum of their individual effects. Despite one initial report supporting this hypothesis (Hazuch and Bates, 1975), this concern has not been verified experimentally (Bell et al., 1977; Folinsbee et al., 1985; Kleinman et al., 1981). In conclusion, it is probable that SO_2 may cause problems with athletic performance in asthmatics but at current ambient levels, it is unlikely to be of concern to the performer with otherwise normal lungs. Furthermore, the SO_2 induced bronchoconstriction can be inhibited by the prior administration of cromolyn sodium (disodium cromoglycate) (Sheppard et al., 1981c).

1.1.4. Summary

Athletes to whom elevated pollutant levels would be of principal concern are those who participate in events which last 30 minutes or longer (e.g. distance running, soccer, field hockey, cycling road races). However, a prolonged warm-up period prior to a shorter-lasting event could produce effects which would disturb performance. If an air pollution episode ocurs during a major athletic competition, the athletes may be hampered by exposures to carbon monoxide, especially if their COHb levels are raised above 5%. Submaximal performance will not be affected below 15% COHb yet cognitive functions will be affected when COHb levels exceed 5% and, therefore, errors in judgment may become apparent as exposure to CO continues.

In terms of preparing for competition in an area which has a history of high levels of photochemical oxidant, it would be wise to have some experience with exercising under such conditions. Since 'smog episodes' are intermittent, such experience in the ambient environment may require several weeks to obtain as compared to 4 - 5 days in the laboratory controlled ozone experiments. Secondly, photochemical air pollution episodes are usually associated with high ambient temperatures and it has been well established that heat acclimatization should be a part of any endurance performers pre-competition preparation. Thus, it may be prudent for endurance athletes to consider several weeks of training in a photochemical smog area in order to become acclimatized to both heat and ozone which will presumably minimize the potential effect of these two environmental stressors on competitive performance.

Finally, the exercise-induced asthmatic athletic performer may need to experiment with prophylactic medication in areas where sulphur dioxide is prevalent. Specifically, the upcoming Olympic Games in Seoul, Korea, is an example of an area high in sulphur oxide pollution which may prove detrimental to an SO_2 sensitive individual.

Acknowledgement

The Author wishes to express his appreciation of the efforts of the World Processing Center Personnel of Texas College of Osteopathic Medicine, whose professional expertise enabled completion of this manuscript in a timely fashion.

References

Except for those references cited below all other references can be found in the following two review articles:

1. Folinsbee, L.J. and Raven, P.B. 'Exercise and air pollution.' Journal of Sports Sciences 2:57-75, 1984.

2. Raven, P.B. 'Heat and air pollution: The cardiac patient.' Chapter 28 in Heart Disease and Rehabilitation, 2nd Edition, edited by Pollock, M.L. and Schmidt, D.H. John Wiley and Sons, New York, N.Y., 1985, pp. 549-574.

Additional references

Adams, W.C., Saving, W.M., Christo, H.E. (1981). Detection of ozone toxicity during continuous exercise via the effective dose concept. J. Appl. Physiol. 51:415-422.

Adams, W.C. and Schelegle, E.S. (1983). Ozone toxicity effects consequent to prolonged high intensity exercise in trained endurance athletes. J. Appl. Physiol. 55:805-812.

Aizawa, H., Caung, K.F., Leikauf, G.O., Ueki, I., Bethel, R.A., O'Byrne, P.M., Hirose, T., Nadel, J.A. (1985). Significance of thromboxane generation in ozone induced-airway hyperresponsiveness in dogs. J. Appl. Physiol. 59:1918-1923.

Aronow, W.S and Goldsmith, J.R. Carbon monoxide and coronary artery disease. Environ. Res. 10:236-248, (1975). Academic Press, Inc.

Avol, E.L., Linn, W.S., Venet, T.G. A comparison of ambient oxidant effects to ozone dose-response relationships. Interim Annual Report to Southern California Edison. March, 1983.

Ayres, S.M., Grannelli, S. Jr., Mueller, H. (1970). Effects of low concentrations of carbon monoxide: Myocardial infarction in monkeys. Ann NY Acad Sci 17:268-293.

Bates, D.V., Bell, G.M., Burnham, C.D., Hazucha, M., Manthan, J., Pengelly, L.D., Silverman, F. (1972). Short-term effects of ozone on the lung. J. Appl. Physiol. 32:176-181.

Beckett, W.S., McDonnell, W.F., Horstman, D.H., House, D.E. (1985). Role of parasympathetic nervous system in acute lung response to ozone. J. Appl. Physiol. 59: 1879-1885.

Bedi, J.F., Folinsbee, L.J., Horvath, S.M., Ebenstein, R.S. (1979). Human exposure to sulfur dioxide and ozone: Absence of a synergistic effect. Arch. Environ. Health 34:233-239.

Bedi, J.F., Horvath, S.M., Folinsbee, L.J. (1982). Human exposure to sulfur dioxide and ozone in a high temperature-humidity environment. Am. Ind. Hyg. Assoc. J. 43:26-30.

Bell, K.A., Linn, W.S., Hazucha, M., Hackney, J.D., Bates, D.V. (1977). Respiratory effects of exposure to ozone plus sulfur dioxide in Southern Californians and Eastern Canadians. Am. Ind. Hyg. Assoc. J. 38:695-705.

Bennett, G. (1962). Oxygen contamination of high altitude aircraft cabins. Aerosp. Med. 33:969-973.

Bethel, R.A., Epstein, J., Sheppard, D., Nadel, J.A., Boushey, H.A. (1983). Potentiation of sulfur dioxide-induced bronchoconstriction by airway cooling. Am. Rev. Respir. Dis. 127 (#4, pt. 2): 160, Abst.

Bromberg, P.A. and Hazucha, M.J. (1982). Is 'adaptation' to ozone protective? Am. Rev. Respir. Dis. 125:489-490, 1982.

Clamann, H. and Bancroft, R. (1959). Toxicity of ozone in high altitude flight. Adv. Chem. Ser. 21:352-359.

Chevalier, R.B., Bowers, J.A., Bondurant, S., Ross, J. (1963). Circulatory and ventilatory effects in smokers and nonsmokers. J. Appl. Physiol. 18:357-360.

Coburn, R.F., Forster, R.E., Cane, P.B. (1965). Considerations of the physiological variables that determine the blood carboxyhemoglobin concentration in man. J. Clin. Invest. 44:1899-1910.

Dahms, T.E., Horvath, S.M., Gray, D.J. (1975). Technique for accurately producing desired carboxyhemoglobin levels during rest and exercise. J. Appl. Physiol. 38:366-368.

Debias, D.A., Bancyu, C.M., Burkhead, N.C., et al. (1973). Carbon monoxide inhalation effects following myocardial infarction in monkeys. Arch. Environ. Health 27:161-167.

DeLucia, A.J. and Adams, W.C. (1977). Effects of O_3 inhalation during exercise on pulmonary function and blood biochemistry. J. Appl. Physiol: Respirat. Environ. Exercise Physiol. 43:75-81.

Demedts, M. and Anthonisen, N.R. (1973). Effects of increased airway resistance during steady state execise. J. Appl. Physiol. 35:361-366.

Deno, N.S., Kamon, E., Kiser, D.M. (1981). Physiological responses to resistance breathing during short and prolonged exercise. Am. Ind. Hyg. Assoc. J. 42:616-623.

Dimeo, M.J., Glenn, M.G., Holtzman, M.J., Sheller, J.R., Nadel, J.A., Boushey, H.A. (1981). Threshold concentration of ozone causing an increase in bronchial reactivity in humans and adaptation with repeated exposures. Am. Rev. Resp. Dis. 124:245-248.

Dressendorfer, R.H., Wade, C.E., Bernauer, E.M. (1977). Combined effects of breathing resistance and hyperoxia on aerobic work tolerance. J. Appl. Physiol. 42:444-448.

Drinkwater, B.L., Raven, P.B., Horvath, S.M., Gliner, J.A., Ruhling, R.O., Bolduan, N.W. (1974). Air pollution, exercise and heat stress. Arch. Environ. Health 28:177-182.

Ekblom, B. and Huot, R. (1972). Response to submaximal and maximal exercise at different levels of carboxyhemoglobin. Acta. Physiol. Scand. 86:473-474.

Farrell, B.P., Kerr, H.D., Kulle, T.J., Sauder, L.R., Young, J.L. (1979). Adaptation in human subjects to the effects of inhaled ozone after repeated exposure. Am. Rev. Respir. Dis. 119:725-730.

Folinsbee, L.J., Silverman, F., Shephard, R.J. (1975). Decrease of maximum work performance following O_3 exposure. J. Appl. Physiol: Respir. Environ. Exercise Physiol. 42:531-536.

Folinsbee, L.J., Horvath, S.M., Raven, P.B., Bedi, J.F., Morton, A.R., Drinkwater, B.L., Bolduan, N.W., Gliner, J.A. (1977b). Influence of exercise and heat stress on pulmonary function during ozone exposure. J. Appl. Physiol: Respir. Environ. Exercise Physiol. 43:409-413.

Folinsbee, L.J., Drinkwater, B.L., Bedi, J.F., Horvath. S.M. (1978). The influence of exercise on the pulmonary changes due to exposure to low concentrations of ozone. In: Folinsbee, L.J., Wagner, J.A., Borgia, J.F., Drinkwater, B.L., Gliner, J.A., Bedi, J.F., eds. Environmental Stress Individual Human Adaptations. New York: Academic Press; pp.125-145.

Folinsbee, L.J., Bedi, J.F., Horvath, S.M. (1980). Respiratory responses in humans repeatedly exposed to low concentrations of ozone. Am. Rev. Respir. Dis. 121:431-439.

Folinsbee, L.J. (1981). Effects of ozone exposure on lung function in man: A review. Rev. Environ. Health. 3(3):211-240.

Folinsbee, L.J., Bedi, J.F., Gliner, J.A., Horvath, S.M. (1983). Concentration dependence of pulmonary function adaptation to ozone. Chap. 13 in: The Biomedical Effects of Ozone and Related Photochemical Oxidants. Lee, S.D., Mustafa, M.G., Mehlman, M.A. (eds), Princeton Junction, NJ: Princeton Scientific, pp. 175-187.

Folinsbee, L.J., Bedi, J.F., Horvath, S.M. (1984). Pulmonary function changes after 1 hr continuous heavy exercise in 0.21 ppm ozone. J. Appl. Physiol. 57:984-988.

Folinsbee, L.J., Horstman, D.H., Norona, R.D., Prince, J.M., Berry, (1986). Determinants of endurance performance during ozone inhalation. (Abstract) Fed. Proc.

Folinsbee, L.J., Raven, P.B. (1984). Exercise and air pollution. J. of Sports Sciences 2:57-75.

Forbes, W.H., Sargent, F., Roughton, F.J.W. (1945). The rate of carbon monoxide uptake by normal men. Am. J. Physiol. 143:594-608.

Frank, N.R., Amdur, M.O., Worcester, J., et al. (1961). Effects of acute controlled exposure to SO_2 on respiratory mechanics in healthy male adults. J. Appl. Physiol. 17:252-258.

Frank, N.R. Studies on the effects of acute exposure to sulfur dioxide in human subjects. Proc. R. Soc. Med. 57:1029-1033.

Gertner, A., Bromberger-Barnea, B., Troystman, R., Menkes, H. (1983a). Responses of lung periphery to 1.00 ppm ozone. J. Appl. Physiol. 55:770-776.

Gertner, A., Bromberger-Barnea, B., Troystman, R., Menkes, H. (1983b). Effects of ozone on peripheral lung reactivity. J. Appl. Physiol. 55:777-784.

Gertner, A., Bromberger-Barnea, B., Kelly, L., Troystman, R., Menkes, H. (1984). Local vagal responses in lung periphery. J. Appl. Physiol. 57:1079-1088.

Gliner, J.A., Raven, P.B., Horvath, S.M., Drinkwater, B.L., Sutton, J.C. (1975). Man's physiologic response to long-term work during thermal and pollutant stress. J. Appl. Physiol. 39:628-632.

Gliner, J.A., Horvath, S.M., Folinsbee, L.J. (1983). Pre-exposure to low ozone concentrations does not diminish the pulmonary function response on exposure to higher ozone concentration. Am. Rev. Respir. Dis. 127:51-55.

Gregg, D.E., Fischer, L.C. (1963). Blood supply to the heart, in Hamilton, W.F., Dow, P. (eds) Handbook of Physiology, vol.2, section 2, Washington, D.C., American Physiological Society, p. 1547.

Hackney, J.D., Linn, W.S., Mohler, J.G., Pedersen, E.E., Breisacher, P., Russo, A. (1975a). Experimental studies on human health effects of air pollutants. II. Four hour exposure to ozone and in combination with other pollutant gases. Arch. Environ. Health 30:379-384.

Hackney, J.D., Linn, W.S., Law, D.C., Karuzer, S.R., Greenberg, H., Buckley, R.D., Pedersen, E.E. (1975b). Experimental studies on human health effects of air pollutants. III. Two hour exposure to ozone alone and in combination with other pollutant gases. Arch. Environ. Health 30:385-390.

Hackney, J.D., Linn, W.S., Buckley, R.D., Hislop, H.J. (1976). Studies in adaptation to ambient oxidant air pollution effects of ozone exposure in Los Angeles residents vs. new arrivals. Environ. Health Perspect. 18:141-146.

Hackney, J.D., Linn, W.S., Mohler, J.G., Coller, C.R. (1977a). Adaptation to short-term respiratory effects of ozone in men exposed repeatedly. J. Appl. Physiol. 43:82-85.

Hackney, J.D., Linn, W.S., Karuza, S.K., Buckley, R.D., Law, D.C., Bates, D.V., Hazucha, M., Pengelly, L.D., Silverman, F. (1977b). Effects of ozone exposure in Canadians and Southern Californians. Evidence for adaptation? Arch. Environ. Health 32:110-116.

Haldane, J.S. and Priestly, J.G. (1935). Respiration, London, Oxford University Press.

Hallett, W.Y. (1965). Effect of ozone and cigarette smoke on lung function. Arch. Environ. Health 10:295-302.

Hazucha, M., Silverman, F., Parent, C., Field, S., Bates, D.V. (1973). Pulmonary function in man after short-term exposure to ozone. Arch. Environ. Health 27:183-188.

Hazucha, M. and Bates, D.V. (1975). Combined effect on ozone and sulfur dioxide on human pulmonary function. Nature 257:50-51.

Higgins, E.A., Lategola, M.T., McKenzie, J.M., Melton, C.E., Vaughn, J.A. (1979). Effects of ozone on exercising and sedentary adult men and women representative of the flight attendant population. FFA Technical Report #FFA-AM-79-20.

Holtzman, M.J., Fabri, L.M., Skoogh, B.E., O'Byrne, P.M., Walters, E.H., Aizawa, H., Nadel, J.A. (1983). Time course of airway hypernea responsiveness induced by ozone in dogs. J. Appl. Physiol. 55:1232-1236.

Horstman, D.H., Folinsbee, L.J., Vorona, R.D., Prince, J.M., Berry, J.M. (1986). Ozone induced flow changes are not related to decreased maximum respiratory effort (Abstract) Fed. Proc.

Horvath, S.M., Raven, P.B., Dahms, T.E., Gray, D. (1975). Maximal aerobic capacity at different levels of carboxyhemoglobin. J. Appl. Physiol. 38:300-303.

Horvath, S.M., Gliner, J.A., Matsen-Twisdale, J.A. (1979).
Pulmonary function and maximum exercise responses following
acute ozone exposure. Aviat. Space Environ. Med.
40:901-905.

Horvath, S.M., (1981a). Impact of air quality on exercise
performance. Exercise Sport Sci. Rev. 9:265-296.

Horvath, S.M., Gliner, J.A., Folinsbee, L.J. (1981b). Adaptation
to ozone: duration of effect. Am. Rev. Respir. Dis.
123:496-499.

Kirkpatrick, M.B., Sheppard, D., Nadel, J.A., Boushey, H.A.,
(1982). Effect of oronasal breathing route on sulfur dioxide
induced bronchoconstriction in exercising asthmatic subjects.
Am. Rev. Dis. 125:627-631.

Kleinman, M.T., Bailey, R.M., Chang, Y.C., Clark, K.W., Jones,
M.P., Linn, W.S., Hackey, J.D. (1981). Exposures of human
volunteers to a controlled atmospheric mixture of ozone, sulfur
dioxide, and sulfuric acid. Am. Ind. Hyg. Assoc. J.
42:61-69.

Kulle, T.J. (1983). Duration of pulmonary function and bronchial
reactivity adaptation to ozone in humans. Chap. 12 in: The
Biomedical Effects of Ozone and Related Photochemical Oxidants.
Lee, S.D., M.G., Mehlman, M.A. (eds), Princeton Junction, NJ:
Princeton Scientific, pp. 161-173.

Lategola, M.T., Melton, C.E., Higgins, E.A., (1980). Pulmonary and
symptom threshold effects of ozone in airline passengers and
cockpit crew surrogates. Aviat. Space Environ. Med.
51:878-884.

Lauritzen, S.K. and Adams, W.C. (1985). Ozone inhalation effects
consequent to continuous exercise in females: comparison to
males. J. Appl. Physiol. 59:1601-1606.

Lawther, P.J. (1955). Effects of inhalation of sulfur dioxide on
respiration and pulse rate in normal subjects. Lancet 2:745-
748.

Lehmann, K.B. (1908). Neue Untersuchungen uber die quantitative
Absorption einiger giftiger Gase von Tier und Mensch durch die
Respirationstraktus und seine Tiele. Arch. Hyg. 67:57-98.

Lewis, T.R., Moorman, W.J., Sudmanns, W.F., et al. (1973).
Toxicity of longterm exposure to oxides of sulphur. Arch.
Environ. Health 26:16-31.

Linn, W.S., Medway, D.A., Anzar, U.T., Valencia, L.M., Spier, C.E.,
Tsao, F.S-O, Fischer, D.A., Hackney, J.D. (1982). Persistence of
adaptation to ozone in volunteers exposed repeatedly over six
weeks. Am. Rev. Respir. Dis. 125:491-495.

Linn, W.S., Venet, T.G., Shamoo, D.A., Valencia, L.M., Anzar, U.T.,
Spier, C.E., Hackney, J.D. (1983). Respiratory effects of sulfur
dioxide in heavily exercising asthmatics. Am. Rev. Respir. Dis.
127:278-283.

McCafferty, W.B. (1981). Air Pollution and Athletic Performance,
Springfield: Thomas.

McDonnell, W.F., Horstman, D.H., Hazucha, M.J., Seal, E., Jr.,
Haak, E.D., Salaam, S. (1983). Pulmonary effects of ozone
exposure during exercise dose-response characteristics.
J. Appl. Physiol. 54:1345-1352.

Nadel, J.A., Salem, H., Tamplin, B., et al. (1959). Mechanism of bronchoconstriction during inhalation of sulfur dioxide. J. Appl. Physiol. 197:1317-1321.

Nadel, J.A., Salem, H., Tamplin, B., et al. (1965). Mechanism of bronchoconstriction. Arch. Environ. Health 10:175-178.

Nielson, B. (1971). Thermoregulation during work in carbon monoxide poisoning. Acta. Physiol. Scand. 82:98-106.

Ogura, J.H. and Harvey, J.E. (1971). Nasopulmonary mechanics - experimental evidence of the influence of the upper airway upon the lower. Acta. Otolaryngol. (Stoch) 71:123-132.

Petersen, J.E. and Stewart, R.D. (1970). Absorption and elimination of carbon monoxide by inactive young men. Arch. Environ. Health. 21:176-181.

Petersen, J.E. and Stewart, R.D. (1975). Predicting carboxyhemoglobin levels from carbon monoxide exposures. J. Appl. Physiol. 39:633-638.

Raven, P.B., Drinkwater, B.L., Ruhling, R.O., Bolduan, N.W., Tauchi, S., Gliner, J.A., Horvath, S.M. (1974a). Effect of carbon monoxide and peroxyacetyl-nitrate on man's maximal aerobic capacity. J. Appl. Physiol. 36:288-293.

Raven, P.B., Drinkwater, B.L., Horvath, S.M., Ruhling, R.O., Gliner, J.A., Sutton, J.C., Bolduan, N.W. (1974b). Age, smoking habits, heat stress and their interactive effects with carbon monoxide and peroxyacetylnitrate on man's aerobic power. Int. J. Biometerol. 18:222-232.

Savin, W. and Adams, W. (1979). Effects of ozone inhalation on work performance and $\dot{V}O_2$max. J. Appl. Physiol. 46:309-341.

Sheppard, D., Saisho, A., Nadel, J.A., Boushey, H.A. (1981a). Exercise increases sulfur dioxide-induced bronchoconstriction in asthmatic subjects. Am. Rev. Respir. Dis. 123:486-491.

Sheppard, D., Wong, W.S., Vehara, C.E., Nadel, J.A., Boushey, H.A. (1981b). Lower threshold and greater bronchomotor responsiveness of asthmatic subjects to sulfur dioxide. Am. Rev. Respir. Dis. 122:873-878.

Sheppard, D., Nadel, J.A., Boushey, H.A. (1981c). Inhibition of sulfur dioxide-induced bronchoconstriction by disodium cromoglycate in asthmatic subjects. Am. Rev. Respir. Dis. 124:257-259.

Sheppard, D., Epstein, J., Bethel, R.A., Nadel, J.A., Boushey, H.A. (1983a). Tolerance to sulfur dioxide-induced bronchoconstriction in subjects with asthma. Environ. Res. 30:412-419.

Sheppard, D., Eschenbacher, W.L., Boushey, H.A., Bethel, R.A. (1983b). Magnitude of the interaction between the bronchomotor effects of sulfur dioxide and those of dry (cold) air. Physiologist 26:A-23, Abst.

Silverman, F., Folinsbee, L.J., Bernard, J. (1976). Pulmonary function changes in ozones - interaction of concentration and ventilation. J. Appl. Physiol. 41:859-864.

Silverman, P.S., Shephard, R.J., Folinsbee, L.J. (1977). Effect of physical activity on lung responses to acute ozone exposure. Proc. 4th Intl. Clean Air Congress, pp. 15-19.

Sim, V.M. and Pattle, R.E. (1957). Effects of possible smog irritants on human subjects. JAMA 175:1908-1913.

Snell, R.E. and Luchsinger, P.C. (1969). Effects of sulfur dioxide
on expiratory flow rates and total respiratory resistance in
normal human subjects. Arch. Environ. Health. 10:175-178.

Speizer, F.E. and Frank, N.R. (1966). A comparison in pulmonary
flow resistance in health volunteers acutely exposed to SO_2 by
mouth and by nose. Br. J. Ind. Med. 23:75-79.

Stewart, R.D., Petersen, J.E., Baretta, E.D., Bachand, R.,
Husko, M., Herman, A. (1970). Experimental human exposure to
carbon monoxide. Arch. Environ. Health 21:154-156.

Stewart, R.D. (1975). The effect of carbon monoxide on humans.
Annu. Rev. Pharmacol. 409-424.

Vogel, J.A., Gleser, M.A., Wheeler, R.C., Whitten, B. (1972a).
Carbon monoxide and physical work capacity. Arch. Environ.
Health 24:198-203.

Vogel, J.A. and Gleser, M.A. (1972b). Effect of carbon monoxide
transfer during exercise. J. Appl. Physiol. 32:234-239.

Vorona, R.D., Folinsbee, L.J., Prince, J.M., Horstman, D.H. (1986).
Sustained arterial hypoxemia during prolonged heavy exercise
by trained runners. (Abst.) Fed. Proc.

Wayne, W.S., Wehrle, P.S., Carroll, R.E. (1967). Oxidant air
pollution and athletic performance. JAMA 199:151-154.

Wright, G.R., Jewezk, S., Onrot, J., Tomlinson, P., Shephard, R.
(1975). Carbon monoxide in the urban atmosphere. Arch.
Environ. Health 30:123-129.

Young, W.A., Shaw, D.B., Bates, D.V. (1964). Effect of low
concentrations of ozone on pulmonary function. J. Appl.
Physiol. 19:765-768.

Discussion

Dr Lloyd, Edinburgh, Scotland
It is sometimes difficult to separate different environmental
factors. You reported a relationship between SO_2 levels and excess
deaths in London in the winter of 1953, but I recall that that
period was also associated with extreme cold. Could this have been
a factor in the higher than expected mortality rates observed?

Dr Raven, Texas, USA
Most of the deaths seen during this period were due to exacerbation
of bronchitis and emphysema and I do not think that cold was a
factor. These mortality patterns have not been observed since the
Clean Air Act was introduced so it seems likely that pollution was
the major factor.

Dr Prior, Vancouver, Canada
Does it matter which lung function test is used to assess
impairment of function?

Dr Raven
No: the effect on maximal mid-expiratory flow is similar to that
on FEV_1.

Dr Prior
Aerosols are available, at least in Canada, which have an atropine-like action and I wonder whether these have been used prophylactically.

Dr Raven
These aerosols have not yet been approved by the FDA, but they are looking at them. So far, however, we have no data as to their possible effectiveness.

Dr Harrison, Farnborough, England
Do you have any data relating to the effects of air pollution on the performance of top-class athletes?

Dr Raven
Some studies were made on elite cyclists just prior to the 1984 Olympic Games. The cyclists exercised at ventilation of over $120 l.min^{-1}$ for 1 1/2 hours at comparatively low levels of O_3 (0.12ppm) and showed significant decrements in performance after exposure. This was the reason for the construction of the cycling velodrome well away from the polluted areas. There is however only limited evidence due to reluctance of top class athletes to volunteer for these studies.

Dr Loucks, California, USA
Is there any evidence to support the idea of adaptation to these pollutants?

Dr Raven
Yes: Haldane, Krogh and others realised that adaptation took place when they used CO for pulmonary diffusion tests on a daily basis. They found that they could tolerate levels as high as 500ppm; however, if they went on vacation, they found significant effects when they returned. Cigarette smokers, of course, also adapt to CO; they show polycythaemia and elevations of 2,3-DPG. There is less evidence for an adaptation to SO_2 concentration, airway resistance is maximal within 10 minutes of exposure. There is, of course, a very large variability between individuals in sensitivity, with asthmatics being particularly affected.

Circadian rhythms and exercise

T. REILLY

1. Introduction

Stability is a rare feature of nature as most living things exhibit
fluctuations in their states. These changes may be regular,
recurring on a cyclical and predictable basis. The focus of this
review is on circadian variation or rhythmic changes in humans
within each solar day. Clocks are probably ubiquitous in mammalian
tissue and circadian rhythms are not completely isolated from
other time structures with different periodicities (Simpson, 1976).
Circadian rhythms are found at levels ranging from cell division
to whole-body activity and so may have implications for exercise
and sports performance.

Circadian rhythms usually form a sinusoid with a period of about
24 hours (Fig. 1). The changes can also reflect the sharp contrast
between night and day. Circadian rhythms found in humans tend to
be a mixture of endogenous or self-sustained causes and exogenous
factors. The internally structured rhythms implicate a biological
timing mechanism, evidence favouring the cells of the supra-
chiasmatic nucleus of the hypothalamus as the clock. In some
animals a direct link between the retina and the supra- chiasmatic
nucleus has been shown (Minors and Waterhouse, 1981). Important
time-keeping functions are also attributed to the pineal gland,
which is sensitive to changes in light during the solar day. Other
external influences which give shape to many diurnal rhythms
include temperature, social factors, physical activity and diet.
The discovery of local time-keepers, in heart cells and skeletal
muscle for example, suggest that there is a family of oscillators,
probably arranged in hierarchical order. Whether individual rhythms
are endogenous or exogenous can be established by experimental
procedures (Conroy and Mills, 1970): the innate rhythms do not
rigidly adhere to environmental cycles. This separation may be
important if the rhythm is to be manipulated in preparing for
sports performance. The curve of body temperature (Fig. 2) is
regarded as the fundamental variable in circadian rhythmicity,
conforming to the criteria of an internally structured cycle
(Colquhoun, 1971). Many types of human performance closely follow
this curve: most activities are especially favoured by the higher
temperatures in the evening. The performance rhythms are also
linked to the state of biological arousal which affects the
readiness for intense physical efforts: a low state of arousal
predisposes towards errors and increased injury risk. Though

arousal is influenced by body temperature, its cyclical form throughout the day is mainly due to a rhythm in sleep-wakefulness which is independent of that in temperature (Minors and Waterhouse, 1981).

There are many potential applications of circadian rhythmicity to exercise. The influence of time of day on industrial tasks has been thoroughly researched, yet studies in sporting contexts are not so prolific. In experimental work on exercise, the need to control for time of day when measurements are taken is generally accepted. The potency of many drugs is time-of-day dependent: though chronopharmacology is a productive area of research, its principles have not been carefully examined in treatment of sports injuries. Athletes are creatures of habit and so are acutely aware of departures from their usual time of training or competing. The existence of circadian rhythms is most obvious when they are perturbed by loss or disruption of sleep. Crossing time zones causes desynchronisation of a multitude of biological rhythms, leading to disorientation until all adjust completely to the new environment.

In the sections that follow the implications of human circadian rhythms for exercise are considered. The evidence for existence of rhythms in field conditions is treated first before progressing to review laboratory studies of acute reactions to exercise. Physical and psychological factors are included before finally considering the effects of desynchronisation.

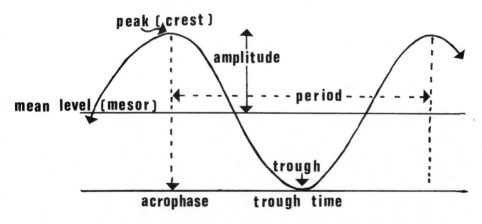

Figure 1. The form and characteristics of typical circadian rhythm.

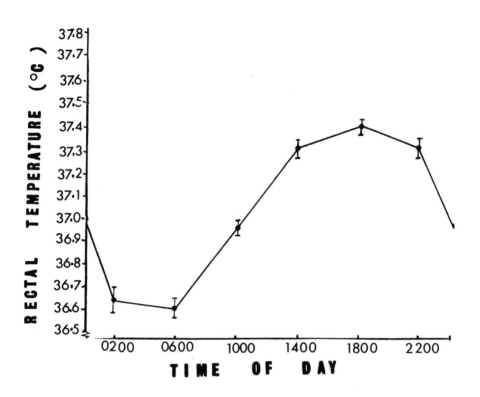

Figure 2. The circadian rhythm in rectal temperature.

2. Sports performance

Major sports contests are not evenly distributed over a
sufficiently broad span of the day to yield conclusions about the
optimal time for competing. In practice there seems to be a
preference for evening contests. All the World Records for running
distances from 1500m to 5000m during the 1985 season were set
between 1900 and 2300 hours. Prior to the javelin throw by Fatima
Whitbread at the 1986 European Championships, the last World Record
in track and field to be set in the morning was by shot-putter
Charles Fonville over 30 years ago. Most of the best athletic
performances at the French national championships were reported to
occur in the afternoon (Laporte, 1982). Heats and qualifying
events frequently take place in the morning, championship finals
where tactics are important are usually in the afternoon while
organised record attempts are generally scheduled for the
evening. The environmental temperature is usually more favourable
to performance in the evening; besides, on hot days the mid-day
peak in ambient temperature is best eschewed to reduce heat
stress. Consequently any comparison of morning, afternoon and
evening records, even when weighted for frequency of occurrence,
may merely reflect organisational factors.

As sports performance represents a cluster of abilities which may not be encompassed by a single biological rhythm, findings may be specific to the sport in question. Analysis of French International sabre fencers showed that their best scores, as far as they related to speed and skill, were around noon (Reinberg et al., 1985). In field and court games, players may have to play tournament matches at start times ranging from 0800 to 2200 hours: the skills of these games differ from those executed in sabre fencing or track and field athletics and so may not share a common circadian cycle. Without a sensitive measure of the quality of individual performance in match-play, inferences may be invalid. Nevertheless, an underlying rhythm can be detected if the self-selected level of activity during play at different times of day is examined.

A study of 5-aside soccer play sustained for four days demonstrated that the work-rate of players varied rhythmically (Reilly and Walsh, 1981). The pace of play showed a peak at about 1800 hours and a trough at 0500-0600 hours. Feelings of fatigue were negatively correlated with levels of activity and with muscular strength. The self-paced level of exercise conformed closely to the curve in body temperature and was not obliterated by sleep deprivation. As the rhythm applies to light exercise sustained for a supra-normal period, it does not necessarily indicate psychological and biological predispositions for more intensive exercise. This requires experimental manipulation of subjects according to time of day in simulated contests.

3. Simulated contests

Study of time trials or simulated competition generally supports the existence of a time of day effect on performance. The work of Conroy and O'Brien (1974) was the first systematic study of diurnal variation in performance of sportsmen. Six runners, 3 weight-throwers and 3 oarsmen were found to do better in the evening than in the morning. Rodahl et al. (1976) found that swimmers produced faster times over 100m at 1700 hours compared with 0700 hours in 3 out of 4 strokes studied. More frequent sampling of a 5 min run showed that the variation in speed of performance agreed closely with changes in body temperature within the day (Stockton et al., 1978).

A recent study (Baxter and Reilly, 1983) of swimming 100m and 400m at 5 times of the day between 0630 and 2200 hours boosted the evidence for superior performance predispositions in the evening (Fig. 3). The times for both distances showed a linear trend, the steady improvement throughout the day being 3.5% for 100m and 2.5% for 400m. Improvement in the evening was noted even after the body temperature had begun to decline. This suggests that although the curves in performance and body temperature are close in phase, they are not necessarily causally related.

Despite their relevance to realistic conditions none of these
studies covered a complete 24 hour cycle and so the characteristics
of a rhythm could not be ascertained. There remains a question
about extrapolating results to full scale competition where
motivational and environmental circumstances may be very different.
This uncertainty also applies to discrete components of exercise
performance such as muscle function - strength, anaerobic power and
endurance - flexibility, reaction and movement time.

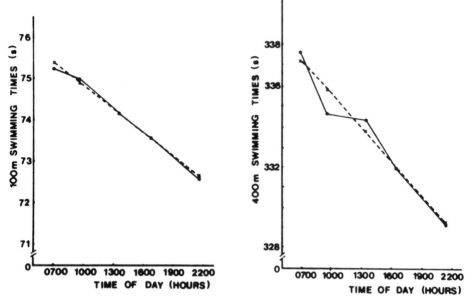

Figure 3. Performance of swimmers in 100m and 400m front crawl at
different times of day (Baxter and Reilly, 1983). The dashed line
represents values predicted by a linear trend.

4. Motor performance

There is wealth of literature on circadian variation in motor and
psychomotor performance (Colquhoun, 1971). Measures which exhibit
rhythmicity include isometric strength, simple reaction time, co-
ordination as measured by a pursuit rotor task, agility and tapping
speed. Most of these variables retain their cycles during
prolonged sleep loss. The close correlation between body
temperature and motor performance persists in shift workers during
adaptation of both rhythms to a nocturnal regimen.
    The ties between body temperature and motor performance
(Rutenfranz and Colquhoun, 1979), suggest that exercise is best
performed at the crest time of core temperature. The optimal core
and muscle temperature for exercise is about $38.3^{\circ}C$ and $40^{\circ}C$
respectively (Åstrand and Rodahl, 1977); the resting temperature is
closest to these values in the evening. Stockton et al. (1978)
reported that 12 out of 17 discrete components of sports
performance showed a significant time-of-day effect. The curves
in the tasks chosen were close in phase to that of oral temperature.

- 350 -

Faster performances at the crest time of body temperature may be linked with local temperatures in active muscle and other soft tissues. A circadian variation has been reported for joint stiffness (Wright et al., 1969); the increased resistance to motion as the joint cools should impair flexibility as well as speed of movement. A variation in trunk flexibility was found by Baxter and Reilly (1983), the trough occurring in the morning and the peak in the afternoon. The phase lead of the trunk flexibility curve over that of body temperature may be due to the onset of truncal stiffness with habitual day-time acitivity.

Although circadian influences on brief explosive efforts are small, they are nevertheless potentially significant. Analysis of standing broad jump data at six equally spaced times of day demonstrated no significant cycle until the inter-subject variability was removed (Reilly and Down, 1986). This was achieved by expressing observations as deviations from trough values before fitting a cosine function to them. The amplitude of the rhythm in the distance jumped was about 3%. The performance curve was relatively flat through the later part of the day compared to the smooth sinusoid of rectal temperature, suggesting that the jumping performance may not be entirely dependent on the temperature rhythm.

Performance in short-term exercise at unusual times of day may be hampered by a circadian variation in anaerobic power. A study of arm ergometry by Reilly and Down (1986a) failed to find a rhythm in anaerobic power or anaerobic capacity as expressed by the 30s Wingate Anaerobic Test. Subjects were well warmed up prior to exercise and were well motivated to work all-out for its duration. In such conditions the circadian variation in power production may be less than the measurement error associated with this test. The conclusion that the maximal anaerobic power of the arms is a relatively stable function which is not significantly altered by time of day leaves unexplained the biological source of rhythms in motor performance that are usually noted.

5. Resting physiological rhythms

There is evidence of rhythmicity in hormonal secretions at rest that affect metabolism and so have a potential impact during exercise. As endocrine secretions are episodic and episodes vary between individuals, the circadian rhythms reported represent the smoothed 24 hour picture of grouped data. Even then hormonal rhythms do not fit classical sinusoid patterns. The rhythm in adrenaline is stronger than that of noradrenaline, though both peak early afternoon and reach a nadir at night. The changes in adrenaline seem to have more importance for arousal than for metabolism as it has been found to correlate significantly with rifle shooting performance and negatively with self-rated fatigue (Akerstedt, 1979).

Cortisol has a large endogenous component in its dozen or so secretions during the day. Secretion seems also to be related to time of sleep onset and highest plasma concentrations are evident in the morning. The spurts of growth hormone output are most pronounced during slow wave sleep and seem unrelated to the smooth curve in metabolism which is similar in form to that of body temperature.

Impaired glucose tolerance in the afternoon (Zimmet et al., 1974) suggests the body is less well able to deal with glucose as the day progresses. This is associated with impaired insulin release and insulin resistance (Whichelow et al., 1974). Blood glucose levels tend to be lower in the morning than in the afternoon and liver glycogen is reduced after an overnight fast. Conlee et al. (1976) concluded that muscle glycogen also shows a diurnal variation: this could not be explained by their hormonal or metabolic data. There does not seem to be a consistent pattern in endocrine and metabolic rhythms that would explain why exercise performance is best in the evening.

There are also circadian rhythms in renal and circulatory functions (Conroy and Mills, 1973; Minors and Waterhouse, 1981). The changes in renal function may not be so important in exercise because of the relative shut down of blood flow to the kidneys. A rhythm in blood pressure is observed when intra-arterial measurements are made. Normally the rhythm is not apparent with sphygmomanometry (Reilly, Robinson et al., 1984). The amplitude or mean to peak change in the heart rate rhythm is about 4 beats min^{-1}: this might be important if resting pulse rate is interpreted as a sensitive index of cardiovascular status.

The rhythms in physiological functions related to metabolism are not all in phase agreement at rest, though this in itself is not evidence of independent oscillation. The heart rate tends to lead the $\dot{V}O_2$ and $\dot{V}E$ peaks which are in turn in advance of that of body temperature. The phase lead of heart rate is probably due to a mechanism intrinsic to heart cells which is independent of temperature. Calculations which assume a Q_{10} of 2.0 show that the circadian change in core temperature explains about 37% of the range observed in $\dot{V}O_2$ and 25% of that in $\dot{V}E$ (Reilly and Brooks, 1982). [When Q_{10} is 2.0, then for each 10° rise in temperature the metabolic rate increases by 100%]. The rhythm in $\dot{V}CO_2$ agrees in phase and amplitude with that of $\dot{V}O_2$. The rhythm in $\dot{V}E$ is stronger than either of these due to the increased airway resistance and a shift in CO_2 sensitivity and pulmonary diffusing capacity at night. In general the amplitudes of the rhythms are 7-11% of the mean value, except for body temperature whose amplitude is best expressed by reference to its physiological range.

6. Sub-maximal exercise

Physiological rhythms apparent at rest might be eliminated or attenuated, maintained or amplified under exercise conditions. Research reports can be marshalled to provide support for all possibilities. Much of the conflict is due to a failure to adequately control the environment and masking factors such as diet and previous activity of subjects. When these variables are considered carefully, a consistent picture begins to emerge. The rhythm in heart rate, for example, that is apparent at rest is still evident at light and moderate exercise. The consistency of its phase and amplitude has been shown for arm (Cable and Reilly, 1986) and leg exercise (Reilly and Brooks, 1982a).

If the heart rate response to submaximal exercise at different times of day is used to estimate the $\dot{V}O_2$max, it gives the erroneous impression that maximal aerobic power is best at night. This does not represent a true variation in $\dot{V}O_2$max. The calculation of the physical working capacity at a heart rate of 170 beats min^{-1} (PWC$_{170}$) would have a similar source of variance.

The rhythm in heart rate is not paralleled by the $\dot{V}O_2$ and $\dot{V}E$ throughout the range of submaximal work rates. This seems to apply to arm exercise as well as leg exercise. In a longitudinal study of one subject (Reilly and Brooks, 1982), the rhythm in $\dot{V}O_2$ was gradually lost as the exercise intensity increased. The rhythm at a moderate exercise level was explained by variations in body weight. No circadian variation during moderate exercise was found for $\dot{V}CO_2$ or the respiratory exchange ratio. This suggests that choice of substrate as fuel for exercising muscle is not determined by time of day, once diet, environmental temperature and activity are controlled.

The most robust rhythm seems to be that of $\dot{V}E$ which is amplified at light and moderate exercise intensities. This is due to a combination of autonomic and endocrine mechanisms, narrower airways increasing the resistance to breathing at cool body temperatures. There is also a fall in pulmonary diffusing capacity during the day (Cinkotai and Thompson, 1966). Even when $\dot{V}E$ is expressed as ventilation equivalent of oxygen the rhythm is clearly evident (Fig. 4). This may partly explain the mild dyspnoea sometimes associated with training in the early morning. At vigorous work rates, the ventilation threshold - which indicates the point where ventilation begins to increase disproportionately to $\dot{V}O_2$ - does not vary with time of day (Reilly and Brooks 1982a).

As temperature in soft tissues around the joints can affect their resistance to the joint's action, this could alter the energy expenditure. The muscular efficiency - which represents the mechanical work done as a percent of its energy cost - can be calculated as gross or net efficienty. Where more than one steady rate of exercise is performed the delta efficiency can be computed. For a given exercise mode the muscular efficiency is affected by the work-rate and the mode of calculation rather than by time of day (Reilly and Brooks, 1982). Nor does the greater joint viscosity at night significantly affect the time to attain 'steady state' metabolic conditions during exercise (Reilly, 1982).

In summary the heart rate response to submaximal exercise does vary with time of day reflecting the circadian rhythm at rest and is unaffected by any circadian change in plasma volume. The rhythm in $\dot{V}E$ is discernible in submaximal exercise, even as $\dot{V}E/\dot{V}O_2$. The $\dot{V}O_2$ rhythm gradually fades as the exercise intensity is raised. Nor is there a rhythm in muscular efficiency or in the choice of substrate by active muscles. Consequently it is necessary to look at maximal physiological functions in the attempt to explain circadian variations in exercise performance.

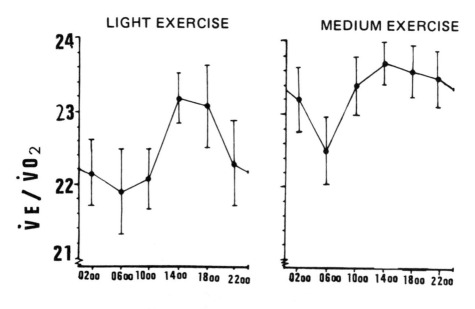

TIME OF DAY (hours)

Figure 4. The rhythm in the ventilation equivalent of oxygen at light and medium exercise levels (Reilly, 1982).

7. Maximal physiological functions

In attributing maximal values to measurements the question arises as to whether the ceiling of physiological capacity was realised during the exercise test. Consequently, recognised criteria are applied when assessing $\dot{V}O_2$max. Data collected during graded exercise to volitional exhaustion may merely reflect the reluctance of subjects to work at $\dot{V}O_2$max at night-time. For a well trained individual with a body weight of about 70kg, the normal amplitude of the $\dot{V}O_2$ rhythm at rest would be less than 0.5% of the mean maximal value. It is difficult to pick this up against the background of biological variation and measurement error associated with $\dot{V}O_2$max. It is hardly surprising, therefore, that the most carefully conducted studies fail to detect a circadian variation in $\dot{V}O_2$max. Faria and Drummond (1983) used twelve different times of day and duplicate measurements at each time point. Reilly and Brooks (1982, 1982a) used a longitudinal design to eliminate variability between subjects as well as a cross-sectional approach: the coefficient of variation of $\dot{V}O_2$max was 2.9%. Both research groups concluded that $\dot{V}O_2$max is a stable function, independent of time of day. This is in sharp contrast to the value predicted from sub-maximal heart rate (Fig.5), demonstrating an error in estimating $\dot{V}O_2$max not usually recognised.

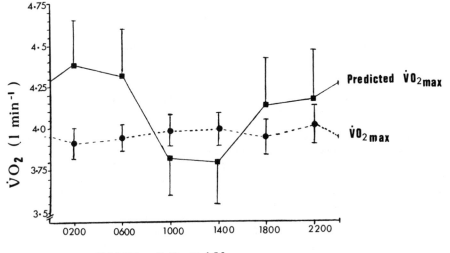

Figure 5. The $\dot{V}O_2$max estimated from heart rate response to sub-maximal exercise differs from the $\dot{V}O_2$max measured at 6 times of day.

Similarly it seems that the circadian rhythm in $\dot{V}E$ apparent during light and moderate exercise, disappears under maximal aerobic conditions. In arm exercise the highest metabolic measurements do not generally demonstrate a plateau and are referred to as peak rather than maximal values. In a study of arm ergometry the $\dot{V}O_2$ peak, $\dot{V}E$ peak and highest heart rate did demonstrate a circadian rhythm, the highest values being observed close to the crest time of rectal temperature (Cable and Reilly, 1986). The result reflected a rhythm in the total work performed in the incremental arm-exercise test to exhaustion.

The maximal heart rate does consistently show an influence of time of day (Reilly, Robinson et al., 1984). The rhythm is similar in phase to that seen at rest and submaximal exercise but is reduced in amplitude. This is compatible with expectations of any biological function as it approaches the ceiling of its physiological range. The rhythm may reflect a thermogenic as well as metabolic influence and may partly be due to altered sympathetic

drive. It is not reflected in cardiac output which in the study of
Davies and Sargeant (1975) showed no circadian variation.
Physiological variables have been examined post-exercise,
especially for short periods after graded ergometry tests to
exhaustion. The excess oxygen consumption for 3 min following a
$\dot{V}O_2$max exercise protocol was found to be invariant with time of
day (Reilly and Brooks, 1982). The circadian rhythm in heart rate
is evident soon after maximal exercise ceases (Reilly, Robinson et
al., 1984). Fitness indices such as the Harvard Test Score could
therefore have an error as large as 5% due to the time of day the
test is performed.

8. Thermoregulation

Body temperature may impose a limit to endurance performance,
especially if the exercise is conducted in the heat. During
strenuous exercise the cardiac output serves a thermoregulatory
function by distributing blood to the skin for cooling. This may
compromise blood flow to the active muscles but will not
necessarily do so if cardiac output is sub-maximal. There is no
compelling reason to suppose that the highest core temperature
that can be tolerated without risk of injury does vary with time
of day. Most guidelines for avoiding heat stress operate
implicitly or explicitly on the basis of absolute core temperature
values for the stages of heat illness. This would mean that the
margin from resting baseline to the risk threshold is about
$0.5°C$ greater in the morning than in the afternoon. This
supports the argument for starting marathon races in the morning
rather than in the afternoon in hot climates, which is based on
the lower environmental heat stress in the morning. In cold and
wet conditions a morning start would place the slower performers at
increased risk of hypothermia.
  Core temperatures of marathon runners often exceed the optimal
level suggested by Åstrand and Rodahl (1977). One advantage of
starting sustained exercise at a sub-optimal core temperature is
that the onset of heat stress is retarded and the overall strain on
thermoregulatory mechanisms is reduced. Experimental evidence
supporting this view was provided by Hessemer and co-workers (1984).
Pre-cooling oesophogeal temperature by $0.4°C$ and mean skin
temperature by $4.5°C$ before 60 min of submaximal exercise produced
a 6.8% overall increase in work-rate compared with control conditions.
  The circadian variation in core temperature during exercise
represents a fixed thermal load superimposed on the resting
baseline temperature. The rhythm in rectal temperature apparent at
rest persists in phase and amplitude at different levels of
exercise. Data of Brooks and Reilly (1984) displayed closely
related cyclical changes in rectal and skin temperatures. The time
course of skin temperature changes varied with the location and the
rhythm in the exercising limb tended to disappear during exercise.
  The cyclical rise and fall in core temperature represent a
combination of heat loss and heat gain mechanisms. If the change
in skin temperature was due solely to changes in heat loss, then
skin and core temperatures should be mirror images. Circadian
variation in metabolism implicates heat gain mechanisms in the

nexus causing the rhythm in core temperature. The peak of adrenergic activity which would cause increased vasoconstriction and promote a rise in core temperature occurs about mid-day or early in the afternoon. In warming up after experimental cold immersion, blood flow to the skin is greater in the morning than in the afternoon (Hildebrandt, 1974). The threshold for onset of sweating and forearm blood flow has been shown to be higher at 1600 and 2000 hours compared to 2400 and 0400 hours (Stephenson et al., 1984). All these observations are consistent with the conclusion that it is the control of body temperature rather than the loss or gain of heat that varies in a circadian fashion.

9. Perception of effort

A variation in the subjective reaction to exercise could conceivably explain why performance is generally better in the evening than in the morning. The perception of effort does not seem to vary at light exercise loads up to 150W, though the slope of the relationship between heart rate and perceived exertion does change with time of day (Reilly, Robinson et al., 1984). Faria and Drummond (1982) obtained ratings of exertion at treadmill running speeds eliciting heart rates of 130, 150 and 170 beats min^{-1}. As the heart rate response to a fixed submaximal exercise intensity is lowest at night, it follows that more exercise can be performed at a given heart rate at that time. The higher subjective ratings reported at night may have been due to the work-rate and not an inherent variation in effort perception. Ilmarinen and co-workers (1980) also examined the circadian variation in perceived exertion and reported a significant result only at one submaximal load (245W), although several lower exercise levels were rated. It is possible that a circadian variation in the rating of exertion is evident only at high steady rates of ergometry. This is supported by findings of Reilly and Baxter (1983) whose subjects first cycled at 40% $\dot{V}O_2$ for 5 min before cycling to exhaustion at 95% $\dot{V}O_2$max at two different times of day, 0630 hours and 2200 hours. There was no difference in perceived exertion with time of day at either work-rate, although the higher work-rate was sustained for longer in the evening.

A standard weight-training circuit is felt to be more severe in the morning than in the evening (Wilby et al., 1985). An alternative paradigm employs light work-bouts every 4 hours for 24 hours but this may include a cumulative fatigue effect. With this protocol exercise was rated harder at night time, and perceived exertion was marginally elevated in the afternoon (Reilly and Young, 1982). This may represent a sub-harmonic in the circadian rhythm of biological arousal, which is sometimes reflected in a post-lunch dip in performance (Rutenfranz and Colquhoun, 1979).

As variations in aerobic power cannot explain the better performance predisposition in the evening compared to the morning, and most exercise contests are performed at a high fractional utilization of aerobic power rather than at $\dot{V}O_2$max, the answer may lie in motivation rather than metabolic factors. This was tested by comparing time to exhaustion at two different times of

day cycling at 95% $\dot{V}O_2$max (Reilly and Baxter, 1983). Total
work done before desisting was 41% greater at 2200 hours than at
0630 hours and higher blood lactate levels were produced. A
significant negative correlation between endurance time and
perceived exertion was due to the less fit subjects showing
greater distress at exhaustion and desisting earlier. As the
subjects were more prepared to sustain a fixed level of subjective
discomfort in the evening the results did not strictly correspond
to the conventional arousal model (Martens, 1974).

10. Shrinkage

There are physical as well as physiological and psychological
factors that vary with time of day and that have implications for
exercise. The day-night cycle of activity and rest provides an
alternation of weight bearing associated with the upright posture
and recovery while sleeping. Weight bearing imposes compressive
loading on the spine and leads to a loss of disc height due to
expulsion of water through the disc wall. This loss of height is
known as shrinkage and with apropriate apparatus is reflected in
measurements of changes in stature. The spinal shrinkage during
the day is about 1% of stature (Reilly, Tyrrell et al., 1984).
    Although the data illustrated in Fig. 6 conform to a cosine
curve, a power function best fits the shrinkage during the day,
the rate of loss declining as the discs stiffen. Shrinkage is
reversed at night while recumbent, the rate of regain in height
being greater in the first part of the night's sleep. It is
possible that an endogenous rhythm in stature is reinforced or
masked by the changes in posture and spinal loading between day
time and night time. Observations on the rate of reversal of
shrinkage lead to the conclusion that circadian variation in
stature is largely attributable to spinal loading (Reilly,
Tyrrell et al., 1984).
    The loss of disc height could render the spine more vulnerable
to injury as its stiffness increases, so making lifting and similar
activities more hazardous as stature recedes throughout the day.
As loss of disc height causes changes in the dynamic response
characteristics of the disc, there is a time of day effect on the
shrinkage resulting from a fixed exercise regimen. Wilby et al.
(1985) compared the losses of height with a 20 min circuit weight-
training regimen at 0730 and 2300 hours. The disc was a more
effective shock absorber in the morning when shrinkage was 5.4 mm
compared to a value of 4.3 mm in the evening. This greater
stiffness is partly compensated for by greater back muscle strength
in the evening. A high negative correlation was found between back
strength and height lost, the greater the muscle strength the less
height that was lost.
    The habitual activity level and the postures engaged in can
affect the amount of shrinkage during the day. Intervention
procedures for unloading the spine prior to heavy physical training
in the evening have been advocated. An example is the Fowler
position at rest with the trunk supine and the legs raised to rest
on a bench. Gravity inversion systems have also proved effective
(Troup et al., 1985).

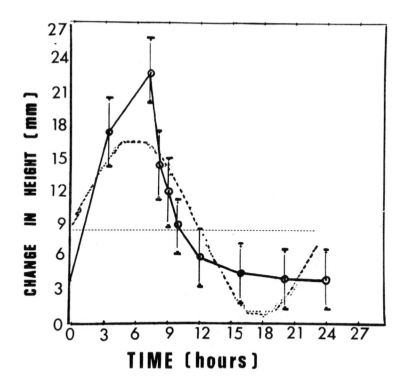

Figure 6. The circadian variation in stature (Reilly, Tyrrell and
Troup, 1984). The midnight baseline is set at 3.5mm and variation
is shown as changes from the baseline. The unbroken line indicates
observed mean values (n = 8): the dashed line is the cosinor curve
fitted to the data.

11. Desynchronisation

Biological rhythms may reflect the operation of multiple
oscillators and so the different rhythms are not all in phase.
Apparently healthy subjects may commonly show an internal
desynchronisation of a set of circadian rhythms. Competitive
athletes with internally synchronised rhythms generally have a
better chance of winning than individuals with an internal
desynchronisation. This was corroborated in a study of French
fencers competing at the Los Angeles Olympics (Reinberg et al.,
1985).
    Circadian rhythms are externally desynchronised if the
individual switches to a nocturnal work schedule or rapidly crosses
a series of time zones. Physiological rhythms affected include
body temperature, the sleep-wake cycle, pulse rate, ventilation,
arterial pressure, diuresis and excretion of electrolytes (Winget
et al., 1984). The resulting disorientation can impair

performances of athletes on busy competitive schedules until the major rhythms adjust to the new time zone. As about 20% of workers in technologically advanced countries are on some form of shift system and this number inevitably includes sports participants, they also will suffer from disturbed ryhthms.

Wright et al. (1983) showed that cardiovascular functions and perceived exertion during submaximal and maximal exercise were impaired by a six hour time zone change five days after the phase shift. Sprint and endurance running were adversely affected two-three days after the change and some muscular strength measures were depressed for five days. Empirical data on runners crossing the Atlantic support the practice of allowing one day to adjust for each time zone crossed. Data on pistol shooters with a maximal time shift suggested that complex skills need longer to adjust (Antal, 1975).

Adjustment to westward travel tends to be faster than for travelling in an easterly direction. This probably reflects the fact that in 'free-wheeling' conditions where the major environmental time-givers are absent, the period is lengthened to 25-27 hours. Performance of psychomotor and athletic skills tend to suffer more following eastward than after westward flights (Winget et al., 1985).

There are recognised individual differences in the phasing of rhythms. Introverts show an earlier rise in core temperature than extroverts and their rhythms peak earlier in the afternoon. This earlier curve is found also in many measures of human performance (Rutenfranz and Colquhoun, 1979). Differences in behaviour profiles are referred to as 'morning' and 'evening' types. Morning types are phase advanced compared to evening types and tend to suffer worse from night work and day sleep.

Athletes are unlikely to endure shift work systems well because these would disrupt their habitual training routines. They necessarily will encounter jet-lag when travelling to international competitions. Ameliorative measures to cope with the disturbances that are apropriate for business personnel may not be suitable. Ehret and Scanlon (1983) proposed a dietary regimen which would accelerate adaptations to a new time zone. This incorporated alternations of feeding and fasting which would be unacceptable to athletes preparing for impending contests. The recommended use of methylxanthines to aid adaptation would be unacceptable for similar reasons. Chronobiotic drugs facilitate adaptation by shifting the phases of the rhythms in the direction of the time zone at destination but the drugs must be administered at the right time of day. Use of orally ingested melatonin to reduce or eliminate effects of jet-lag may have value in the future (Arendt et al., 1986).

Altering bed-time for a few days before departure and for a few days after arrival can minimise the disruptive effects of travelling across time zones. The changes in sleeping should correspond with the direction of intended travel, so that the change of circadian rhythms is smooth. Sleep rather than meal times or social activity is the synchroniser of the rhythm: prolonged naps at the new location should be avoided as these would operate against adaptation by anchoring the rhythm at its previous phase (Minors and Waterhouse, 1981a). Anchoring circadian rhythms is a tactic used by non-sports personnel regularly crossing time zones: its use by athletes would be practical when they fly in for single contests but this might be counteracted by the effects of travel fatigue.

12. Ultradian rhythms

Circadian rhythms are typically envisaged as a single sinusoid with a period of 24 hours. Chronobiologists have also observed cycles that recur within each day and these are known as ultradian. The most common has a cycle of 90 min and is evident in the electroencephalograms (EEG). Appearance of sleep-like EEG waves in the afternoon may be a relic of the sleep of infancy and vindicate the customary siesta of Hispanic cultures.

An afternoon drop in mental performance tests has been reported by Rutenfranz and Colquhoun (1979). This is referred to as the 'post-lunch' dip, though it persists in the absence of lunch. This sub-harmonic may be a function of the habitual activity during the day. When a light exercise bout was successively presented every 4 hours of a 24 hour period, perceived exertion was highest at night and showed a slight rise in the afternoon (Reilly and Young, 1982). This is contrary to observations of the trend in perceived exertion when the subject has one short steady-rate work bout to perform. Cognitive functions, when superimposed on a light exercise work load, show a similar post-lunch dip in performance.

It can be supposed that a nap could counteract the fall in arousal underlying any sub-harmonic in the performance curve. There has been no substantive research concerned with the refreshing effects of napping on subsequent exercise performance. A nap taken early in the day should be better than a late afternoon nap; the latter would contain the more slow-wave sleep and the less REM sleep and would take longer to arouse from after waking. Athletes would be expected to have the mental drive to overcome this de-arousal. The advocation of a nap would depend on its interaction with such factors as the timing of the contest and pre-competitive meal-time: most importantly the personal preference of the athlete must be acknowledged.

13. Conclusion

All-out exercise performance does seem to show circadian variation. Although the optimal time varies with the type of activity, in general the variation is in phase with changes in body temperature and is usually about 3%. Similar cycles are noted in motor and psychomotor performances. Many physiological mechanisms which could account for this do not seem to operate differentially with time of day when physiological capacities are examined. Endogenous metabolic, respiratory and endocrine rhythms fade when exercise becomes strenuous whilst heart rate and body temperature rhythms are evident at maximal exercise. Motivation does exert an influence, tending to tolerate the discomfort of exercise better in the evening. In sports events where thermoregulatory functions can limit exercise performance, such as marathon running in the heat, competitions may be best arranged for morning, in contrast to evening schedules which are recommended for the majority of sports. Plans for optimising performance in the afternoon or evening should allow recovery from spinal shrinkage and ultradian falls in arousal. The clearest demonstration of the importance of circadian rhythms in exercise is when they are desynchronised, either by jet-lag or by nocturnal work schedules. It is possible to ease the disruptions by appropriate behavioural changes.

References

Akerstedt, T. (1979). Altered sleep/wake patterns and circadian rhythms. Acta Physiologica Scandinavica, Suppl. 469.

Antal, L.C. (1975). The effects of the changes of the circadian body rhythm on the sports shooter. British Journal of Sports Medicine 9:9-12.

Arendt, J., Aldhous, M. and Marks, V. (1986). Alleviation of jet lag by melatonin: preliminary resuls of controlled double blind trial. British Medical Journal 292:1170.

Åstrand, P.O. and Rodahl, K. (1977). Textbook of Work Physiology. New York: McGraw-Hill.

Baxter, C. and Reilly, T. (1983). Influence of time of day on all-out swimming. British Journal of Sports Medicine 17:122-127.

Brooks, G.A. and Reilly, T. (1984). Thermoregulatory responses to exercise at different times of day. Journal of Physiology 354:99P.

Cable, T. and Reilly, T. (1986). Influence of circadian rhythms on arm exercise. Journal of Human Movement Studies, 12 (in press).

Cinkotai, F.F. and Thompson, M.L. (1966). Diurnal variation in pulmonary diffusing capacity for carbon monoxide. Journal of Applied Physiology 21:535-541.

Colquhoun, W.P. (1971). Biological Rhythms and Human Performance. New York Academic Press.

Conlee, R.K., Rennie, M.J. and Winder, W.W. (1976). Skeletal muscle glycogen content: diurnal variation and effects of fasting. American Journal of Physiology 231:614-618.

Conroy, R.T.W.L. and Mills, J.N. (1970). Human Circadian Rhythms. London Churchill.

Conroy, R.T.W.L. and O'Brien, M. (1974). Diurnal variation in athletic performance. Journal of Applied Physiology 236:51P.

Davies, C.T.M. and Sargeant, A.J. (1975). Circadian variation in physiological responses to exercise on a stationary bicycle ergometer. British Journal of Industrial Medicine. 32:110-114.

Ehret, C.F. and Scanlon, L.W. (1983). Overcoming Jet-Lag. New York: Berkeley Publishing Corporation.

Faria, I.E. and Drummond, B.J. (1982). Circadian changes in resting heart rate and body temperature, maximal oxygen consumption and perceived exertion. Ergonomics 25:381-386.

Hessemer, V., Langusch, D., Bruck, K., Bodeker, R.K. and Breidenbach, T. (1984). Effects of slightly lowered body temperatures on endurance performance in humans. Journal of Applied Physiology: Respiratory Environmental and Exercise Physiology 57:1731-1737.

Hildebrandt, G. (1974). Circadian variation in thermoregulatory response in man. In Chronobiology (edited by L.E. Scheving, F. Halberg and J.E. Pauly), pp. 234-240. Tokyo: Igakashoin Ltd.

Ilmarinen, J., Ilmarinen, R., Korhonen, O. and Nurminen, M. (1980). Circadian variation of physiological functions related to physical work capacity. Scandinavian Journal of Work and Environmental Health 6:112-122.

Laporte, G. (1982). Chronobiologie et sport. Medicin et Sport 56:248-252.

Martens, R. (1974). Arousal and motor performance. Exercise and Sport Sciences Reviews 2:155-188.

Minors, D.S. and Waterhouse, J.M. (1981a). Anchor sleep as a synchroniser of abnormal routines. International Journal of Chronobiology 7:165-188.

Reilly, T. (1982). Circadian variation in ventilatory and metabolic adaptations to submaximal exercise. British Journal of Sports Medicine 16:115-116.

Reilly, T. and Baxter, C. (1983). Influence of time of day on rections to cycling at a fixed high intensity. British Journal of Sports Medicine 17:128-130.

Reilly, T. and Brooks, G.A. (1982). Investigation of circadian rhythms in metabolic responses to exercise. Ergonomics 25:1093-1197.

Reilly, T. and Brooks, G.A. (1982a). Circadian constancy in work stress indices and physiological capacity. Ergonomics 25:329-330.

Reilly, T. and Down, A. (1986). Circadian variation in the standing broad jump. Perceptual and Motor Skills 62:830

Reilly, T. and Down, A. (1986a). Time of day and performance of all-out arm ergometry. In Kinanthropometry III (edited by T. Reilly, J. Watkins and J. Borms). pp. 296-300 London: E. and F.N. Spon.

Reilly, T. and Walsh, T.J. (1981). Physiological, psychological and performance measures during an endurance record for 5-a-side soccer play. British Journal of Sports Medicine 15:122-128.

Reilly, T. and Young, K. (1982). Digit summation, perceived exertion and time of day under submaximal exercise conditions. In Proceedings 20th International Congress of Applied Psychology (Edinburgh) pp/344.

Reilly, T., Robinson, G. and Minors, D.S. (1984). Some circulatory responses to exercise at different times of day. Medicine and Science in Sports and Exercise 16:477-482.

Reilly, T. Tyrrell, A. ans Troup, J.D.G. (1984). Circadian variation in human stature. Chronobiology International 1:121-126.

Reinberg, A., Proux, S., Bartal, J.P., Levi, F. and Bicakova-Rocher, A. (1985). Circadian rhythms in competitive sabre fencers: internal desynchronisation and performance. Chronobiology International 2:195-201.

Rodahl, A., O'Brien, M. and Firth, P.G.R. (1976) Diurnal variation in performance of competitive swimmers. Journal of Sports Medicine and Physical Fitness 16:72-76.

Rutenfranz, J. and Colquhoun, W.F. (1979). Circadian rhythms in
human performance. Scandinavian Journal of Work and
Environmental Health 5:167-177.

Simpson, H.W. (1976). A new perspective: chronobiochemistry.
Essays in Medical Biochemistry 2:115-187.

Stephenson, L.A., Wenger, C.B., O'Donovan, B.H. and Nadel, E.R.
(1984). Circadian rhythm in sweating and cutaneous blood flow.
American Journal of Physiology 246:R321-R324.

Stockton, I.D., Reilly, T., Sanderson, F.H. and Walsh, T.J. (1978).
Investigations of circadian rhythms in selected components of
sports performance. Communication to the Society of Sports
Sciences. (Crewe and Alsager College).

Troup, J.D.G., Reilly, T., Eklund, J.A.E. and Leatt, P. (1985).
Changes in stature with spinal loading and their relation to the
perception of exertion or discomfort. Stress Medicine 1:303-307.

Whichelow, M.J., Sturge, R.A., Keen, H., Jarret, R.J., Stimmler, L.
and Grainger, S. (1974). Diurnal variation in response to
intravenous glucose. British Medical Journal 1:485-488.

Wilby, J., Linge, K., Reilly, T. and Troup, J.D.G. (1985).
Circadian variation in effects of weight-training on spinal
shrinkage. British Journal of Sports Medicine 19:236.

Winget, C.M., De Roshia, C.W. and Holley, D.C. (1985). Circadian
rhythms and athletic performance. Medicine and Science in
Sports and Exercise 17:498-516.

Winget, C.M., De Roshia, C.W., Markley, C.L. and Holley, D.C.
(1984). A review of human physiological and performance changes
associated with desynchronosis of biological rhythms.
Aviation, Space and Environmental Medicine 55:1085-1096.

Wright, J.E., Vogel, J.A., Sampson, J.T., Knapik, J.J., Patton,
J.F. and Daniels, W.L. (1983). Effects of travel across time
zones (jet-lag) on exercise capacity and performance.
Aviation, Space and Environmental Medicine 54:132-137.

Wright, V., Dawson, D. and Longfield, M.D. (1969). Joint stiffness
-its characterisation and significance. Biology and Medicine
in Engineering 4:8-14.

Zimmet, P.Z., Wall, J.R., Rome. L., Stimmler, L. and Jarrett, R.J.
(1974). Diurnal variation in glucose tolerance: associated
changes in plasma insulin, growth hormone and non-esterified
fatty acids. British Medical Journal 2:485-488.

Discussion

Dr Raven, Texas, USA

What happens when you change time zones? Also, many athletes are
changing rhythms, for example by training hard in the morning and
evening and perhaps sleeping in between; does this have any
implications for performance?

Dr Reilly, Liverpool, England

Little information is currently available on the effects of phase
shifts on athletes. The time course of changes in the rhythm for
variables such as rectal temperature can give some information.
The rhythm in rectal temperature is resistant to change and
requires about one day per time zone to adapt. Athletes who train

twice a day introduce masking factors so that the endogenous rhythm in whatever function becomes less clear. There may be residual effects of morning training on evening performance but athletes would not normally train <u>hard</u> on the morning of an evening contest. It is also worth noting that there is a rhythm in arousal levels which is very much dependent on the sleep-wake cycle. If subjects are placed in an isolation chamber for prolonged periods, the rhythms begin to freewheel and after about 15 days, core temperature establishes a rhythm with a period of about 25 hours; the sleep-wakefulness pattern desynchronises from that and adjusts to a period of about 27 hours. This illustrates that the various biological rhythms adapt at different rates to phase shifts.

Dr Raven
It is worth noting that the risk of sudden cardiac death during exercise is greater in the morning than at night. How do you reconcile this fact with the recommendation that marathons should be run in the morning?

Dr Reilly
There are of course qualifications to that recommendation and I would stress that it applies to warm conditions and fit athletes seeking to achieve their best possible performance.

Dr Harrison, Farnborough, England
There is some evidence that people sweat more during exercise in the morning than in the afternoon. Nadel also has some results showing that temperature is higher during steady state exercise in the afternoon, coincident with the circadian shift in resting core temperature: this was associated with an enhanced vasoconstrictor tone and an altered sweat rate. This was ascribed to a shift in the set point, or a threshold shift to the right. Do you have any comment?

Dr Reilly
There is indeed a shift in the threshold for sweating and blood flow responsiveness but I think it unlikely that the circadian rhythm in temperature can be explained entirely by variation in sudomotor or vasomotor activity.

Dr Jacobs, Toronto, Canada
How do you account for the effects of dietary-induced thermogenesis on body temperature in these studies, given that most individuals eat 2-4 meals per day.

Dr Reilly
Diet is one of the factors which tends to swamp endogenous rhythms or impose sub-harmonics on them. We tried to control this as far as possible. The last meal before the beginning of test periods was a snack containing about 1500kJ given at least 3 hours before exercise; after exercise subjects were allowed to eat if they wished. In nychthemeral conditions of everyday life the effects of the specific dynamic activity of food on the circadian rhythm in core temperature are still relatively small.

Dr Frederick, New Hampshire, USA

What is the effect of overtraining on the various rhythms? Many top athletes spend the last few weeks leading up to peak performances in a state of incipient or frank overtraining. Without knowing what the rhythm effects are, it is clear that these athletes show changes in rectal temperature, body weight, mood and so on.

Dr Reilly

I think one important thing here is to control for the time of day at which measurements are made. It is likely that in the majority of cases, rhythms would still be evident as circadian variations around a new set point. It is conceivable also that some rhythms would be damped, especially if the normal sleep-wake cycle is disturbed as a result of overtraining. These are at best guesses as there is no substantive research on this particular question.

Dr Legg, Farnborough, England

Is there a relationship between daily change in stature and spinal flexibility? One might expect less flexibility with reduced stature and possibly an increased risk of back pain.

Dr Reilly

I agree with your predictions but our data do not support a straight forward relationship. Imbibition of fluid from the disc should increase its stiffness, decreasing the flexibility of the spine, and alleviate the risk of injury. In the studies of trunk flexibility the turning point occurs around midday or early afternoon whereas stature generally continues to decline. Spinal flexibility is influenced by the back muscles and ligamentous structures and their status would affect the flexibility rhythm. Although modelling studies of the disc have shown that it is a poor shock absorber when compressed, we still await convincing epidemiological evidence in whole-body contexts.

Fluid balance as a limiting factor for exercise

M.H. HARRISON

The importance of fluid balance as a factor influencing the
capacity for prolonged exercise is too often understated. Mild
dehydration equivalent to as little as 1% of body weight can reduce
cardiovascular capacity, while dehydration in excess of 5% of body
weight can precipitate physical collapse and heat stroke. In
reviewing fluid balance as a limiting factor for exercise, the
present paper considers three aspects; the conditions which lead to
dehydration; how dehydration impairs exercise capacity; and how
this impairment can be reduced.

Dehydration during exercise is likely above a wet bulb globe
temperature (WBGT) index of $18^{o}C$, while above a WBGT of
$25^{o}C$ endurance athletes are at risk from heat stroke. The
effects of dehydration on performance seem to be mediated by
specific changes in thermoregulatory and cardiovascular function.
Dehydration-induced intravascular hyperosmolality and hypovolaemia
induce a relative hyperthermia during exercise. The hypovolaemia,
and a peripheral redistribution of central blood volume, reduce
cardiac filling presure and, hence, cardiac output. These effects
of dehydration can be attenuated by over-hydration before exercise,
and regular drinking during exercise. Small volumes are usually
all that can be taken, and water is to be preferred. Carbohydrate
solutions are acceptable if dilute, or if in polymer form.
Electrolyte drinks should be avoided.

1. Introduction

Fluid balance can be an important limiting factor for exercise.
Under conditions of environmental heat stress, and when high-
intensity exercise is performed for prolonged periods, sweating
leads to an increasingly negative fluid balance (dehydration). This
cumulative loss of body water can dramatically reduce the capacity
for exercise, and in extreme cases precipitate physical collapse
(Pugh et al., 1967) and even heat stroke (Wyndham, 1977). Although
the adverse effects of dehydration can be attenuated, or even
prevented, by replacing the sweat water loss, drinking during
exercise is generally found to be difficult and uncomfortable.

The present paper addresses three questions: what conditions cause dehydration? how does dehydration reduce exercise capacity?; and how can this impairment best be minimised? Thus, the intention is to consider both practical and physiological aspects of fluid balance as a limiting factor for exercise.

2. Conditions predisposing to dehydration

It is important to dispel the myth that the environment is the primary source of thermal stress. As Nadel (1977) has pointed out, environmental heat loads rarely exceed 200W. Four times this amount of heat is produced by a 60kg athlete completing a marathon in 2.5 hours by running at 75% of a 4 $l.min^{-1}$ maximal oxygen uptake ($\dot{V}O_2$max; Harrison, 1986). If this metabolic heat was dissipated entirely by evaporation of sweat, the athlete would lose 3kg (5%) of his body weight. In fact, body weight losses of this order of magnitude are not uncommon during marathon runs in moderate and hot environments (Adams et al., 1975; Pugh et al., 1967). Exceptionally fit individuals may sustain heat production rates in excess of 1.2kW for protracted periods (Nadel, 1983).

As the environmental temperature rises and approaches the mean skin temperature, heat losses by convection and radiation decrease, but are counterbalanced by increased sweat production and evaporation (Nielsen, 1938). Sweat secretion rates can approach $30g.min^{-1}$ under conditions of maximal demand (Nadel et al., 1977), providing an evaporative potential equivalent to the 1.2kW of heat produced by very fit endurance athletes. It will be appreciated, however, that such a sweat rate, if sustained, would quickly produce significant dehydration.

Conditions of maximal thermal demand are not necessarily restricted to situations where the environmental temperature is high. If termperature regulating mechanisms were not activated, a 60 to 70kg athlete producing 1.2kW of heat would experience a $1°C$ rise in body temperature every 5 mins (Nadel et al., 1977). Within the prescriptive zone (i.e. the zone of physiological temperature regulation; Lind, 1963), and assuming again a work rate equivalent to 75% of $\dot{V}O_2$max, this rate of heat production will, because of the activation of thermoregulatory mechanisms, produce a steady-state core temperature of about $38.5°C$ (Saltin and Hermansen, 1968). Even allowing for the inhibitory effect of a cool skin on sweat rate (Kerslake, 1972), a core temperature of this magnitude will still provide a powerful stimulus to sweat secretion (Nadel et al., 1971). Hence, prolonged runs performed under relatively cool conditions of $10°C$ dry bulb can still produce a 2% decline in body weight as a result of sweat (and respiratory) water loss (Adams et al., 1975).

It is impossible to define precise environmental conditions under which fluid balance is likely to be a significant limiting factor for exercise. Heat dissipation by convection and radiation is profoundly affected by factors such as wind speed and the solar radiation load. Heat dissipation by evaporation is similarly affected by humidity. As a guide, however, for the 'average' athlete producing heat at a rate of 600W, thermal, and hence fluid balance problems are unlikely at a wet bulb globe temperature

(WBGT) index (i.e., [0.7 x wet bulb temperature]+[0.2 x black globe temperature] + [0.1 x dry bulb temperature]) below 18°C (Greenleaf and Harrison, 1985). Above a WBGT index of 25°C, however, endurance athletes are at risk from heat stroke, while above 28°C athletic events should be cancelled (Wyndham, 1977).

3. Dehydration and exercise performance

That dehydration reduces the capacity for prolonged exercise in hot environments by impairing temperature regulation was first demonstrated over forty years ago by Pitts et al. (1944). Since then many studies have confirmed the importance of fluid balance as a limiting factor for exercise, and especially for exercise performed in hot environments (Gosselin, 1947; Ladell, 1955; Buskirk et al., 1958; Pearcy, et al., 1959; Grande et al., 1959; Saltin, 1964a;b; Craig and Cummings, 1966; Greenleaf and Castle, 1971; Claremont et al., 1976; Harrison et al., 1978; Nadel et al., 1980; Sawka et al., 1985). But, despite this wealth of information regarding the hazards of dehydration, fluid balance does not generally figure prominently in texts devoted to sports medicine and sports science. Rather, and perhaps understandably, fluid balance tends to be discussed in the much broader context of thermal stress as a limiting factor for exercise. This may be a reflection of a failure to recognise just how important fluid balance per se can be as a factor influencing exercise performance. Thus, dehydration equivalent to as little as 1% of body weight will significantly impair temperature regulation (Ekblom et al., 1970), while above 2% dehydration, degradation of physical work capacity becomes increasingly apparent (Craig and Cummings, 1966; Saltin, 1964b).

There may also be a failure to appreciate that thirst alone is not an effective antidote to dehydration during exercise. Thirst is not a particularly well-developed stimulus in homo sapiens, and a fluid deficit approaching 1% of body weight is normally incurred before drinking is initiated (Fitzsimons, 1979). Thirst sensations are less intense during exercise, and in the heat fluid losses tend to be replaced only when food is available (Adolph and Wills, 1947). Furthermore, even when drinking is initiated, the volume consumed voluntarily is always less than the volume of the deficit, so that a state of 'involuntary dehydration' persists (Fitzsimons, 1979). Consequently, dehydration, albeit mild dehydration, must be regarded as an inevitable accompaniment of virtually all endurance-type sporting activities.

The body water lost during thermal sweating, or during dehydration induced by fluid restriction, comes from all the fluid compartments. However, because sweat is hypotonic to plasma (Robinson and Robinson, 1954), extracellular osmolality rises, and osmotic transfer of water from the the intracellular to the extracellular compartments occurs i.e. the intravascular and interstitial compartments tend to be maintained at the expense of the cells, although, in absolute terms, the volumes of all three compartments are depleted. It may be hypothesised, therefore, that the detrimental effects of dehydration on temperature regulation and physical work capacity can be attributed to:

(i) the increase in extracellular osmolality, and/or
(ii) the decrease in extracellular volume, and/or
(iii) the decrease in intracellular volume.

3.1 Dehydration and temperature regulation.
The greater the body water deficit incurred during exercise,
the greater the rise in core temperature (Wyndham and Strydom,
1969). At rest, the magnitude of the body water deficit is
positively correlated with plasma osmolality (Senay, 1968; Senay
and Christensen, 1965). Hence, an association between core
temperature and plasma osmolality is suggested. This association
is confirmed by the findings that in dogs (Kozlowski et al.,
1980) and in man (Nielsen, 1974a; Nielsen et al., 1971; Harrison
et al., 1978), extracellular hyperosmolality induces an excessive
rise in core temperature, and that core temperature and plasma
osmolality are directly correlated during exercise (Greenleaf et
al., 1974; 1977).

The first study to demonstrate unequivocally that osmolality is
a causal factor in dehydration hyperthermia was that of Harrison et al.
(1978). This showed that core temperature during exercise was
very similar in subjects previously dehydrated, and in the same
subjects in whom dehydration was completely prevented by drinking
1% saline. If dehydration was prevented by drinking water, rather
than saline, core temperature was regulated at a lower level
(Fig.1). Later, Fortney et al. (1984) showed that hyperosmolality
modified thermoregulation by elevating the threshold for sweating
during exercise, and both elevating the threshold, and reducing the
sensitivity, of the cutaneous vasodilator response to the thermal
strain induced by exercise.

The interaction between plasma osmolality and core temperature
led Snellen (1972) to propose that the former might represent a non-
thermal input to the hypothalamic thermoregulatory centre. If
plasma osmolality provided an index of body volume, and interacted
(in some as yet undefined manner) with body temperature, then a
link would be established between the homeostatic mechanisms
concerned with heat balance and fluid balance. Such a link is a
logical necessity if the conflicting demands imposed upon the
circulation for heat dissipation and metabolism are to be met. Put
another way, if the ability of the circulation to supply oxygen and
substrates to vital tissues is to be maintained under conditions of
severe thermal stress, a limit must be imposed upon the volume of
fluid which can be removed from the circulation. It appears that an
elevated plasma osmolality reduces fluid losses by inhibiting
sweating, and helps maintain central blood volume be reducing
cutaneous blood flow. Reductions in plasma volume of more than 20%
are rare during exercise, even under conditions of severe thermal
stress (Harrison, 1985).

A possible objection to this attractive hypothesis is that
plasma osmolality, with sodium and chloride concentrations,
increases quickly during exercise, the magnitude of this increase
depending upon the intensity and duration of the exercise (see
Harrison, 1985, for references). It could be argued (Greenleaf et
al., 1977) that if plasma osmolality during exercise is determined
by the associated redistribution of water and electrolytes

(Harrison, 1985) rather than by body water content, then it is difficult to ascribe to osmolality the role in temperature regulation suggested by the studies of Nielsen et al. (1971) and Harriso:: et al. (1978). On the other hand, plasma osmolality, sodium, and chloride are all, like core temperature (Saltin and Hermansen, 1966), linearly related to exercise intensity (Senay et al., 1980; Wilkerson et al., 1982), and it is therefore conceivable that exercise-induced changes in plasma osmolality could influence thermoregulatory responses to exercise.

A second objection is that dehydratiòn could also increase body temperature by stimulating metabolic heat production. Although this possibility does not appear to have been adequately considered, studies that have included measurements of oxygen consumption have generally found no increase attributable to dehydration (Ekblom et al., 1970; Sawka et al., 1985).

A third objection is that dehydration and exercise are both generally accompanied not only by an elevated plasma osmolality, but also by a reduction in plasma volume (Harrison, 1985). In fact, it seems that hypovolaemia and hyperosmolality have similar effects on thermoregulation. By using diuretics (Nadel et al., 1980; Fortney et al., 1981b), or phlebotomy (Fortney et al., 1981a) to reduce blood volume, hypovolaemia can be induced without hypernatraemia or hyperosmolality. As with hyperosmolality, hypovolaemia acts to reduce heat dissipation by inhibitory actions on sweating and cutaneous blood flow, although hyperosmolality appears to have a dominant effect on sweat rate (Sawka et al., 1985). In contrast to hyperosmolality, the threshold of the sudomotor response to the increased metabolic heat production of exercise does not appear to be changed by hypovolaemia. Rather, the sensitivity of the response is attenuated (i.e. the quantity of sweat secreted per unit increment in core temperature is reduced), but only over the inactive muscles (Fortney et al., 1981b). This suggests that the greater heat production of the active muscles may have a local facilitatory effect, overcoming the inhibitory effect of the hypovolaemia. Isotonic hypervolaemia induced by albumin infusion has no effect on sweat rate (Fortney et al., 1981b). Effects of isotonic hypo- and hypervolaemia on cutaneous vasomotor responses to exercise are far less clear-cut. Initially, Nadel et al. (1980) observed an increase in the vasodilator threshold with hypovolaemia induced by diuretics, but no change in sensitivity, and no changes in either threshold or sensitivity with hypervolaemia induced by anti-diuretic hormone and water administration. In a later study, however, Fortney et al. (1981a) found that hypovolaemia induced by phlebotomy had no statistically significant effect on the vasodilator threshold, but that, compared to responses to hypervolaemia induced by replacing, 2 weeks later, the blood previously removed, the sensitivity of the vasodilator response to exercise was reduced. Clearly, further studies are required to resolve these conflicting observations.

At present it is unclear how alterations in blood volume and osmolality modulate thermoregulation, or even whether the effects of hypovolaemia and hypersomolality are mediated peripherally or centrally. Two factors suggest a predominantly central mechanism, however. First, as already noted, the sudomotor response to

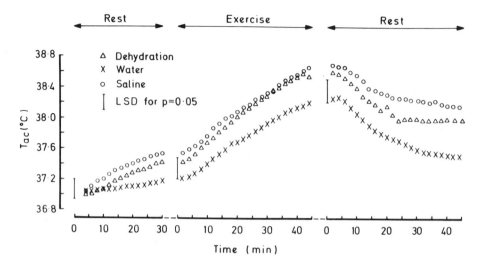

Figure 1. Deep body temperature (T_{ac}) at rest, during cycling exercise, and during recovery from exercise, at an environmental temperature of $45°C$ dry bulb, 30% relative humidity. Mean of four subjects who were: (i) dehydrated by 2.5% of body weight at time zero (by a preliminary dehydration phase; see Harrison et al., 1978) and by 5% of body weight at the end of the experiment; (ii) had dehydration prevented by oral administration of a., distilled water, and b., 1% saline. LSD indicates least significant difference between hydration conditions. Rest, exercise and recovery periods were contiguous. Reproduced with permission, The American Physiological Society.

dehydration is modified by purely local (peripheral) factors (Fortney et al., 1981b). Second, the apparent increases in sweating and vasodilator thresholds with hyperosmolality and hypovolaemia imply a decrease in central thermoregulatory drive at a given core temperature; in other words, an increase in the set-point at which effector thermoregulatory responses are initiated. Since the set-point is determined by the integrated balance of multiple thermal, and probably non-thermal, inputs, a change in set-point could occur if, for example, some alteration in blood or interstitial fluid osmolality or sodium concentration changed the sensitivity of neurones in the thermoregulatory pathways (Snellen, 1972). Also, hyperosmotic dehydration is invariably accompanied by a decrease in mean corpuscular volume (Harrison, 1985). Assuming that this intracellular water loss is representative of the intracellular compartment generally, then volume changes of cells within the hypothalamus might also influence effector thermoregulatory responses (Fortney et al., 1984). Cellular dehydration is, of course, an important stimulus to drinking.

Thermoregulatory responses to decreases in blood volume could be triggered by the reduced stimulation of cardio-pulmonary baroreceptors as cardiac filling pressure falls (Fortney et al., 1981b). These receptors, which have a powerful influence on forearm vascular resistance (Mark and Mancia, 1983), appear to have inputs to both the medullary vasomotor and hypothalamic

thermoregulatory centres. Therefore, a decrease in cardiac filling
pressure might simultaneously increase sympathetic vasoconstrictor
outflow, and decrease central thermoregulatory drive, thereby
reducing both skin blood flow and sweating.

It may be concluded, therefore, that the effects of dehydration
on temperature regulation are probably mediated by both extracellular
and intracellular factors, with the primary stimuli being changes
in osmolality and volume. Whether it is osmolality per se which
is important, or some component of osmolality such as sodium, or
whether endocrine factors are also involved, remains uncertain. It
is worth noting, however, that while Nielsen (1974b) has reported a
direct effect of plasma sodium on temperature regulation, Kozlowski
et al. (1980) found that in dogs hyperosmolality without
hypernatraemia still induced an excessive rise in core temperature
during exercise.

3.2 Dehydration and work capacity
Brown (1947) has provided a graphic account of the physical
debilitation and distress caused by water shortage in the desert.
Some years later Saltin (1964a;b) showed that aerobic and
anaerobic work capacity are both reduced by dehydration. At
submaximal work rates in an upright position heart rate is higher,
and stroke volume lower, after dehydration than before. Although
Saltin observed no significant decrease in cardiac output, studies
by Nadel et al. (1980) indicate that as exercise intensity
increases, the relative tachycardia becomes increasingly unable
to compensate for the reduced stroke volume, and so cardiac output
decreases. This accounts for the reduction in submaximal
endurance generally observed following dehydration (Armstrong et
al., 1985; Craig and Cummings, 1966).

Maximal exercise time is markedly decreased by dehydration
(Saltin, 1964b). However, despite the contrary report of Buskirk
et al. (1958), this does not seem to be a result of any decrease in
$\dot{V}O_2$max (Rowell, 1974). Dehydration, then is an excellent
example of a situation where $\dot{V}O_2$max does not provide a reliable
measure of physical work capacity. Although levels of dehydration
producing measurable effects on physical performance tend to range
from 2 to 5% of body weight, it is important to appreciate that the
heart rate response to exercise becomes accentuated by a level of
dehydration equivalent to as little as 1% of body weight (Ekblom et
al., 1970). Thus, very mild dehydration can encroach upon
cardiovascular reserve, even though changes in blood volume are
minimal at this level of dehydration (Harrison et al., 1986a;b).
It is hardly surprising, therefore, that homeostatic mechanisms
have evolved to maintain central blood volume under conditions of
dehydration and hyperthermia by reducing blood flow to the skin,
and to blood depots such as the splanchnic and renal circulations
(Rowell, 1974; 1983). Almost certainly these mechanisms are
activated by a fall in blood pressure detected by low, and possibly
high, pressure baroreceptors (Fortney et al., 1981a).

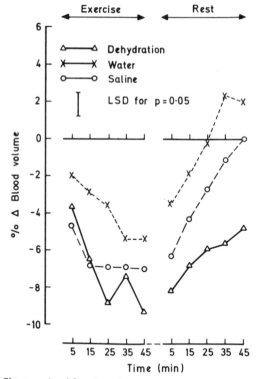

Figure 2. Change in blood volume during cycling exercise, and during recovery from exercise, following dehydration, and prevention of dehydration with water or 1% saline. Experimental details as Fig. 1. Blood volume changes were calculated from alterations in the haemoglobin concentration compared to values at rest preceding the exercise. After Harrison et al. (1978).

Dehydration may also influence work capacity by specific effects on the magnitude of the haemoconcentration response to exercise. Harrison et al. (1978) found that the decrease in blood volume occuring during cycling exercise in a hot environment was greater in thermally dehydrated subjects than in subjects in whom dehydration had been prevented by drinking water sufficient to replace all sweat losses (Fig.2). If dehydration was prevented not by drinking water, but by drinking 1% saline, the magnitude of the exercise haemoconcentration was similar to that seen with dehydration, but the haemodilution following cessation of exercise (Harrison, 1985) occurred much more quickly (Fig.2). Both water and saline attenuated the increase in heart rate during cycling exercise compared to dehydration (Fig.3). Since core temperatures with dehydration and with prevention of dehydration by drinking saline are similar during cycling exercise, (Fig.1), this demonstrates that dehydration can influence work capacity independently of its effect on temperature regulation.

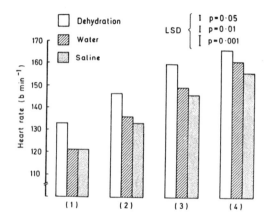

Figure 3. Steady-state values of heart rate at four rates of work
in a thermoneutral environment (21°C dry bulb) with dehydration,
and with prevention of dehydration with water or 1% saline. Mean of
five subjects. Reproduced with permission, The American
Physiological Society.

The reduced heart rate response to cycling exercise following
prevention of dehydration with water reflects both the attenuated
haemoconcentration, and the lower core temperature. Similar
beneficial effects of preventing dehydration with water have been
demonstrated for bench stepping (Gaebelein and Senay, 1980),
walking (Moroff and Bass, 1965; Sawka et al., 1984), and running
(Costill, 1970). Perhaps less immediately obvious is the mechanism
of the reduced heart rate response to cycling exercise following
prevention of dehydration with saline, since the magnitude of the
haemoconcentration, and the rise in core temperature, were similar
to dehydration alone. The explanation is the differing absolute
blood volumes. In the study of Harrison et al. (1978) the
hypertonic saline drunk during the period of dehydration preceding
exercise caused a 4% increase in the blood volume (as determined
from a decrease in the haemoglobin concentration). But
dehydration, and, surprisingly, prevention of dehydration by water
replacement, both resulted in a 4% decrease in blood volume.
Hence, although in relative terms the magnitudes of the exercise
haemoconcentrations were similar for dehydration and saline, the
absolute blood volumes immediately before the exercise began were
substantially different. Assuming a five litre blood volume, the
intravascular fluid content would have been some 400ml greater
following saline. Isotonic hypervolaemia has a similar beneficial
effect on cardiovascular responses to exercise (Fortney et al.,
1981a; Sawka et al., 1983a).
    Contrary to the findings of Harrison et al. (1978), Fortney et
al. (1981b) have described a smaller haemoconcentration response
to cycling exercise following a reduction in blood volume, and a
greater response following an increase in blood volume, compared
with normovolaemic controls. As they point out, this is a sensible
arrangement, since hypovolaemia acts to inhibit further volume
reduction. The reason for the discrepancy between these two
studies is not entirely clear, but one probably important
difference between them is that the hypovolaemia following thermal

dehydration in the study of Harrison et al. (1978) was accompanied
by a substantial increase in plasma osmolality; in the study of
Fortney et al. (1981b) the hypovolaemia, induced using a diuretic,
occurred isotonically. Consequently, the balance of filtration and
absorption forces acting along the capillary beds (where fluid
exchanges between the intravascular and interstitial compartments
take place (Harrison, 1985)) may have been different in the two
studies.

In conclusion, two factors can be identified as limiting
exercise performance, especially in the heat. One is dehydration,
which reduces blood volume and impairs temperature regulation. The
other is competition for blood flow between the muscle and skin
circulations as the cardiovascular system attempts to meet the
conflicting demands of metabolism and thermoregulation. This
competition, together with dehydration induced hypovolaemia,
reduces venous return, and, consequently, cardiac output. Because
it takes time for negative fluid and positive thermal balances to
develop, dehydration tends to degrade performance only when
exercise is performed for a protracted period of time, such as
running events of 5000 metres or longer (Armstrong et al., 1985).
The underlying cause of this degradation of performance is reduced
cardiac filling.

4.   Preventing dehydration

Obviously, the only way to prevent dehydration is to drink.
Unfortunately, as those who participate in sport will appreciate,
this is usually difficult, if not impossible, during exercise.
Opportunities for liquid refreshement are generally severely
circumscribed either by rules and regulations, or simply by
practicalities. By the time the opportunity for drinking does
arise, the fluid deficit can already be too great to make up
without inducing intense gastric discomfort (Costill, 1979). Then
there is the question of what to drink. As Greenleaf and Harrison
(1985) point out: 'A bewildering array of hydration drinks is
available commercially that bombard the individual with a variety
of claims, some of which border on the ludicrous'.

The first and most important point is that a little often is far
better than either none at all, or large volumes taken at one
time. The second important point is that, within reason, any drink
is better than no drink. It is the stomach emptying time which
determines how much liquid can be consumed comfortably while
exercising; the greater the volume, the greater the inevitable
consequences to comfort of the inertia possessed by a large liquid
mass constrained within what is essentially an elastic bag.
Contrary to popular belief, gastric emptying time does not appear
to be increased by exercise, at least up to relative intensities
of approximately 70% of $\dot{V}O_2$max (Costill and Saltin, 1974; Fordtran
and Saltin, 1967). While large volumes leave the stomach
proportionately more quickly than small volumes (Costill and
Saltin., 1974), emptying time is powerfully inhibited by
carbohydrates even in very small quantities (Costill and Saltin,
1974; Coyle, 1978). This inhibition seems to be a function of the

osmolar concentration of the stomach contents, and can be attenuated by providing carbohydrates in drinks as polymers (Seiple et al., 1983). Cold water tends to be absorbed more quickly than warm water (Costill and Saltin, 1974). It is also more palatable (Hubbard et al., 1984), and obviously has a greater cooling effect. Metabolic water makes a minimal contribution to the relief of dehydration (Pivarnik et al., 1984). However, it is worth noting the glycogen utilised during exercise releases more metabolic water than fat (Greenleaf and Harrison, 1985; Olsson and Saltin., 1971); each gram of glycogen releases 2.7g of water of association.

Carbohydrate feeding during exercise appears to enhance performance (Hargreaves et al., 1984; Ivy et al., 1983). If the adverse effect on gastric emptying is overcome by either taking glucose as a polymer supplement, or minimizing the glucose content of solutions (a concentration not exceeding $2.5g. 100ml^{-1}$ of water is ideal (Costill and Saltin, 1974)), then preventing dehydration with 'energy drinks' is acceptable. On the other hand, contrary to assertions in the popular sporting press, and sometimes in the scientific literature (e.g. Seiple et al., 1983), minerals lost in sweat need not, and should not, be replaced during exercise. As already noted, because sweat is hypotonic to plasma (Robinson and Robinson, 1954), thermal- and exercise-induced dehydration elevate blood electrolytes and osmolality. Only during recovery from exercise does intravascular tonicity decrease below the pre-exercise level, and then largely as a result of the consumption of hypotonic drinks. As we have seen, elevations of plasma osmolality reduce the sensitivity of heat dissipation mechanisms. The message is clear. No useful purpose is served by adding electrolytes to rehydration drinks during most sporting activities; avoid electrolyte drinks! The only exception might be when exercise is performed over many hours in the heat - as in ultra-marathon events, for example. Then, a very dilute salt solution may be appropriate, although not exceeding a concentration of $0.5g.100ml^{-1}$ (Greenleaf and Harrison, 1985). Salt tablets should be assiduously avoided, as they cause gastric irritation. The time to replace electrolytes lost in sweat is after, not during, exercise. But if the diet is adequate, electrolyte supplements will still not be necessary.

What, therefore, is the optimum strategy for preventing dehydration? In point of fact, some dehydration will be inevitable during prolonged sporting activities. The adverse effects of dehydration can, however, be attenuated. Adequate, even over-hydration before exercise is recommended, although the diuretic effect of a water load must not be overlooked. A positive fluid balance will stimulate diuresis with possibly unfortunate consequences during the early stages of an event. The excess fluid needs to be lost as sweat, not urine. Glucose should not be taken with liquids consumed before an event, since this stimulates insulin secretion, and may precipitate hypoglycaemia (Costill et al., 1977; Galbo et al., 1979). Caffeine, however (e.g. in coffee or tea), may have a beneficial effect by enhancing lipolysis, (Costill et al., 1978; Ivy et al., 1979).

During exercise, especially exercise in the heat, liquids should be consumed whenever possible, even in the absence of sensations of thirst. It is the opinion of the author that water alone is not only adequate, but is to be preferred for endurance events lasting less than one to two hours. Carbohydrates are probably best taken towards the end of such events, when glycogen stores are becoming depleted. As much liquid as possible, compatible with comfort, should be taken, although in practice this will rarely be found to exceed 100 to 125 ml per drink (Greenleaf and Harrison, 1985). No electrolytes should be added to, or taken with, drinks for any event lasting less than about four hours, even under hot environmental conditions.

A brief word is appropriate about heat acclimatization. There is some evidence to suggest that heat acclimatization, in addition to its favourable effects on thermoregulation and salt balance (Davies et al., 1981; Harrison et al.,1981), may attenuate the effects of dehydration. Greenleaf et al. (1983) have shown that acclimatization may reduce the magnitude of involuntary dehydration by increasing predisposition to drinking; i.e. thirst sensitivity may be increased. Also, adaptive responses to heat may attenuate the adverse effects of dehydration on cardiovascular responses to heat and exercise (Sawka et al., 1983b). What must be emphasised, however, is that there is absolutely no evidence to support the myth that it is possible to adapt (acclimatise) to dehydration per se.

Perhaps the best way to minimise the effects of dehydration during exercise is to follow the advice of the American Dietetic Association (1980); begin increasing water intake two hours before competitions by drinking 600 ml, and then drinking anouther 400 to 500ml approximately 15 minutes before the start. But if the start is delayed, this could all be a waste of time!

Acknowledgements

Research by the author was conducted at the Royal Air Force Institute of Aviation Medicine, Farnborough, and at NASA Ames Research Center, Moffett Field, California.

Thanks are due to Mrs K. Rose for typing the manuscript.

References

Adams, W.C., Fox, R.H., Fry, A.J. and MacDonald, I.C. (1975). Thermoregulation during marathon running in cool, moderate, and hot environments. J. Appl. Physiol. 38:1030-7.
Adolph, E.F. and Wills, J.H. (1947). Thirst. In Physiology of Man in the Desert, (by E.F. Adolph and Associates) chapt. 15, pp. 241- 53. New York. Interscience Publishers Inc.
American Dietetic Association (1980). Position Statement : nutrition and physical fitness. J. Am. Diet. Ass. 76:437-43.

Armstrong, L.E., Costill, D.L. and Fink, W.J. (1985). Influence of diuretic-induced dehydration on competitive running performance. Med. Sci. Sports Exerc. 17:456-61.

Brown, A.H. (1947). Dehydration exhaustion. In Physiology of Man in the Desert (by E.F. Adolph and Associates), chapt.13:208-25. New York: Interscience Publishers Inc.

Buskirk, E.R., Iampietro, P.F. and Bass, D.E. (1958). Work performance after dehydration; effects of physical conditioning and heat acclimatization. J. Appl. Physiol. 12:189-94.

Claremont, A.D., Costill, D.L., Fink, W. and van Handel, P. (1976). Heat tolerance following diuretic induced dehydration. Med. Sci. Sports 8:238-43.

Costill, D.L. (1979). A Scientific Approach to Distance Running. Track and Field News.

Costill, D.L., Coyle, E., Dalsky, G., Evans, W., Fink, W. and Hoopes, D. (1977). Effects of elevated plasma FFA and insulin on muscle glycogon usage during exercise. J. Appl. Physiol. 43:695-99.

Costill, D.L., Dalsky, G.P. and Fink, W.J. (1978). Effects of caffeine ingestion on metabolism and exercise performance. Med. Sci. Sports 10:155-8.

Costill, D.L., Kammer, W.F. and Fisher, A. (1970). Fluid ingestion during distance running. Arch. Environ. Health 21:520-5.

Costill, D.L. and Saltin, B. (1974). Factors limiting gastric emptying during rest and exercise. J. Appl. Physiol. 37:679-83.

Coyle, E.F. (1978). Gastric emptying rates for selected athletic drinks. Res. Q. 49:119-243.

Craig, F.N. and Cummings, E.G. (1966). Dehydration and muscular work. J. Appl. Physiol. 21:670-4.

Davies, J.A., Harrison, M.H., Cochrane, L.A., Edwards, R.J. and Gibson, T.M. (1981). Effect of saline loading during heat acclimatization on adrenocortical hormone levels. J. Appl. Physiol. 50:605-12.

Ekblom, B., Greenleaf, C.J., Greenleaf, J.E. and Hermansen, L. (1970). Temperature regulation during exercise dehydration in man. Acta Physiol. Scand. 79:475-83.

Fitzsimons, J.T. (1979). The physiology of Thirst and Sodium Appetite. Monographs of the Physiological Society, No.35. Cambridge : Cambridge University Press.

Fordtran, J.S. and Saltin, B. (1967). Gastric emptying and intestinal absorption during prolonged severe exercise. J. Appl. Physiol. 23:331-5.

Fortney, S.M., Nadel, E.R., Wenger, C.B. and Bove, J.R. (1981a). Effect of acute alterations of blood volume on circulatory performance in humans. J. Appl. Physiol. 50:292-8.

Fortney. S.M., Nadel, E.R., Wenger, C.B. and Bove, J.R. (1981b). Effect of blood volume on sweating rate and body fluids in exercising humans. J. Appl. Physiol. 51:1594-600.

Fortney, S.M., Wenger, C.B., Bove, J.R. and Nadel, E.R. (1984). Effect of hyperosmolality on control of blood flow and sweating. J. Appl. Physiol. 57:1688-95.

Gaebelein, C.J. and Senay, L.C. Jr. (1980). Influence of exercise type, hydration, and heat on plasma volume shifts in men. J. Appl. Physiol. 49:119-23.

Galbo, H., Holst, J.J. and Christensen, N.J. (1985). Glucagon and plasma catecholamine responses to graded and prolonged exercise in man. J. Appl. Physiol. 38:70-6.

Gosselin, R.E. (1947). Rates of sweating in the desert. In Physiology of Man in the Desert (by E.F. Adolph and Associates), chapt.4, pp. 44-76. New York : Interscience Publishers Inc.

Grande, F., Monagle, J.E., Buskirk, E.R. and Taylor, H.L. (1959). Body temperature responses to exercise in man on restricted food and water intake. J. Appl. Physiol. 14: 194-8.

Greenleaf, J.E., Brock, P.J., Keil, L.C. and Morse, J.T. (1983). Drinking and water balance during exercise and heat acclimation. J. Appl. Physiol. 54:414-9.

Greenleaf, J.E. and Castle, B.L. (1971). Exercise temperature regulation in a man during hypohydration and hyperhydration. J. Appl. Physiol. 30:847-53.

Greenleaf, J.E. Castle, B.L. and Card, D.H. (1974). Blood electrolytes and temperature regulation during exercise in man. Acta Physiol. Pol. 25:397-410.

Greenleaf, J.E., Convertino, V.A., Stremel, R.W., Bernauer, E.M., Adams, W.C., Vignau, S.R. and Brock, P.J. (1977). Plasma $[Na^+]$, $[Ca^{2+}]$, and volume shifts and thermoregulation during exercise in man. J. Appl. Physiol. 43:1026-32.

Greenleaf, J.E. and Harrison, M.H. (1985). Water and electrolytes. In Nutrition in Aerobic Exercise (edited by D.K. Layman), chapt. 8, pp. 107-24. Washington, D.C. : American Chemical Society.

Hargreaves, M., Costill, D.L., Coggan, A., Fink, W.J. and Nishibata, I. (1984). Effect of carbohydrate feedings on muscle glycogen utilization and exercise performance. Med. Sci. Sports Exercise 16:219-22.

Harrison, M.H. (1985). Effects of thermal stress and exercise on blood volume in humans. Physiol. Rev. 65:149-209.

Harrison, M.H. (1986). Heat and exercise : effects on blood volume. Sports Med. 3:214-223, 1986.

Harrison, M.H., Edwards, R.J. and Fennessy, P.A. (1978). Intravascular volume and tonicity as factors in the regulation of body temperature. J. Appl. Physiol. 44:69-75.

Harrison, M.H., Edwards, R.J., Graveney, M.J., Cochrane, L.A. and Davies, J.A. (1981). Blood volume and plasma protein responses to heat acclimatization in humans. J. Appl. Physiol. 50:597-604.

Harrison, M.H., Hill, L.C., Spaul, W.A. and Greenleaf, J.E. (1986a). Effect of hydration on some orthostatic and haematological responses to head-up tilt. Europ. J. Appl. Physiol. 55:187-194,1986.

Harrison, M.H., Keil, L.C., Wade, C.A., Silver, J.E., Geelen, G. and Greenleaf, J.E. (1986b). Effect of hydration status on plasma volume and endocrine responses to water immersion. J. Appl. Physiol. In print.

Hubbard, R.W., Sandick, B.L., Mattnew, W.T., Francesconi, R.P., Sampson, J.B., Durkot, M.J., Maller, O. and Engell, D.B. (1984). Voluntary dehydration and alliesthesia for water. J. Appl. Physiol. 57:868-75.

Ivy, J.L., Costill, D.L., Fink, W.J. and Lower, R.W. (1979). Influence of caffeine and carbohydrate feedings on endurance performance. Med. Sci. Sports 11:6-11.

Ivy, J.L., Miller, W., Dover, V., Goodyear, L.G., Sherman, W.M., Farrell, S. and Williams, H. (1983). Endurance improved by ingestion of a glucose polymer supplement. Med. Sci. Sports. Exerc 15:466-71.

Kerslake, D. McK. (1972). The Stress of Hot Environments. Monographs of the Physiological Society, No.29, Cambridge : Cambridge University Press.

Kozlowski, S., Greenleaf, J.E., Turlejska, E. and Nazar, K. (1980). Extracellular hyperosmolality and body temperature during physical exercise in dogs. Am. J. Physiol. 239 (Regulatory Integrative Comp. Physiol.8) : R180-3.

Ladell, W.S.S. (1955). The effects of water and salt intake upon the performance of men working in hot and humid environments. J. Physiol., London. 127:11-46.

Lind, A.R. (1963). A physiological criterion for setting thermal environmental limits for everyday work. J. Appl. Physiol. 18:51-6.

Mark, A.L. and Mancia, G. (1983). Cardiopulmonary baroreflexes in humans. In Handbook of Physiology : The Cardiovascular System III, (edited by J.T. Shepherd and F.M. Abboud) chapt. 21, pp. 795-813. Bethesda : American Physiological Society.

Moroff, S.V. and Bass, D.E. (1965). Effects of overhydration on man's physiological responses to work in the heat. J. Appl. Physiol. 20:267-70.

Nadel, E.R. (1977). A Brief Overview .... In Problems with Temperature Regulation during Exercises. (edited by E.R. Nadel), pp. 1-9. New York : Academic Press Inc.

Nadel, E.R. (1983). Factors affecting the regulation of body temperature during exercise. J. Therm. Biol. 8:165-9.

Nadel, E.R., Bullard, R.W. and Stolwijk, J.A.J. (1971). Importance of skin temperature in the regulation of sweating. J. Appl. Physiol. 31:80-7.

Nadel, E.R., Fortney, S.M. and Wenger, C.B. (1980). Effect of hydration state on circulatory and thermal regulations. J. Appl. Physiol. 49:715-21.

Nadel, E.R., Wenger, C.B., Roberts, M.F., Stolwijk, J.A.J. and Cafarelli, E. (1977). Physiological defences against hyperthermia of exercise. Ann. N.Y. Acad. Sci. 301:98-109.

Nielsen, M. (1938). The control of body temperature in muscular work. Skandinav. Arch. 79:193-230.

Nielsen, B. (1974a). Effects of changes in plasma volume and osmolarity on thermoregulation during exercise. Acta. Physiol. Scand. 90:725-30.

Nielsen, B. (1974b). Effects of changes in plasma Na^+ and Ca^{++} ion concentration on body temperature during exercise. Acta. Physiol. Scand. 91:123-9.

Nielsen, B., Hansen, G., Jorgensen, S.O. and Nielsen, E. (1971). Thermoregulation in exercising man during dehydration and hyperhydration with water and saline. Intern. J. Biometeorol. 15:195-200.

Olsson, K.-E. and Saltin, B. (1971). Diet and fluids in training and competition. Scand. J. Rehab. Med. 3:31-8.

Pearcy, M., Robinson, S., Miller, D.I., Thomas, J.T. and DeBrota,
 J. (1959). Effects of dehydration, salt depletion, and pitressin
 on sweat rate and urine flow. J. Appl. Physiol. 8:621-6.
Pitts, G.C., Johnson, R.E. and Consolazio, F.C. (1944). Work in
 the heat as affected by intake of water, salt, and glucose.
 Am. J. Physiol. 142:253-9.
Pivarnik, J.M., Leeds, E.M. and Wilkerson, J.E. (1984). Effects of
 endurance exercise on metabolic water production and plasma
 volume. J. Appl. Physiol. 56:613-8.
Pugh, L.G.C.E., Corbett, J.L. and Johnson, R.H. (1967). Rectal
 temperatures, weight losses, and sweat rates in marathon
 running. J. Appl. Physiol. 23:347-52.
Robinson, S. and Robinson A.H. (1954). Chemical composition of
 sweat. Physiol. Rev 34:202-20.
Rowell, L.B. (1974). Human cardiovascular adjustments to exercise
 and thermal stress. Physiol. Rev. 54:75-159.
Rowell, L.B. (1983). Cardiovascular adjustments to thermal
 stress. In Handbook of Physiology : The Cardiovascular System
 III (edited by J.T. Shepherd and F.M. Abboud). chapt. 27, pp.
 967-1023. Bethesda : American Physiological Society.
Saltin, B. (1964a). Aerobic and anaerobic work capacity after
 dehydration. J. Appl. Physiol 19:114-8.
Saltin, B. (1964b). Circulatory response to submaximal and maximal
 exercise after thermal dehydration. J. Appl. Physiol.
 19:1125-32.
Saltin, B. and Hermansen, L. (1966). Esophageal, rectal, and muscle
 temperature during exercise. J. Appl. Physiol. 21:1757-1762.
Sawka, M.N., Francesconi, R.P., Pimental, N.A. and Pandolf, K.B.
 (1984). Hydration and vascular fluid shifts during exercise in
 the heat. J. Appl. Physiol. 56:91-6.
Sawka, M.N., Hubbard, R.W., Francesconi, R.P. and Horstman, D.H.
 (1983a). Effects of acute plasma volume expansion on altering
 exercise-heat performance. Eur. J. Appl. Physiol. 51:303-12.
Sawka, M.N., Toner, M.M., Francesconi, R.P. and Pandolf, K.B.
 (1983b). Hypohydration and exercise : effects of heat
 acclimation, gender, and environment. J. Appl. Physiol.
 55:1147-53.
Sawka, M.N., Young, A.J., Francesconi, R.P., Muza, S.R. and Pandolf,
 K.B. (1985). Thermoregulatory and blood responses during exercise
 at graded hypohydration levels. J. Appl. Physiol.
 59:1394-401.
Seiple, R.S., Vivian, V.M., Fox, E.L. and Bartels, R.L. (1983).
 Gastric- emptying characteristics of two glucose polymer-
 electrolyte solutions. Med. Sci. Sports Exerc. 15:366-9.
Senay, L.C. Jr. (1968). Relationship of evaporative rates to serum
 $[Na^+]$, $[K^+]$, and osmolarity in acute heat stress.
 J.Appl. Physiol. 25:149-52.
Senay, L.C. Jr. and Christensen, M.L. (1965). Changes in blood
 pressure during progressive dehydration. J. Appl. Physiol.
 20:1136-40.
Senay L.C. Jr. Rogers, G. and Jooste, P. (1980). Changes in blood
 pressure during progressive dehydration. J. Appl. Physiol.
 49:59- 65.

Snellen, J.W. (1972). Set point and exercise. In Essays on Temperature Regulation (edited by J. Bligh and R.E. Moore), pp. 139-48. Amsterdam : North-Holland Publishing Company.

Wilkerson, J.E., Horvath, S.M., Gutin, B., Molnar, S. and Diaz, F.J. (1982). Plasma electrolyte content and concentration during treadmill exercise in humans. J. Appl. Physiol. 53:1529-39.

Wyndham, C.H. (1977). Heat-stroke and hyperthermia in marathon runners. Ann. N.Y. Acad. Sci. 301:128-38.

Wyndham, C.H. and Strydom, N.B. (1969). The danger of an inadequate water intake during marathon running. S. Afr. Med. J. 43:893-6.

Discussion

Dr Maughan, Aberdeen, Scotland

We have been looking at water absorption in the small intestine and it is quite clear that the rate of water absorption is increased in the presence of small amounts of glucose and electrolytes compared with plain water. Perhaps even more interestingly, if a concentrated solution is given, there is a net movement of water into the lumen of the gut and this can lead to a decrease in plasma volume. I agree entirely that electrolyte replacement is not necessary, and indeed the glucose in these solutions may contribute little to metabolism, but they do promote water uptake.

Dr Raven, Texas, USA

No drinking stations are allowed for the first 10km of championship marathon races. What is your view of this?

Dr Harrison, Farnborough, England

I think it is insane, and also possibly dangerous under conditions of severe heat stress. In endurance events longer than 10 miles, water should be taken as early as possible. Because large amounts cannot be taken at once due to gastric discomfort, small amounts should be taken at frequent intervals.

Dr Sutton, Hamilton, Canada

Tim Noakes has recently reported some interesting observations in the Comrades (88km) Marathon. He reported four cases of overhydration and hyponatraemia in runners who took water continually throughout the event. Serum sodium levels as low as 115mmol.1^{-1} were recorded. Do you think there is any way for an individual to estimate fluid requirements during an event of this type?

Dr Harrison

I saw that report and found it very surprising. I would expect at these low work loads that urine production would not be inhibited and that the sensation of a full bladder would restrict further fluid intake. It is very difficult to maintain a state of hyperhydration.

Dr Spurway, Glasgow, Scotland
Obviously isotonic saline is too strong; sweat is hypotonic with respect to plasma. Have you any evidence to support the use of water rather than drinks which are approximately isotonic with sweat?

Dr Harrison
My argument is based on the fact that the aim is to reduce the intravascular tonicity as far as possible and consequently the more dilute the drink the better. In ultramarathon events, of course, the situation changes and there may be a need for some electrolyte replacement.

Dr Frederick, New Hampshire, USA
You said that exercise did not appear to affect the rate of water absorption, but you also showed a slide which indicated that gastric emptying decreased very significantly as exercise intensity increased. Can you clarify this? Can you also tell us how gastric emptying relates to water absorption in the small intestine, or are these processes independent?

Dr Harrison
There seems to be no inhibition of gastric emptying until the workload exceeds 60-65% of $\dot{V}O_2$max. Top class marathon runners can run at about 80% of $\dot{V}O_2$max but I don't know of any evidence to show that they retain water in the stomach.

Professor Saltin, Copenhagen, Denmark
We have done some studies which showed that there was no reduction in the uptake of water, sodium, potassium or glucose at workloads close to 80% of $\dot{V}O_2$max. In some other species, such as the dog, a dramatic decrease in uptake from the gut during exercise has been reported.

IN CONCLUSION

Physiological compared with clinical aspects of physical activities

P. -O. ÅSTRAD

It is an advantage to try and separate the strictly physiological
effects of habitual physical activity from its importance in the
primary and secondary prevention of disease. Many physiological
effects are evident and benefit various structures and organ
functions (Table 1). However, from a clinical point of view their
beneficial effects are in many cases still controversial.
Detailed epidemiological studies are complicated. Individuals or
patients devoting an increasing proportion of their time to
exercise often change other aspects in their lifestyle in
conjunction with their increased physical activity. It may well be
that they are genetically self-selected when they adhere to a
sustained programme of physical activity. When asking the
physician whether or not there are scientific data proving that
physical exercise is beneficial it is inevitable that the physician
will concentrate in his or her reply on whether or not such training
has positive beneficial effects in the prevention of disease. As I
have already indicated epidemiological studies in this field are
complicated and the results often inconclusive. For this reason
many physicians do not actively recommend exercise and I believe,
somewhat provocatively, that this is because they have no real
understanding of exercise physiology. In most medical schools very
few lectures are devoted to exercise physiology. Early in this
Conference, Dr Young mentioned that in June 1980, 57% of British
final-year medical students did not know that physical training
reduced the heart rate response to any given exercise in elderly
individuals.

Table 1 lists a number of positive effects of regular exercise.
These effects are positive while the individual participates in
regular exercise but whether they are sustained, for example, one
month after all exercise has been stopped is unknown. I believe
that there is a total, even unanimous agreement, shared by all
exercise physiologists, that regular exercise is essential for
optimal function of the human body. Therefore one of our ambitions
must be to convince the medical profession that exercise is most
likely to be good for a patient even if it can be doubted whether
this increase in activity can 'treat' disease as such.

Table 1.

Beneficial effects of habitual physical activity

Increase in maximal oxygen uptake and cardiac output - stroke
volume (Åstrand et al. Chap.10, 1986 and Blomqvist et al., 1983.)
Reduced heart rate at given oxygen uptake (Åstrand et al.
Chap.10, 1986.)
Reduced blood pressure? (Seals et al., 1984.)
Reduced heart rate x blood pressure product (Blomqvist et al., 1983.)
Improved efficiency of heart muscle (Åstrand et al. Chap.4, 1986.)
Improved myocardial vascularization? (Hammond, 1985.)
Favourable trend in incidences of cardial morbidity and mortality
(Hammond, 1985, Haskell et al., 1983, Paffenbarger et al., 1986
and Shephard, 1986.)
Increased capillary density in skeletal muscle (Saltin et al., 1983.)
Increased activity of 'aerobic' enzymes in skeletal muscles
(Saltin et al., 1983.)
Reduced lactate production at given percentage of maximal oxygen
uptake (Åstrand et al. Chap.10, 1986, Holloszy et al., 1986 and
Hurley et al., 1984.)
Enhanced ability to utilize free fatty acid as substrate during
exercise - glycogen saving (Saltin et al., 1983.)
Improved endurance during exercise (Åstrand et al. Chap.10, 1986.)
Increased metabolism - advantageous from a nutritional viewpoint
(Åstrand et al. Chap.12, 1986.)
Counteracts obesity (Garrow, 1986 and Tremblay et al., 1985.)
An increase in the HDL/LDL ratio (Haskell, 1986 and
Wood et al., 1985.)
Improved structure and function of ligaments, tendons and joints
(Tipton et al., 1986.)
Increased muscular strength (Atha, 1981 and Saltin et al., 1983.)
Reduced perceived exertion at given work rate (Åstrand et al.
Chap.10, 1986.)
Increased release of endorphins (Dearman et al., 1983.)
Enhanced fifer sprouting? (Stebbins et al., 1985.)
Enhanced tolerance to hot environment - increased rate of sweating
(Åstrand et al. Chap.13, 1986.)
Reduced platelet aggregation? (Rauramaa, 1986 and
Rauramaa et al., 1984.)
Counteracts osteoporosis (Smidt et al., 1986.)
Can normalize glucose tolerance (Holloszy et al., 1986.)

References in brackets

When prescribing medication or pills many physicians do not
demand as much scientific proof that the medication is justified
for a particular patient compared to any demand of the patient to
modify their lifestyle. Admittedly it is easier to induce a
patient to take a pill than to modify his/her lifestyle. However,
considering again the many positive effects elicited by regular
physical activity one can question whether it is, from a medical

point of view, ethical <u>not</u> to prescribe exercise. It has been
pointed out that it is essential that physiologists and clinicians
work together and undertake the necessary epidemiological studies.
This Symposium served a very useful purpose by its integration of
different disciplines in human biology, treated as both basic and
applied sciences. 'In the Bond the Strength', to quote the motto
of the Edinburgh Post-Graduate Board for Medicine. No doubt it
becomes more and more complicated to function as an exercise
physiologist considering that exercise in its acute and chronic
effects engages almost all organ functions in the body. At this
Symposium I have, from the lectures of Drs Newsholme and Prior,
understood that more attention should be devoted to the brain
and how the production of neurotransmittors can be affected by
exercise.

1. Limiting Factors

This Symposium is not an exception as far as devoting time to an
analysis of what specific factors limit physical performance. Where
are the crucial bottle necks in the anaerobic and aerobic energy
yielding process, the myofibrillar machinery, etc? We will debate
these points over many future meetings but as yet we have no
definitive answers. For a physiologist who is not an expert in
biochemistry it has been interesting to follow how the development
of new methods in some way guides our research programmes. For
instance, in conjunction with the new development of scientific
methodology one tends to concentrate on one after another enzyme
engaged in substrate breakdown. We note carefully significant
correlations between enzyme activity and maximal oxygen uptake,
anaerobic power, muscular strength, etc. It is however just
possible that a significant correlation may have little or no
biological meaning. I advise my students that a textbook written
1.5 billion years ago dealing with glycolysis, Krebs citric cycle
and electron transport chains could still be recommended today (see
Scientific American, 1978). Once upon a time one enzyme system may
have been very important for the survival of specific species or
even the animal kingdom but at a later stage other factors were
more crucial. In the genetic code there are factors which were
inscribed 100000 million billion years ago. To prevent damage to
vital functions there are probably several safety systems. If one
regulatory system or 'limiting factor' fails there is an
alternative back-up system or brake which can come into action.
There are definite problems when studying 'limiting factors', in
some tasks. As for example in an emergency situation or when
offered a substantial reward, or in an important competition, the
individual can usually perform better in an 'all out' test than in
a conventional laboratory experiment. The design reported by
Professor Eric Hultman and others to stimulate the muscles by
electrical currents is one way of trying to exclude the effects of
motivation in studies of muscle metabolism and its impact on
muscular fatigue.
Until some two decades ago most studies on muscle metabolism
were done on animals. With the development of needle biopsy
techniques it has been possible to obtain samples of human skeletal

muscle. At the early stages the analyses of enzymes and metabolites were done on homogenate made up from human muscle and with improved methodology we were able to study the single muscle fibre. Our ambition is now to look into the events in various compartments of the cell and this is the modern and essential challenge.

2. Nutrition

The more physically active a person is the higher can be their energy intake without risking obesity. From a nutritional point of view the advantage that activity bestows is that a higher energy intake will better secure an adequate intake of essential nutrients (Åstrand and Rodahl, 1986, Chapter 12). From an evolutionary point of view our intake of energy, and more or less automatically, of essential nutrients, was quite high. It may become critical for the low energy consumer i.e. a sedentary person, to be nutritionally well off with regard to essential nutrients particularly if they are exposed to the so called 'junk-food'. As an individual ages there is a gradual reduction in basal metabolic rate but there is not a proportional reduction in the need for essential nutrients. Just for this reason it is very important that elderly people stay physically active and are high energy consumers. If they do not take in an adequate diet, concentrating on foods with a high density of essential nutrients, they may develop dietary deficiencies. It should be emphasised that an increase in physical activity is not accompanied by a proportional increase in demand for vitamins, minerals and protein but just for energy in the form of carbohydrate and fat. Normally protein is not an energy source for skeletal muscle. I agree with Dr Durnin who writes: 'Anyone seriously interested in suggesting that there are increased protein requirements as a result of heavy physical exercise has to be prepared to combat an enormous wealth of classical studies which have shown the opposite' (Durnin, 1982). It would be very unwise if skeletal muscle fibres consumed their neighbours or even themselves.

There are reports that habitual physical activity does not counteract obesity (Pace et al, 1986). One aspect neglected in such reports is that (a) any increase in physical activity demands an extra energy yield; (b) it is a voluntary decision of an individual whether he/she decides to consume extra energy. In a review Tremblay et al, (1985) concluded that habitual physical activity effectively can contribute to weight loss in obese individuals.

An individual with a body weight of 65 kg needs approximately one litre of oxygen per minute when walking at a speed of 5 km.hr^{-1}. For the average 70 year old male individual this amounts to moderately heavy exercise and heavy exercise for his female counterpart. With a body weight of 100 kg that walk would, for many persons, tax their aerobic power up to maximum levels (oxygen demand of 1.5 l.min^{-1}. Therefore it is evident that the ageing individual should try to stay slim and fit.

3. Age

During this Symposium we have discussed the ageing individual both from a physiological and clinical point of view. We are all agreed, I think, that chronological age is a very poor guide for classification of an individual's health and fitness. An individual's development and function are based on individually different genetic codes, in a way very undemocratic, but a fundamental 'force' behind evolution. In human history it is a very recent event that we retire from work at a given age, in many countries at approximately 65 years old. Before being 'civilized' the North American Indian who was no longer able to participate as a hunter, scout or warrior became responsible for the education of the young boys. He continued to contribute in a meaningful, intellectual, social and physical role in his society until it finally was a 'good day to die' (Hill, 1979). In the small village where I grew up the ageing farmer who was no longer physically able to go behind the plough or handle a scythe was still very important because he had valuable experience and knowledge to teach the younger men. However, with the onset of more sophisticated machinery, fertilizers, agricultural and veterinary procedures, the 'old man' has become completely out of date with self-evident and mostly negative consequences.

Slightly provocatively medical scientists have promised that if they are given more money they will solve most medical problems. Maybe that is a factor behind society's demand for increased medical care. 'Why can't you help me?' Both Drs Young and Gray in their papers emphasized that the attitude of society towards elderly people too often promotes passivity. At a higher age there is inevitable deterioration of organ function but this occurs at different times and at different rates in different individuals. The North American Indian and the old farmer were very realistic in their acceptance of the 'rules' of life and death, health and disease. We are much more unrealistic and in my opinion there is an important educational task ahead whereby the population at large has to be taught that there are medical problems one has to accept and live with. The other educational task that must be undertaken is to emphasize that body structures and organ functions deteriorate more rapidly as a result of a 'poor lifestyle'. The problem is that we still do not have scientific data as a platform for a prescription of an individualised optimal lifestyle. There are many symptoms very similar which can result from either a 'poor lifestyle' or a disease, e.g. fatigue, headache, gastrointestinal problems, breathlessness during mild exercise to mention some more subjective symptoms. Objective clinical findings can be equally confusing e.g. tachycardia, reduced glucose tolerance, low maximal oxygen uptake, iron deficiency anaemia and osteoporosis to mention but a few. There are many question marks in the zone between optimal health and established disease.

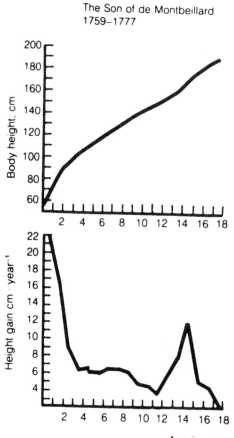

The Son of de Montbeillard
1759–1777

Figure 1a. Illustrates the growth in height of a French boy
recorded by his father (de Montbeillard). The upper curve shows
the gradual gain during an 18 year period, the lower curve the
height gain each year. Note the accelerated growth around the age
of 14-15 years ('peak height velocity'). (After Tanner, 1962).

   Another problem is that human beings are by nature gamblers; we
do not like being told what is 'good for us'.
   There is good scientific data confirming that habitual physical
exercise can prevent, maintain and significantly increase maximal
oxygen uptake even at very advanced ages (Astrand and Rodahl, 1986,
Chapter 10). In this way a given physical demand in daily activities
is less fatiguing and a potential self-help, and an active leisure
time is much improved, as compared with the situation for the
sedentary individual.
   It is very impressive that many musicians at a very advanced age
can perform perfectly. As examples one could mention Arthur
Rubenstein playing very demanding Chopin compositions at the age of

88 and Andre Segovia giving concerts at the age of 91 on the classical guitar. Quick and precise finger movements are usually considered impossible at advanced ages. However, by hours of daily practice, very demanding neuromuscular skills can apparently be maintained throughout a long life span.

I would like to add some comments about the discrepancy between chronological and biological age in children. Tanner (Tanner, 1981), who is one of the pioneers in this field, has established the general framework of biological age. It is evident that a longitudinal recording of a child's height over many years gives a good picture of the onset of puberty and the development of secondary sexual characteristics. The so called peak height velocity (PHV) (Fig.1a) is the easily determined marker for this period of maturity. Fig.1b illustrates how the PHV may, in girls, occur as early as the age of nine and a half for one girl, but not until the age of fifteen years for another girl. In boys the adolescent growth spurt ranges from eleven to seventeen years old.

Since the adolescent growth spurt has a profound effect on physical performance it is not only unfair but is also possibly a psychological trauma, to group children athletically in classes according to their age. One individual who develops early may dominate his/her class athletically for a long period of time, causing the parents, coach and the child to overestimate his/her athletic talent. In due course classmates may catch up only to confirm that the early success was not due to a particular talent but more a matter of early maturation. Another point: at the age of thirteen years the majority of girls are already young ladies while boys are still children.

While it is practical to characterize an individual on the basis of an age scale it is biologically very unsound. However, it is not easy to find an alternative basis for any such classification. In her lecture Dr Prior referred to the bushman society. For the bushman as well as our ancient ancestors, recording age was a waste of time. When educating their children as to what was of vital importance to survival the bushman's lecture hall was outdoor and I take it for granted that the curriculum was filled with thrill and excitement and appealed to curiosity. That is in definite contrast to our modern day classroom. I regret that an important part of curriculum today does not include more outdoor activities including the study of nature. When studying flora and fauna the initial lessons can take a long time to learn but enriched knowledge in these subjects is very rewarding throughout a long life. There are those individuals who do not like to walk just for the sake of walking but if a hobby like bird-watching or picking mushrooms demands some walking then they will enjoy this form of physical activity.

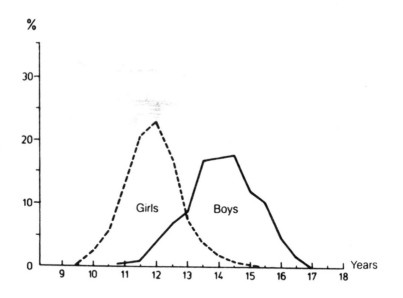

Figure 1b. Distribution of age at Peak Height Velocity (PHV age) for girls (n=358) boys (n=373). (After Lindgren, 1978).

4. Risk

Eventually physical activity may induce injuries and other negative effects. We have discussed this vigorous physical activity with regard to cardiovascular risk. Vuori has reviewed the literature on this subject and reports that the incidence of sudden death in connection with jogging was one death per approximately 400000 jogging hours and one death per 600000 hours of cross-country skiing. In this particular activity it was estimated there were 500000 skiers enjoying this sport each year per case of sudden cardiovascular death in the age group between 20 to 40 years. The corresponding figure for skiers between 50 to 69 years of age was 31000. In the deceased men approximately 40% had been suspected or diagnosed as suffering from coronary heart disease during their life. Therefore, it is very important that we maintain our awareness of the risk factors with relevance to coronary heart disease. (Vuori, personal communication). The overall picture is that the incidence of sudden death during physical activity is exceptionally low (Shephard, 1986).

5. Recommended activities

Bearing in mind the beneficial effects of regular physical exercise listed in Table 1, I would recommend the following activities:-
    Daily - at least 60 minutes of physical activity, not necessarily vigorous and not all at the same time. This would

include activities during the normal daily working routine,
walking, climbing stairs etc, whether for one minute 60 times a day
or twelve minutes 5 times a day as long as the daily total achieves
60 minutes. This is equivalent to an individual using 300 kcal
(1.2 MJ) of energy.

Weekly - at least three periods of 30 minutes of more vigorous
exercise should be undertaken each week. I would suggest brisk
sustained walking, jogging, cycling, swimming, aerobics, rowing,
skiing and skipping. These activities are efficient in their
ability to achieve and maintain good cardiovascular fitness and may
consume an additional 750 kcal (3 MJ) per week.

References

Åstrand, P.-O. and Grimby, G. (1986). Physical activity in health
    disease. Acta Med. Scand. 220:(suppl. 711).
Åstrand, P.-O. and Rodahl, K. (1986). 'Textbook of Work
    Physiology' New York: McGraw-Hill: 3rd ed.
Atha, J. (1981). Strengthening muscle, Exerc. Sport Sci. Rev.
    9:1-73.
Blomqvist, C.G. and Saltin, B. (1983). Cardiovascular adaptation
    to physical training. Ann. Rev. Physiol. 45:169-89.
Dearman, J. and Francis, K.T. (1983). Plasma levels of
    catecholamines, cortisol and beta-endorphins in male athletes
    after running 26.2, 6 and 2 miles. J. Sports Med. 23(1):30-8.
Durnin, J.V.G.A. (1982). Muscle in sports medicine - nutrition and
    muscular performance. Int. J. Sports Med. 3:52-7.
Garrow, J.S. (1986). Effect of exercise on obesity. In ref. 1.
Hammond, H.K. (1985). Exercise for coronary heart disease
    patients: Is it worth the effort? J. Cardiopulmonary
    Rehabil. 5:531-9.
Haskell, W.L. (1986). The influence of exercise training on plasma
    lipids and lipoproteins in health and disease. In ref. 1.
Haskell, W.L., Savin, W., Oldrige, N. and DeBusk, N. (1983).
    Factors influencing estimated oxygen uptake during exercise
    testing soon after myocardial infarction. Am. J. Cardiol.
    50:299-304.
Henriksson, H. and Reitman, J.S. (1977). Time course of changes in
    human skeletal muscle succinate dehydrogenase and cytochrome
    oxidase activities and maximal oxygen uptake with physical
    activity and inactivity. Acta. Physiol. Scand. 99:91-7.
Hill, R.B. (1979). Hanta Yoo - an American Saga, New York: Warner
    Books.
Holloszy, J.O., Schultz, J., Kusnierkiewicz, J., Hagberg, J.M. and
    Ehsani, A.A. (1986). Effects of exercise on glucose tolerance
    and insulin resistance. In ref. 1.
Hurley, B.F., Hagberg, J.M., Allen, W.K., Seals, D.R., Young, J.C.,
    Cuddihee, R.T. and Holloszy, J.O. (1984). Effect of training on
    blood lactate levels during submaximal exercise.
    J. Appl. Physiol: Resp. Environ. Exerc. Physiol. 56:1260-4.
Lindgren, G. (1978). Growth of school children with early, average
    and late ages of peak height velocity. Ann. Human Biol.
    5:253-67.

Pace, P.J., Webster, J. and Garrow, J.S. (1986). Exercise and
    Obesity. Sports Med. 3:89-113.
Paffenbarger, R.S., Hyde, R.T., Hsieh, C.C. and Wing, A.L. (1986).
    Physical activity, other life-style patterns, cardiovascular
    disease, and longevity. In ref. 1.
Rauramaa, R. (1986). Physical activity and prostanoids. In ref. 1.
Rauramaa, R., Salonen, J.T., Kukkonen, K. et al. (1984).
    Effects of mild physical exercise on serum lipoproteins and
    metabolites of archidonic acid: a controlled randomized trial in
    middle-aged men. Br. Med. J. 288:603-6.
Saltin, B., Blomqvist, G., Mitchell, J.H., Johnson, R.L.,
    Wildenthal, K. and Chapman, C.B. (1986). Response to exercise
    after bed rest and after training. Circulation.
    38:suppl.7: 1-78.
Saltin, B., and Gollnick, P.D. (1983). Skeletal muscle
    adaptability: significance for metabolism and performance. In
    Handbook of Physiology. Section 10, chap.9, pp. 555-63.
    Baltimore: Williams and Wilkins Company.
Scientific American (1978). Evolution. 239(3):39-169.
Seals, D.R. and Hagberg, J.M. (1984). The effect of exercise
    training on human hypertension: a review. Med. Sci. Sports
    Exerc. 16: 107-15.
Shephard, R.J. (1986). Exercise in coronary heart disease.
    Sports Med. 3:26-49.
Smidt, E.L. and Raab, D.M. (1986). Osteoporosis and physical
    activity. In ref.1.
Stebbins, C.L., Schultz, E., Smith, R.T. and Smith, E.L. (1985).
    Effects of chronic exercise during aging on muslce and end-plate
    morphology in rats. J. Appl. Physiol. 58:45-51.
Tanner, J.M. (1962). Growth of Adolescence. Oxford: Blackwell
    Scientific Publications.
Tanner, J.M. (1980). Some methodological problems in analysis of
    human growth, quetelet to the present. In The Biology of
    Normal Human Growth. (edited by M. Ritzen), pp. 309-20. New
    York: Raven Press.
Tipton, C.M., Vailas, A.C. and Matthes, R.D. (1986). Experimental
    studies on the influences of physical activity on ligaments,
    tendons and joints: a brief review. In ref.1.
Tremblay, A.J., Després, P. and Bouchard (1985). The effects of
    exercise-training on energy balance and adipose tissue
    morphology and metabolism. Sports Med. 2:223-33.
Williams, G.A. (1985). Exercise testing and chronic congestive
    heart failure. Learning Center Highlights. 1(2):12.
Wood, P.D., Terry, R.B. and Haskell, W.L. (1985). Metabolism of
    substrates: diet, lipoprotein metabolism and exercise.
    Federation Proc. 44(2):358-63.

Index

This index is compiled from the 'key words' assigned to papers by their authors (plus some additional topics). The page numbers refer to the first page of the paper in which the reference is to be found.